Reverse Osmosis and Nanofiltration

AWWA MANUAL M46

Second Edition

American Water Works Association

Science and Technology

AWWA unites the entire water community by developing and distributing authoritative scientific and technological knowledge. Through its members, AWWA develops industry standards for products and processes that advance public health and safety. AWWA also provides quality improvement programs for water and wastewater utilities.

MANUAL OF WATER SUPPLY PRACTICES—M46, Second Edition

Reverse Osmosis and Nanofiltration

Project Manager and Senior Technical Editor: Melissa Valentine
Production Manager: Melanie Schiff
Manual Coordinator: Beth Behner

Library of Congress Cataloging-in-Publication Data
Bergman, Robert.
  Reverse osmosis and nanofiltration. --2nd ed.
    p.cm. -- (AWWA manual ; M46)
  Includes bibliographical references and index.
  ISBN 1-58321-491-7 (alk. paper)
  1. Water--Purification--Reverse osmosis process. 2. Water--Purification--Membrane filtration.
3. Drinking water--Purification. 4. Nanofiltration. I. Title. II. Series. \

  TD442.5.B47 2007
  628.1'64--dc22

                        2007022961

Printed in the United States of America
American Water Works Association
6666 West Quincy Avenue
Denver, CO 80235

ISBN 1-58321-491-7
978-1-58321-491-6

Contents

Figures

This page intentionally blank.

Tables

Preface

Reverse osmosis (RO) and nanofiltration (NF) are membrane technologies that can be applied to the treatment of various water sources for the production of drinking water. Membrane technologies can remove organic and inorganic substances from water and can replace or be adjuncts to such traditional treatment methods as sand filtration, primary disinfection, lime and soda softening, ion exchange, and evaporative processes. RO and NF are both pressure-driven membrane processes with similar process configurations and equipment. The main differences between the processes are primary treatment focus (demineralization or salt reduction for RO and hardness and/or organics removal for NF) and the degree of necessary applied pressure (higher for RO). However, the two membrane processes exhibit far more similarities than differences, thus their inclusion in the same manual.

RO was commercialized in the United States in the 1960s and has been used for water desalting applications ever since. NF developed from research and development technology as a lower cost membrane process for softening water and removing organic color.

Membrane technology of all types became particularly applicable to drinking water production in the late 1980s when the amendments to the US Environmental Protection Agency's Safe Drinking Water Act (SDWA) required higher-quality drinking water. The amendments were based on health effects research and the ability to detect contaminants at increasingly lower detection limits using sensitive analytical techniques. Because of their ability to remove or reduce many of the substances addressed by SDWA, membranes will play an increasingly important role in enabling water utilities to meet these regulations.

This manual was developed to provide an overview of RO and NF technology for operators, administrators, engineers, scientists, educators, and anyone seeking an introduction to these processes. An introductory chapter, which discusses an overview of RO and NF processes and applications, is followed by chapters discussing RO and NF process design, facility design, and operations and maintenance. The information contained in these chapters includes history, regulations, theory, terminology, water resources, pretreatment, process technology, posttreatment, concentrate disposal, and membrane and system components, configuration, maintenance, chemistry, costing, and safety.

As this is the second edition of AWWA Manual M46, *Reverse Osmosis and Nanofiltration*, the Membrane Processes Committee and the American Water Works Association welcome comments and suggestions for improving future editions. Please send them as an e-mail attachment to the Water Quality Engineer at eharring@awwa.org or in hard copy to 6666 West Quincy Avenue, Denver, CO 80235.

This page intentionally blank.

Acknowledgments

The M46 revision subcommittee members and authors for this edition included the following:

Robert Bergman, Chair, CH2M Hill, Gainesville, Fla.
Brent Alspach, Malcolm Pirnie, Carlsbad, Calif.
Robert Huehmer, CH2M Hill, Herndon, Va.
Scott Freeman, Black & Veatch, Kansas City, Mo.
Nikolay Voutchkov, Poseidon Resources, Stamford, Conn.

The second edition of this manual was reviewed and approved by the Membrane Processes Committee, Water Quality Technology Division. At the time of approval, the review committee consisted of the following:

J.G. Jacangelo, Chair, MWH and The Johns Hopkins University, Lovettsville, Va.
S.A. Adham, MWH Americas Inc., Pasadena, Calif.
J.T. Aguinaldo, Doosan Hydro Technology, Tampa, Fla.
S.C. Allgeier, USEPA Water Security Division, Cincinnati, Ohio
B. Alspach, Malcolm Pirnie Inc., Carlsbad, Calif.
K.Z. Atasi, Wade-Trim Associates Inc., Detroit, Mich.
R.A. Bergman, CH2M Hill, Gainesville, Fla.
G.J. Best, GE Water & Process Technologies, Oakville, Ont.
T.H. Cooke, Black & Veatch, Kansas City, Mo.
P.J. Delphos, Black & Veatch, Charlotte, N.C.
S. Deshmukh, Orange County Water District, Fountain Valley, Calif.
M.I. Dimitriou, Water Innovation, LLC, Richmond, Va.
J.J. Donison, Eastman Water, Weare, N.H.
I.C. Escobar, University of Toledo, Toledo, Ohio
S. Freeman, Black & Veatch, Kansas City, Mo.
P.M. Gallagher, Siemens Water Technologies, Ames, Iowa
M.A. Galloway, Koch Membrane, Wilmington, Mass.
E. Harrington, American Water Works Association, Denver, Colo.
J.A. Herschell, Amiad Filtration Systems, Oxnard, Calif.
K.J. Howe, University of New Mexico, Albuquerque, N.M.
R.P. Huehmer, CH2M Hill, Chantilly, Va.
E.O. Kartinen Jr., Boyle Engineering Corporation, Bakersfield, Calif.
A.A. Karimi, Los Angeles Department of Water and Power, Winnetka, Calif.
C.A. Kiefer, Camp Dresser and McKee Inc., Fort Lauderdale, Fla.
N. Kothari, Manitowoc Public Utilities, Manitowoc, Wis.
D.M. Patton, Malcolm Pirnie Inc., Orchard Park, N.Y.
M. Pilutti, Metcalf & Eddy, Columbus, Ohio
K. Price, US Bureau of Reclamation, Denver, Colo.
S. Rezania, City of Minneapolis, Minneapolis, Minn.
J.K. Schaefer, Metcalf & Eddy, New York, N.Y.
S. Sethi, Carollo Engineers, Sarasota, Fla.
T.F. Speth, USEPA, Cincinnati, Ohio
S. Veerapaneni, Black & Veatch, Kansas City, Mo.

W.A. *Vernon*, Southwest Waters, Phoenix, Ariz.
J.C. Vickers, Separation Processes Inc., Carlsbad, Calif.
N. Voutchkov, Poseidon Resources, Stamford, Conn.
G. Witcher Jr., California Water Service Company, Bakersfield, Calif.

Additional reviewers of this edition included the following:

Khalil Z. Atasi, Wade-Trim Associates, Inc., Detroit, Mich.
Andrew F. DeGraca, San Francisco Public Utilities, Burlingame, Calif.
Steven J. Duranceau, Duranceau Consulting Services, LLC, Orlando, Fla.
Daniel Horne, Virginia Department of Health, Norfolk, Va.
Pamela P. Kenel, Black & Veatch, Gaithersburg, Md.
John T. Morris, Metropolitan Water District, Los Angeles, Calif.
Ben B. Movahed, WATEK Engineering Corporation, Beltsville, Md.
Steve Siverns, Enviro Tower Inc., Toronto, Ont.
John Tobiason, University of Massachusetts, Amherst, Mass.

Original authors and their affiliations of the first edition of the manual, which represented academic, consulting, manufacturing, and utilities backgrounds, included the following:

William J. Conlon, Rust Environment & Infrastructure, Sheboygan, Wis.
Steven J. Duranceau, Chair, Boyle Engineering Corporation, Orlando, Fla.
Harbans S. Kohli, Fluid Systems Corporation, San Diego, Calif.
James C. Lozier, CH2M Hill, Phoenix, Ariz.
Irving Moch Jr., DuPont Permasep Products, Newark, Del.
Stuart A. McClellan, The Dow Chemical Company, West Palm Beach, Fla.
Thomas M. Missimer, Missimer International, Fort Myers, Fla.
Oram J. Morin, Black & Veatch, Orlando, Fla.
David H. Paul, David H. Paul Inc., Farmington, N.M.
Hermann Pohland, DuPont Permasep Products, Newark, Del.
Larry R. Reitz, Phizer Inc., Groton, Conn.
James S. Taylor, University of Central Florida, Orlando, Fla.
Donald M. Thompson, Camp Dresser and McKee Inc., Jacksonville, Fla.

Chapter **1**

Introduction

Brent Alspach

This first chapter provides a general introduction to the reverse osmosis (RO) and nanofiltration (NF) membrane treatment processes. The subjects addressed in this chapter should serve as the basic foundation for a broader understanding of RO and NF processes as applied to potable water, industrial process water, tertiary wastewater, and reclaimed water treatment, and include a general overview of the technology (i.e., types of processes, history of development, general RO/NF system description, and typical performance), specific applications, and membrane materials and configurations. Successive chapters will build on these concepts to provide more detailed information about process design (chapter 2), facility design and construction (chapter 3), and operations and maintenance (O&M) (chapter 4). For readers unfamiliar with RO and NF, a typical facility is shown in Figure 1-1. This picture shows the 10-mgd Scottsdale Water Campus, an RO system treating reclaimed water for aquifer recharge. The RO process itself consists of numerous skids with long horizontal pressure vessels containing the membrane elements, as shown in the center of the picture. The prefiltration (i.e., cartridge filters) to remove particulate matter upstream of the RO process is shown in the foreground at the bottom of the picture, and the high pressure pumps are aligned along the left side.

OVERVIEW

This section first provides a brief overview of the different types of membrane processes. The discussion subsequently narrows to RO and NF processes—the focus of this manual—presenting a brief history of the development of RO and NF membranes and the basics of RO and NF systems.

Types of Membrane Processes

The five membrane processes commonly used in the production of drinking water are RO, NF, ultrafiltration (UF), microfiltration (MF), and electrodialysis/electrodialysis reversal (ED/EDR). Although all five are classified as membrane processes, the technologies and applications are very different in some cases. In general, there are three groups of similar membrane processes: MF/UF, RO/NF, and ED/EDR. Four

Courtesy of Black & Veatch

Figure 1-1   Scottsdale Water Campus—10-mgd RO facility

primary factors distinguish these three groups of membrane processes from each other: the type of membrane, the mechanism of contaminant removal, the process driving force, and the primary application.

MF and UF are pressure-driven membrane processes that use microporous membranes to remove particulate matter (including turbidity and microorganisms), via a sieving mechanism, on the basis of size exclusion. These two processes do not remove ions or other dissolved constituents. Although there are some UF membranes that are used in industrial applications to separate high molecular weight organic molecules from solutions, these membranes are not commercially available for municipal drinking water treatment. In some cases, however, as with conventional media filters, MF and UF processes may be used to reduce levels of dissolved organic material (i.e., total organic carbon [TOC] when applied to coagulated water). MF and UF membranes may be manufactured from a number of different materials, including cellulose acetate and synthetic polymers such as polyvinylidene fluoride, polypropylene, polysulfone, polyether-sulfone, and polyacrylonitrile. For modern water treatment applications, these MF/UF membrane materials are commonly configured into hollow fibers, although other configurations may be available. MF and UF processes are discussed in detail in the American Water Works Association (AWWA) Manual of Practice M53: *Microfiltration and Ultrafiltration Membranes* (2005).

RO and NF are also pressure-driven processes; however, these technologies utilize semipermeable membranes to primarily target the removal of dissolved contaminants via a diffusion-controlled separation process. While RO and NF also remove particulate matter, the nonporous, semipermeable membranes can rapidly foul when subjected to significant particulate loading. When high pressure in excess of the natural osmotic gradient of the system is applied to the feed side of the membrane, water is forced through the molecular structure of the membrane surface while the dissolved solids (i.e., the solutes) are largely rejected. Although solutes can also diffuse through the semipermeable membranes, the rate of mass transfer of these constituents is much slower than that of the water. Consequently, the water that passes through the membrane (i.e., the permeate) contains fewer dissolved solids than does water entering the system (i.e., the feed).

The amount of energy (hydraulic pressure) required to drive the feedwater across the membrane depends on the membrane material and thickness, as well as the osmotic pressure of the feed. The osmotic pressure is the pressure on the membrane created by the naturally occurring process of water flowing from a dilute solution (i.e., lower dissolved solids concentration) across a semipermeable membrane to a more concentrated solution (i.e., higher dissolved solids concentration). Thus, energy in the form of hydraulic pressure is required to overcome both the physical resistance of the membrane itself and the osmotic pressure of the system. Because this pressure is applied to force water against the natural osmotic gradient to produce less saline water from more concentrated water, the treatment process is called *reverse osmosis*.

The first RO membranes were developed at the University of California at Los Angeles in the early 1960s by Loeb and Sourirajan, who produced a membrane to generate drinking water from seawater (Buros 1980). This relatively thick membrane was made from cellulose acetate and required feed pressure in excess of 1,000 psi. Currently, RO membranes used to desalinate seawater require about 800 to 1,200 psi, while brackish water applications may necessitate feed pressure ranging from 100 to 600 psi. For a given membrane system and operating conditions, the feed pressure required depends primarily on the total dissolved solids (TDS) concentration and the temperature of the feedwater—lower TDS levels and warmer waters require lower feed pressure to produce similar quality and quantity of permeate.

NF membranes were developed in the late 1970s as a variant of RO membranes with reduced rejection characteristics for smaller, less charged ions, such as sodium and chloride. Because these membranes also required lower operating feed pressure, NF was well suited for applications such as softening and dissolved organic carbon (DOC)/disinfection by-product (DBP) precursor removal in which TDS was not a primary concern, because treatment objectives could be achieved at lower energy costs than with RO. Common applications for hardness and DOC removal may require only 70 to 120 psi using currently available NF membranes.

The two primary materials used to manufacture RO and NF membranes are cellulose acetate (and its derivatives) and various polyamides used in *thin-film composite* membrane construction. Although both RO and NF membranes are manufactured in several physical configurations, the spiral-wound configuration is the only one that is widely used in municipal treatment applications. (Membrane materials and configurations are discussed in more detail later in this chapter.)

ED/EDR are electrically driven membrane processes that remove dissolved solids using cation- and anion-selective membranes. However, unlike RO and NF, ED/EDR does not provide a barrier to pathogens and does not remove suspended solids or noncharged, nonionic constituents. In RO and NF processes, product water is filtered while passing through the membrane. By contrast, with ED/EDR the demineralized product water passes along the membrane surface in a tangential pattern while charged ions are transported through the membrane and concentrated into the brine stream; thus, the product water does not pass through a membrane barrier. ED/EDR has been used primarily to desalinate brackish waters and applied in specialty applications, such as the removal of fluoride or radionuclides. In addition, because ED/EDR does not affect silica concentrations, it may be advantageous in cases in which silica removal is not needed. Additional information about ED/EDR may be found in the AWWA Manual of Practice M38: *Electrodialysis and Electrodialysis Reversal* (1995).

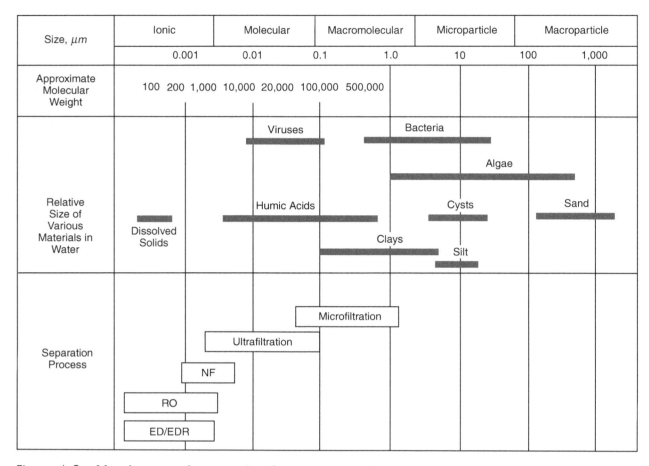

Figure 1-2   Membrane and conventional process overview

Figure 1-2 illustrates the removal abilities of the various types of membrane technology for their respective target drinking water contaminants, based on size of the removed compounds. Table 1-1 summarizes some of this same information in tabular form, including the various membrane process and target contaminants. Note that both Figure 1-2 and Table 1-1 focus on the *target* contaminants, not all the contaminants that the various membrane technologies are capable of removing. For example, while RO and NF processes will remove particulate matter, these technologies are generally not applied specifically for this purpose because the membranes will foul rapidly and in many cases irreversibly.

History of Development

One of the first applications for membrane technology was the conversion of seawater to drinking water through the use of the RO process. Early generation membranes were manufactured with cellulose acetate and were much less permeable than those currently used. The disadvantages of early membranes included the high pressure required and the low recovery rate—only 10 to 25 percent of the source water was converted to desalinated permeate. These factors resulted in extensive and cost-prohibitive energy requirements.

The first commercial application of RO membranes for brackish water desalting began in the early 1960s using the spiral-wound configuration developed in 1967, by General Atomics. In 1969, E.I. DuPont de Nemours, Inc. (DuPont) introduced the

Table 1-1   Membrane processes and target contaminants

Membrane Technology	Target Contaminants Removed
MF	• *Giardia* • *Cryptosporidium* • Bacteria • Turbidity/particulate matter • Coagulated organic matter • Inorganic precipitates
UF	• All contaminants removed by MF, *plus* • Viruses • Large organic macromolecules
NF	• Divalent ions/hardness • Limited monovalent ions • Dissolved organic carbon • Color
RO	• All contaminants removed by NF, *plus* • Monovalent ions
ED/EDR	• Dissolved ions

polyamide hollow fine-fiber membrane in the form of the B-9 permeator for brackish water desalting. These brackish water modules generally operated in the pressure range of 300 to 400 psi. The first municipal brackish water RO plant was located at Key Largo, Florida's, Ocean Reef Club. The plant began operation in October 1971 with an initial operating pressure of 600 psi and a capacity of 0.6 mgd, which was later expanded to 0.93 mgd.

In 1974, DuPont introduced the hollow fine-fiber B-10 permeator, the first RO membrane capable of producing potable water from typical seawater in a single pass at operating pressures of 800 to 1,000 psi. Spiral-wound, thin-film composite RO membranes developed for both seawater and brackish water desalting were introduced in the mid- to late 1970s. Feed pressures for the early composite membranes were approximately the same as for the cellulosic and polyamide hollow fine-fiber modules. Dow Chemical Company's introduction of the low-pressure Dowex™ hollow fine-fiber RO membrane led to a major reduction in the cost of brackish water RO facility operation. The first plant to use the new membrane began operation in 1981, at Venice, Fla., with a 1 mgd capacity. The Dowex™ membrane provided salt rejection and fluxes comparable to the standard pressure cellulosic and polyamide membranes at roughly one half the operating pressure (200 to 250 psi versus 400 to 600 psi).

Low-pressure, thin-film composite, spiral-wound modules were first introduced in the early 1980s by FilmTec Corporation (now part of Dow Chemical Company) and Fluid Systems (now part of Koch Membrane Systems). These composite membranes, currently available from a number of supplier firms, are now commonly used, except in applications in which the better chlorine tolerance of cellulosic membranes is desired.

The expansion of the Englewood Water District's plant in southwestern Florida illustrates the evolution of spiral-wound brackish water RO membrane technology. The original RO process trains (1982) used standard brackish water cellulose acetate blend membranes operating at 400 to 600 psi. New RO trains installed during an initial expansion in 1986 employed the early generation polyurea composite membranes. During an additional expansion in 1989, the new trains and several of the older units were outfitted with more advanced, low-pressure, fully aromatic polyamide composite membranes. As shown in Table 1-2, the energy required for the RO process in 1989 was

Table 1-2   Comparison of three generations of brackish water RO membranes at Englewood Water District, Fla.

	RO Train			
Parameter	Train A (1982), Cellulose Acetate Blend	Train A (1986), Composite (Polyurea)	Trains B and C (1986), Composite (Polyurea)	Trains D and E (1989), Composite (Fully Aromatic Polyamide)
Design feedwater TDS, mg/L	4,700	6,000	6,000	7,000
Maximum design feed pressure, psi (stage 1)	600	420	*	335
Normalized specific flux, $gpd/psi^\dagger$	0.041	0.057	0.069	0.082
Relative membrane energy usage, % of initial plant design	100†	72	59	50

* Trains include interstage booster pumps between the first and second stages.
† All RO trains have the following characteristics: 0.5-mgd permeate capacity at 65 percent minimum and 70 percent design recovery. All trains are normalized to 4,700 mg/L feedwater TDS to permit direct comparison of energy usage at initial plant feedwater conditions. After expansion and upgrade in 2005, a sixth RO train has been added and all trains now use polyamide membranes in single-stage train arrangements with 8 elements per pressure vessel designed to treat 7,000 mg/L TDS design groundwater quality.

50 percent less than the original 1982 plant design, a dramatic decrease made possible by rapid advances in the technology in less than a decade. Train F, installed in 2005, uses even less energy. Currently, all trains use polyamide composite RO membranes in a single-stage arrangement with energy recovery turbopumps that recover energy from the waste concentrate stream and transfer it to the feed. Chapter 3 discusses integrated turbopumps and other commercially available energy recovery devices.

The concept of membrane softening was introduced in 1976, and the following year a 0.25-mgd membrane softening plant was installed in Pelican Bay, Naples, Fla. The plant used a Fluid Systems hydrolyzed (i.e., "loose") RO membrane and was later expanded to 0.5 mgd. Membrane softening was in limited use until 1984, when FilmTec Corporation introduced polyamide NF spiral-wound elements. Other manufacturers subsequently developed similar products.

RO and NF Membrane Systems

A typical RO or NF membrane system consists of three separate subsystems: pretreatment, the membrane process, and posttreatment. Figure 1-3 illustrates a typical system, including one influent stream (i.e., feed) and two effluent streams (i.e., permeate and concentrate). Essentially all sources of water to which RO and NF membrane systems are applied must undergo certain levels of pretreatment. Pretreatment processes usually involve adding acid, scale inhibitor, or both to prevent precipitation of sparingly soluble salts as the rejected ions become more concentrated, followed by 5- to 20-μm cartridge filtration to protect the RO/NF membranes from particulate fouling. Additional pretreatment measures (typically upstream of the standard cartridge filter) may be necessary for water with higher fouling potential, such as most surface waters. Posttreatment may include many unit operations common to conventional drinking water treatment, such as aeration, degasification, pH adjustment, addition of corrosion control chemicals, fluoridation, and disinfection. The unit operations in each subsystem (i.e., pretreatment and posttreatment) are discussed in detail later in subsequent chapters. A thorough understanding of source water characteristics and product water quality goals is

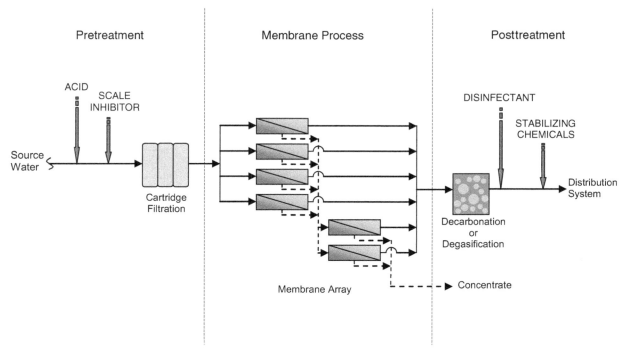

Figure 1-3   Typical RO or NF membrane system

essential to the successful design and operation of a RO or NF treatment plant, because the contaminants found in the source water determine which combination of pre- and posttreatment methods will be necessary.

RO AND NF MEMBRANE APPLICATIONS

This section describes the major current applications of RO and NF membrane processes, including: desalting, the removal/reduction of DBP precursors, hardness (i.e., softening), color, inorganic contaminants (e.g., nitrate, fluoride, arsenic, heavy metals, radionuclides, etc.), synthetic and volatile organic compounds, pathogens, and indirect potable reuse. A short discussion of emerging applications is also provided. Note that RO and NF can also remove suspended solids/particulate matter; however, because the semipermeable membranes are not porous (and therefore not able to be backwashed), any significant particulate loading can rapidly and sometimes irreversibly foul the membranes. Thus, although RO and NF will reduce particulate matter levels (i.e., turbidity, particle counts, etc.), the technology is not applied specifically for this purpose, and pretreatment to remove particulate matter upstream of the membranes is almost always employed.

A flowchart for selecting an appropriate membrane process (including MF, UF, and ED/EDR) is shown in Figure 1-4. Note that this is a very general guideline and does not take into account cost, site-, or application-specific considerations. The figure is primarily intended to serve as an illustrative tool to distinguish the various types of membrane processes on the basis of treatment application.

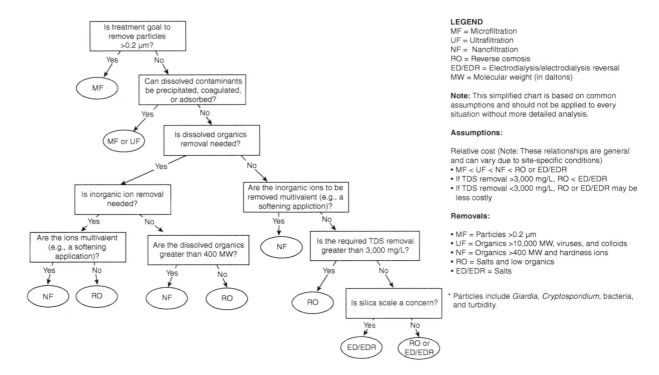

Figure 1-4   Generalized membrane process selection chart

Desalting (TDS Removal)

The primary application of RO and NF membranes is desalting (i.e., TDS removal) from saline surface water, brackish groundwater, seawater, tertiary treated wastewater, or industrial process water. The rejection capabilities of different commercially available products can vary significantly, and in many cases particular membranes are selected specifically for a target TDS range. Because incremental increases in TDS reduction boosts the required pressure, translating to higher energy costs, it can be significant in some cases to ensure that TDS is only reduced to the extent such that the desired treatment objective is satisfied. For example, for saline surface waters that may be relatively low in TDS but high enough to adversely impact the taste of the water for a utility's customers, a low-pressure/low-rejection RO membrane may be used with less efficient rejection characteristics. By contrast, in high purity applications that are common in industry or seawater desalination, RO membranes with much higher rejection of TDS are necessary. For potable water applications, the United States Environmental Protection Agency (USEPA) has established a secondary maximum contaminant level (SMCL) for TDS of 500 mg/L. While this federal SMCL is nonenforceable and established for aesthetic quality, this benchmark is often used as a target for treated water quality, particularly when it may be significantly more expensive to further reduce the TDS. (Note that water quality regulations can vary from state to state, and in some states, the federal SMCLs are enforceable by state mandate.)

Because the removal of TDS by RO and NF is nonselective and relatively high rejections are achieved, the permeate produced by these processes is typically very corrosive and characterized by low alkalinity and minimal buffering capacity. If acid is used as pretreatment to control scaling, the pH may also be low, further compounding the aggressive nature of the permeate. However, RO and NF systems can be designed with appropriate posttreatment processes to produce water that is both low in TDS and well buffered with sufficient alkalinity to help reduce the potential for pipe corrosion in the distribution system.

DBP Precursors

Because DBPs are a significant regulatory concern, RO and NF membranes are increasingly applied to remove DBP precursors such as natural organic matter (NOM)/TOC, which can react with various disinfectants used in the water treatment process to form potential carcinogens. These DBPs include total trihalomethanes (TTHMs) and the sum of five haloacetic acids (HAA5), both of which are strictly regulated in the parts per billion range by the Stage 1 and Stage 2 Disinfectants and Disinfection Byproducts Rules. As a result of these low maximum contaminant levels (MCLs), NOM removal is a significant water treatment objective for many utilities. RO or NF as a stand-alone process has been shown in many cases to reduce TOC to less than 0.5 mg/L. RO can also remove TTHMs and HAAs, albeit less efficiently than their precursor material; however, it is uncommon to apply these membranes for DBP reduction after the disinfection process in water treatment plants as a result of the susceptibility of most such membranes to damage from chemical disinfectants.

Hardness

NF has become a significant alternative to lime softening for reducing the level of calcium and magnesium ions in naturally hard waters where TDS reduction is not a primary treatment goal. Although RO membranes are also capable of reducing hardness, NF membranes have lower rejection characteristics for monovalent ions, allowing them to be operated at lower pressures while still efficiently removing the divalent ions that contribute to hardness, resulting in energy cost savings. Typically, NF membranes used for softening applications remove more than 95 percent of total hardness.

Color

NF is also more effective than lime softening in removing naturally occurring color and DBP precursors, both comprised primarily of organic carbon, and can often be operated more efficiently than RO. NF is generally capable of removing more than 95 percent of color.

Inorganic Contaminants

The USEPA currently recognizes RO as the best available technology (BAT) for removing most inorganic compounds (IOCs) regulated under the Safe Drinking Water Act (SDWA) (Clark and Parrotta 1991), including radionuclides and arsenic, among many others. This classification reflects the broad-spectrum removal capability of the RO process. The ability of NF to remove IOCs is determined to a large extent by the specific dissolved solids character of the water. NF rejection of specific multivalent cations is a function of solution pH and the speciation of other ionic constituents present to a greater degree than for the RO process.

One of the more common applications of RO for treating a specific inorganic contaminant is nitrate removal. RO is considered an effective nitrate removal process for groundwater supplies polluted by the agricultural use of nitrate-containing fertilizers or septic tank discharges. Rejection of nitrate by some RO membranes is significant; composite polyamide low-pressure brackish water membranes typically exhibit sodium nitrate rejection in the range of 93 to 97 percent (FilmTec 1988; Toray 1989). Several RO plants are currently in operation in southern California treating groundwater contaminated with high concentrations of nitrate from past agricultural practices, including those in the cities of Riverside and Tustin, as well as several facilities operated by the Chino Basin Desalter Authority. Note that NF is generally not applied for nitrate removal as a result of its relatively low rejection of this anion compared to RO.

Another inorganic contaminant to which RO is often applied is fluoride. Many groundwater sources in the United States contain elevated levels of naturally occurring fluoride. The USEPA has established a fluoride MCL of 4 mg/L to protect against skeletal fluorosis and a recommended SMCL of 2 mg/L to prevent tooth discoloration. Because levels of naturally occurring fluoride are about the same order of magnitude as the MCL, it is generally not necessary to achieve extremely high rejection, particularly considering that 0.8 to 1.2 mg/L of fluoride in drinking water is recommended for dental health. As a result, in many cases treatment costs can be reduced through the use of split treatment, in which a portion of adequately treated source water is bypassed around the membrane system and blended with the RO permeate.

In general, for water quality constituents or specific inorganic contaminants that are relatively common, RO/NF membrane manufacturers have modeling software that can predict permeate quality fairly accurately. However, for the removal of less common inorganic contaminants for which RO and NF have not been as frequently utilized, rejections are typically based on manufacturer, utility, or independent, third party experience and research. Although increasingly uncommon for many well-known inorganic contaminants, pilot testing can be conducted to quantify or verify rejection levels, if desired.

Synthetic and Volatile Organic Chemicals

Many of the synthetic organic compounds (SOCs) regulated by the USEPA in drinking water supplies are pesticide residuals. Pilot testing has been conducted in a municipality–USEPA partnership to evaluate the pesticide removal efficiency of a number of different types of RO membranes for treatment of groundwater contaminated by various agricultural chemicals (Bailer et al. 1987). This study found that removals were greatest for the polyamide thin-film composite membranes (67 to 95 percent), and it concluded that RO should be considered as a water treatment process for this application (Lykins et al. 1988). Other studies have assessed the capability of a wide range of NF membranes to remove commonly occurring pesticides to below the 0.1 µg/L (Côté et al. 1993; Hofman et al. 1993). Theoretically, specific SOC rejection is primarily a function of molecular size and degree of ionization. This theory was corroborated by a pilot study demonstrating that the degree of rejection is proportional to the molecular weight. Synthetic organic chemicals with a molecular weight greater than 300 Daltons were completely rejected by one type of NF membrane, while those with molecular weights less than 300 Daltons were only partially rejected. For these studies, the degree of rejection was proportional to the molecular weight (Taylor et al. 1989b).

It is less common for RO and NF to be applied for the removal of volatile organic compounds (VOCs), such as trichloroethylene and tetrachloroethylene, among others, because rejection is generally inefficient (albeit varying by specific compound). In addition, many VOCs are solvents that at higher concentrations may dissolve the glue lines on the membrane elements or damage the membranes themselves. It has also been reported that some VOCs may adsorb onto the membrane, potentially reducing permeability or desorbing into the permeate in concentrations higher than the feed until steady state is achieved (Lenz et al. 2005).

Pathogens

Because semipermeable RO and NF membranes are not porous, they have the ability to screen microorganisms and particulate matter in the feedwater. This ability has been verified in a number of studies, such as one that demonstrated that RO membranes provide between 4- and 5-log (i.e., 99.99 to 99.999 percent) removal of viruses normally associated with waterborne disease (Lozier et al. 1994). According to the *Guidance Manual for Compliance with the Filtration and Disinfection Requirements for Public Water Systems Using Surface Water Sources* (commonly referenced as the *Surface Water Treatment Rule [SWTR] Guidance Manual*), RO is listed as an alternate filtration technology that is effective for the removal of *Giardia* and viruses (USEPA 1990), such that unlike many other alternate technologies, no piloting or other studies are necessary to demonstrate that the RO process can achieve 3.0-log (i.e., 99.9 percent) *Giardia* and 4.0-log virus removal when combined with disinfection. The proposed Ground Water Rule also notes the demonstrated ability of RO and NF to achieve 4.0-log virus removal. In addition, under the Long Term 2 Enhanced Surface Water Treatment Rule, both NF and RO are specifically listed as *membrane filtration* technologies that can be applied to achieve significant *Cryptosporidium* removal credit (USEPA 2006).

However, it is important to note that RO and NF are not necessarily absolute barriers. RO and NF membranes are primarily designed for the removal of TDS rather than particulate matter, and thus the elimination of all small seal leaks that have only a nominal impact on the salt rejection characteristics is not the primary focus of the manufacturing process. Consequently, RO and NF spiral-wound elements are not intended to be sterilizing membranes and some passage of particulate matter, including pathogens, may occur despite the absence of pores in the membrane.

Indirect Potable Reuse

Both RO and NF are being increasingly used in the reclamation of municipal wastewaters serving indirectly as future potable water supplies and other reuse applications. In some of these applications, RO and NF remove many contaminants, including nitrogen, heavy metals, TOC, and pathogens, and subsequently the high-quality permeate is injected into groundwater aquifers for recharge. The underground strata serve as an additional filtration step to achieve natural attenuation of the groundwater supply, in some cases over many years, before it is pumped to the surface again for further treatment and distribution. RO technology is often a critical component for groundwater recharge with reclaimed water. The state of California, for example, currently requires all recycled water to be treated via RO prior to injection. The oldest and most widely known groundwater recharge project is the Orange County Water District's Ground Water Replenishment System in Fountain Valley, Calif., which originated as Water Factory 21, and has been in service since 1976. Numerous other utilities in California, Arizona, and other states are also practicing, planning, or studying indirect potable reuse using RO.

Emerging Applications

Because RO and NF achieve significant rejection/removal of a wide assortment of potable water contaminants, these processes are often among the first treatment technologies considered for a variety of emerging applications. For example, perchlorate—an inorganic anion—is one such emerging contaminant that is only effectively removed by a limited range of technologies, such as RO and ion exchange. RO and NF are also likely be among the BATs for removing contaminants such as endocrine disruptors and pharmaceutically active compounds, two broad classes of contaminants that are just beginning to be studied and quantified in drinking water sources. As improved analytical techniques continue to reveal previously unknown contaminants, it is likely that the number of applications for RO and NF will likewise increase.

MEMBRANE MATERIALS AND CONFIGURATIONS

The fundamental components of an RO/NF system are the membrane material and the configuration into which the material is manufactured. This section describes both of these components, elaborating on the different types of materials and configurations used in drinking water applications.

Membrane Materials

The two basic types of membranes currently used are asymmetric homogeneous and composite. A wide variety of materials are used, including cellulose acetate and polymers such as aromatic polyamides. The first commercial membranes were asymmetric (i.e., nonuniform density) brackish water RO membranes with a thin, dense surface, 0.1 to 1.0 μm thick on an otherwise spongy, porous film 80 to 100 μm thick, as illustrated in Figure 1-5. The surface or skin gives the membrane its rejection characteristics, and the porous substrate supports this skin to withstand pressure differentials of over 1,000 psi in some seawater RO applications. These first

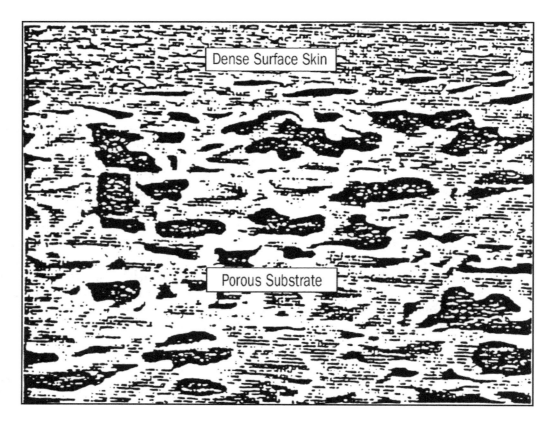

Figure 1-5   Cross-section of an asymmetric membrane

commercial asymmetric RO membranes were made of cellulose acetate material, with the dense skin obtained through an annealing process. Modified cellulosic membranes, including cellulose diacetate and cellulose triaetate, are less expensive than noncellulosic membranes and are thus still used in some applications.

Membranes made from cellulosic materials have some significant limitations. First, cellulose acetate hydrolyzes back to cellulose over a period of time, resulting in a loss of salt rejection even under ideal conditions. As shown in Figure 1-6 the hydrolysis of cellulose acetate is influenced by both pH and temperature. In particular, hydrolysis is accelerated at warmer water temperatures. The optimal feed water pH is approximately 5 for cellulosic membranes, and the pH must be maintained between 4.5 and 6.5 to maximize the membrane's useful life. Accordingly, chemical cleaning must be performed within a relatively narrow pH range (4 to 8), which can limit the effectiveness of the cleaning process in some cases. Cellulosic membranes are also subject to deterioration in the presence of microorganisms capable of cellulose enzyme production. However, because of the material's substantial oxidant tolerance, this risk can be avoided by source water chlorination to 1 mg/L. This same oxidant tolerance is one of the primary advantages of cellulosic membranes.

Asymmetrical membranes, whether manufactured from cellulosic or other materials, are subject to compaction. Compaction occurs mainly in the porous spongy substrate and results in the loss of productivity (i.e., flux) over time. Because the degree of compaction is influenced by the applied pressure, this phenomenon is more pronounced in high-pressure seawater RO applications. However, some degree of compaction also occurs in brackish water applications operating at much lower pressures.

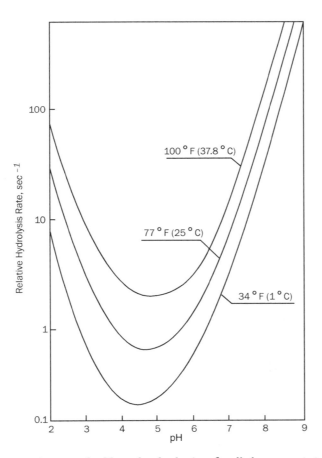

Figure 1-6 Effect of temperature and pH on hydrolysis of cellulose acetate

More recently developed types of membranes are composites of various polymers. Composite membranes are formed by interfacial polymerization on a separate microporous layer, usually polysulfone, which replaces the conventional substrate to support the ultrathin (i.e., 250 to 2,000 Å) salt barrier, as shown in Figure 1-7. A variety of polymers are used for the barrier layer, including the most common fully aromatic polyamides: aryl-alkyl polyamides and polyurea. The initial thin-film composites used aryl-alkyl polyamides as the salt barrier and were extremely sensitive to oxidants, which adversely affected long-term performance. Composites are also made with a salt barrier of fully aromatic cross-linked polyamides that feature more of the desirable characteristics than any other membrane to date. NF employs another type of composite membrane using modified polyamides and piperazinamides for the barrier layer.

Aromatic polyamide membranes, which can tolerate pH levels from 2 to 12 without hydrolysis, can operate over a wider pH range than cellulosic membranes. These membranes are also not susceptible to biological attack. However, because the material is sensitive to oxidants, which can degrade the membrane and result in the loss of salt rejection capabilities, chlorinated water supplies must be dechlorinated prior to the membrane process.

Table 1-3 provides a general summary of key advantages and disadvantages of cellulose acetate and thin-film composite membranes. (It should be noted that properties and characteristics vary somewhat by manufacturers and specific membrane products.)

Primarily due to higher rejection characteristics and lower operating pressures, thin-film composite membranes are most commonly used in water treatment applications. One general exception is the use of membranes in applications in which the source water is higher in organic material. In these cases, the cellulose acetate membranes may offer benefits in terms of more limited membrane biofouling, less frequent cleaning, and potentially reduced pretreatment.

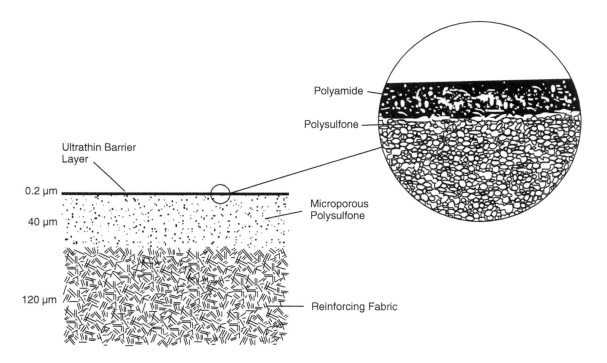

Figure 1-7   Schematic cross-section of a thin-film composite RO membrane

Table 1-3 Comparison of thin-film composite and cellulose acetate membranes

Parameter	Thin-Film Composite Polymer Membranes	Cellulose Acetate Membranes
Salt rejection	Higher (>99.5%)	Lower (up to 95%)
Net driving pressure	Lower	Higher
Surface charge	More negative	Less negative
Chlorine tolerance	Poor	Fair
Cleaning frequency	Higher	Lower
Organics removal	Higher	Lower
Biofouling	More susceptible	Less susceptible
Biodegradation	None	Higher
pH tolerance	High (2–13)	Limited (4–8)

Membrane Element Configurations

A membrane by itself is fragile and must be carefully supported and packaged so that it can be integrated into a unit process. In addition, features are added that enhance permeation of water through the membrane (i.e., flux) and which increase salt rejection. The membrane is generally packaged to minimize hydraulic pressure losses and yet allow sufficient velocities to keep the surface of the membrane flushed clean of concentrated salts and particulate matter. The mechanical design of a membrane element also allows for passage of colloidal and particulate matter through to the concentrate to the extent possible in order to minimize particulate fouling. All of these features are combined with the membrane material itself into a membrane element, which is the smallest discrete unit of an RO or NF system. There are four basic element configurations that have been utilized to at least some extent in commercial applications: tubular, plate-and-frame, hollow fine-fiber, and spiral-wound. Although each of these configurations is described briefly as follows, only the spiral-wound configuration is widely used in modern municipal water treatment applications.

Spiral-wound elements. A membrane utilized in a spiral-wound configuration, as illustrated in Figure 1-8, is manufactured or cast in sheet form on a backing material such as sail cloth (for cellulosic membranes) or a nonwoven polyester web (for the newer composite membranes). Two of these sheets are placed back to back, separated by a spacing fabric/screen that acts as a permeate channel or carrier. Two sides and one end of this sandwich assembly are glued together along the edges to form an envelope or leaf. The open end of the leaf is connected to the permeate tube, around which the leaf is wrapped to form the spiral. An additional sheet of plastic netting (i.e., the feed spacer) is wrapped with each of the numerous leaves to separate the membrane surfaces, maintain the feed channel height, and create turbulence. The spiral assembly, or element, is secured to prevent unraveling by an outer wrap, and a concentrate (i.e., brine) seal is fixed to one end. An antitelescoping device is attached to both ends of the membrane element to maintain a fixed space between elements and facilitate flow from one element to the next. Multiple elements are housed in a series in a cylindrical vessel, as illustrated in Figures 1-9 and 1-10, with the feed and concentrate flowing through the feed-side channels in a straight line along the axis of the element. Some of the water penetrates the membrane and spirals its way to the center, collecting in the central permeate tube. The remaining water passes from the element and out the concentrate port of the pressure vessel. For most applications, several elements, usually six to eight, are housed in a series within the pressure vessel. .The concentrate from one element serves as the feed for

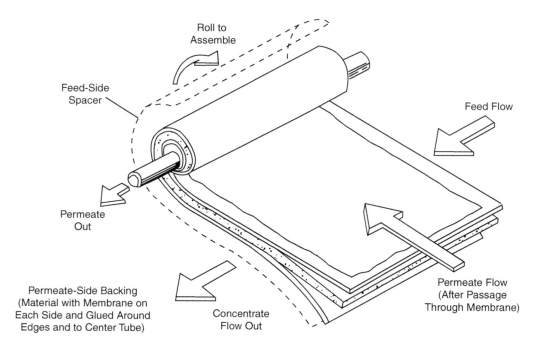

Figure 1-8   Spiral-wound module

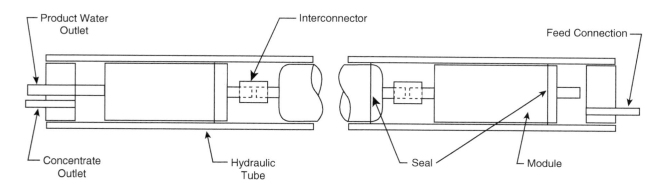

Figure 1-9   Pressure vessel assembly

the next in a series. Permeate can be collected from the back end or both ends of the membrane pressure vessel

Hollow fine-fiber elements.   Sometimes called *hollow fiber membranes*, the additional term *fine* is often used to distinguish this membrane configuration from larger diameter hollow fiber membranes, such as those employed with MF and UF. A hollow fine-fiber membrane is spun with its own support structure. A diagram of a hollow fiber dual-module product is shown in Figure 1-11. The fibers are bundled together as U-shaped tubes with the open ends potted in a tube sheet. The other end of the fiber bundle is also sealed to prevent short-circuiting of the feed stream to the concentrate (i.e., brine) outlet. The bundle is cased in a pressure vessel with the pressurized feed distributed from a tube in the center of the bundle. As it flows radially through the bundle and over the fibers, some of the water penetrates the fibers, flows down the bore, and is collected at the end of the vessel. The remainder

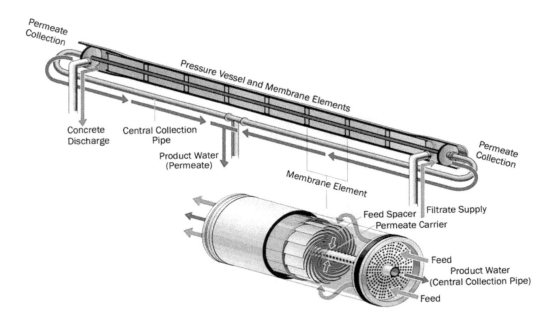

Figure 1-10   Membrane pressure vessel with eight elements

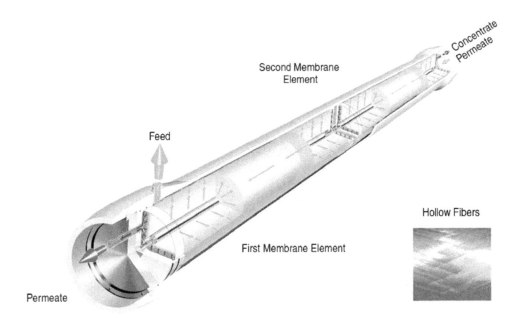

Courtesy of Toyobo, Co., LTD.
Figure 1-11   Hollow fiber membrane module

of the water carries concentrated salts to the concentrate port of the vessel. Because the membrane packaging density is so high, this device has the highest ratio of membrane area to treatment process footprint. The very small diameter fibers dictate lower fluxes with the hollow fine-fiber membrane configuration, but this offers the advantage of minimizing the problem of concentration polarization. The high-density packaging also leaves very little space between the fibers, making it even more critical to remove suspended solids and colloidal matter in order to avoid fouling.

Tubular and plate-and-frame elements.   The use of tubular and plate-and-frame membrane configurations dates back to the beginning of membrane technology. Tubular membranes are essentially a larger, more rigid version of hollow fine-fiber membranes that are not as prone to clogging and that are comparatively easy to clean. The plate-and-frame configuration, one of the earliest membrane designs developed, is simply a series of flat sheet membranes separated by alternating filtrate spacers and feed–concentrate spacers. Both the tubular and plate-and-frame designs have a low membrane-packing density, resulting in a higher capital cost and larger footprint than for spiral-wound or hollow fine-fiber configurations. These designs are used in the food industry (e.g., whey concentration in cheese production and tomato juice concentration) and in some wastewater treatment applications, but seldom compete with spiral-wound and hollow fine-fiber devices in potable applications of brackish water or seawater desalination. One notable exception is in the case of ED/EDR systems, which utilize a design that lends itself well to the use of a plate-and-frame type of membrane arrangement.

REFERENCES

AWWA. 1995. M38–*Electrodialysis and Electrodialysis Reversal*. Denver, Colo.: American Water Works Association.

AWWA. 2005. M53–*Microfiltration and Ultrafiltration Membranes*. Denver, Colo.: American Water Works Association.

Bailer, J.H., B.W. Lykins Jr., C.A. Fronk, and S.J. Kramer. 1987. Using reverse osmosis to remove agricultural chemicals from groundwater. *Jour. AWWA*, 79(8): 55–60.

Bergman, R.A., and J.C. Lozier. 1990. Expanding Applications for Membrane Processes in Water Treatment. In *Proc. of the National Water Supply Improvement Association Biennial Conference*. August 19–23. Lake Buena Vista, Fla.: National Water Supply Improvement Association.

Brunswick, R.J., W. Suratt, and J.E. Burke. 1993. Pilot Testing RO Membranes for Nitrate Removal. In *Proc. of the AWWA Membrane Technology Conference*. Denver, Colo.: American Water Works Association.

Buros, O. 1980. *The USAID desalination manual*. Englewood, N.J.: IDEA Publications.

Clark, S.W., and M.J. Parrotta. 1991. Membrane Technologies and Drinking Water Regulations. In *Proc. of the AWWA Membrane Technologies in the Water Industry Conference*. Denver, Colo.: American Water Works Association.

Côté, P., M.M. Bourbigot, and K. Agbekodo. 1993. Nanofiltration: An Advanced Process for the Production of High Quality Drinking Water. In *Proc. of the AWWA Membrane Technology Conference*. Denver, Colo.: American Water Works Association.

Filmtec Corporation. 1988. *FT-30 Reverse Osmosis Membrane Specifications*. Technical Bulletin. Midland, Mich.: Dow Chemical Company.

Hofman, J.A.M.H., Th.H.M. Noij, J.C. Kruithof, and J.C. Schippers. 1993. Removal of Pesticides with Nanofiltration. In *Proc. of the AWWA Membrane Technology Conference*. Denver, Colo.: American Water Works Association.

Lenz, M., M. Bell, C. Spangenberg, G. Filteau, and E. Owens. 2005. Performance of NF and RO Membranes on VOC Contaminated Groundwaters: Literature Summary and Pilot Test Results. In *Proc. of the AWWA Membrane Technology Conference*. Denver, Colo.: American Water Works Association.

Lozier, J.C., T. McKim, and J. Rose. 1994. *Meeting Stringent Surface Water Discharge Requirements for Reclaimed Water with Membrane Processes*. Paper presented at the ASCE/NCEE Conference July 11–13 at Boulder, Colo.

Lykins, B.W., et al. 1988. *Reverse Osmosis for Removing Organics from Drinking Water: A Cost and Performance Evaluation.* USEPA Publication PB88–225016. Cincinnati, Ohio: US Environmental Protection Agency.

Mickley, M., R. Hamilton, L. Gallegos, and J. Truesdall. 1994. *Membrane Concentrate Disposal.* Denver, Colo.: Awwa Research Foundation and American Water Works Association.

Taylor, J.S., S.J. Duranceau, W.M. Barrett, and J.F. Goigel. 1989a. *Assessment of Potable Water Membrane Applications and Research Needs.* Denver, Colo.: Awwa Research Foundation and American Water Works Association.

Taylor, J.S., L.A. Mulford, S.J. Duranceau, and W.M. Barrett. 1989b. Cost and performance of a membrane pilot plant. *Jour. AWWA,* 81(11): 52–60.

Toray Industries. 1989. *Toray "Romembra" UTC Membrane Reverse Osmosis Module (SU-Series, SU-710L/720L).* Technical Bulletin Series. China 279, Japan: Toray Industries.

USEPA. 2006. *Membrane filtration guidance manual.* Washington, D.C.: USEPA.

USEPA. 1990. *Guidance manual for compliance with the filtration and disinfection requirements for public water systems using surface water sources.* Washington, D.C.: USEPA.

This page intentionally blank.

Chapter **2**

Process Design

Revision Authors: Rob Huehmer and Nikolay Voutchkov (for intakes)

This chapter discusses the general process design principles of RO and NF membrane systems, including the following topics:

- source water

- process design of membrane unit

- posttreatment

Process design fundamentals for selecting and sizing pretreatment, membrane, and posttreatment components of an RO or NF system are discussed in this chapter, as are source water quality and quantity factors. Refer to Figure 1-3 for a schematic view of the typical membrane system used in the subsequent discussions. Table 2-1 summarizes the typical design factors and related unit processes.

This chapter is intended to introduce readers to basic RO and NF design considerations. Reference sources are available for further study in the Additional Sources of Information section at the end of the chapter.

SOURCE WATER SUPPLY

An accurate source water quality analysis of parameters, such as those listed in Table 2-2, is required for NF and RO design. The water quality analysis allows the designer to correctly design the pretreatment and membrane components. The analysis is also used to predict membrane permeate quality. Samples should be split among several certified laboratories with experience in analyzing source water for membrane process treatment as part of the quality assurance and control program. Critical parameters, such as barium, strontium, sulfate, fluoride, and silica, must be accurately analyzed at appropriate detection levels to evaluate scaling potential, particularly for RO and NF applications. For many applications, fouling potential is

Table 2-1   Membrane system design factors and unit processes

Design Factors	Related Unit Processes
Source water supply	
Water quality	Intake, pretreatment, membrane bypass/blending
Water quantity	Pumping, unit operation sizing
Pretreatment	
Fouling potential	
Particulate	Coagulation, flocculation, sedimentation, filtration, MF, UF
Organic	Coagulation, flocculation, sedimentation, filtration, MF, UF
Biological	Coagulation, flocculation, sedimentation, filtration, MF, UF, chlorination, dechlorination
Scaling potential	pH adjustment and scale inhibitor addition
Membrane process	
Feed pressure	Membrane treatment
Permeate recovery rate	Membrane treatment
Permeate flux	Membrane treatment
Permeate quality	Membrane treatment
Posttreatment	
Stabilization	Recarbonation, aeration–degasification, pH adjustment, alkalinity recovery, potential corrosion inhibitor addition
Disinfection	Disinfection
Finished water quality	Membrane bypass and product water blending

also generally predicted by the concentration of DOC, turbidity, and/or biological activity indicators such as heterotrophic plate count (HPC). The reader is cautioned that fouling rates should be determined based on pilot-plant tests for the most accurate indication of fouling potential.

Contaminants of primary concern are:

- Cations that may form scales when concentrated in the membrane system (e.g., calcium, strontium, barium); that may precipitate as hydroxides and foul the membrane elements (e.g., iron, manganese); or are important to meet product water quality objectives (e.g., hardness ions, sodium, boron [for seawater applications])

- Anions that may form scales (e.g., alkalinity ions, sulfate, fluoride, phosphate [water reclamation and reuse application]) and are important for meeting product water quality criteria (e.g., chloride)

- Silica, a nonionic constituent that may precipitate when concentrated, especially in the presence of multivalent cations

- Potential foulants, including bacteria and colloidal material

- Hydrogen sulfide

One of the most important components of any membrane treatment system is a reliable source water supply (Missimer 1994). Even the most sophisticated, well-designed membrane treatment facility has limitations in its ability to treat highly contaminated or varying quality source water.

The required feedwater flow rate will exceed the permeate production because of the limitations in permeate recovery. Assuming permeate recovery rates ranging from 50 to 90 percent, the ratio of required source water to permeate could range from 1.11 to 2.00, as shown in Table 2-3. Figure 2-1 shows the required feedwater flow rates for facilities with capacities of 1 to 40 mgd at various permeate recovery rates. The impact of raw water flow versus system recovery should be considered in the design of wells, pumps, and delivery piping. Also, if two or more water sources of different quality are available, it may be more economical to use one source water over another. Therefore, an analysis of membrane process costs versus source water supply costs should be performed. It is also very important to assess the chemical stability of the source water.

Table 2-2   Suggested parameters for water quality analysis*

Cations		
Aluminum	Ammonium	Barium
Boron	Calcium	Chromium
Copper	Iron (ferrous and ferric)	Lead
Magnesium	Manganese	Potassium
Sodium	Strontium	Zinc

Anions		
Bicarbonate	Carbonate	Chloride
Fluoride	Nitrate	Nitrite
Phosphate (total and ortho)	Sulfate	

Other		
Algae	Alkalinity	Assimilable organic carbon (AOC)
Color	Conductivity	Dissolved oxygen
HPC	Hydrogen sulfide	Ionic strength and ion balance (calculated from analysis)
Oil and grease	Organic carbon (total and dissolved)	pH
Silica (total and reactive)	Silt density index (SDI)	Sulfide-generating bacteria
Temperature	TDS	Total coliform
Total hardness	Total suspended solids	Turbidity
Yeast and mold		

*Not all of these analyses are required for all membrane design efforts. Membrane manufacturers and consultants with expertise in RO/NF design should be consulted for a recommended list of water quality parameters to be tested.

Table 2-3   Feedwater flow rates based on permeate recovery rates

Permeate Flow Rate, mgd	Product Recovery Rate, %	Feedwater Flow Rate, mgd	Concentrate Water Flow Rate, mgd
1.00	50	2.00	1.00
1.00	60	1.67	0.67
1.00	70	1.43	0.43
1.00	75	1.33	0.33
1.00	80	1.25	0.25
1.00	85	1.18	0.18
1.00	90	1.11	0.11

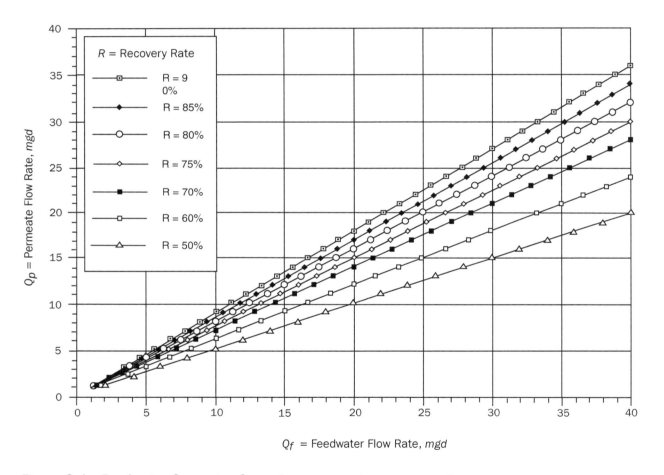

Figure 2-1   Feedwater flow rates for various permeate recovery rates

The following section discusses the development of source water supply and maintenance of water quality. Chapter 3, Facility Design and Construction, presents a discussion of intake design for surface and groundwater sources.

Surface Water

Surface waters present numerous technical problems for pretreatment systems for membrane treatment processes. RO and NF membranes are very sensitive to the concentration of particulates in the water. A surface water source may require construction of comprehensive pretreatment facilities to prevent particulate material from plugging the membranes. Facilities for the coagulation/removal of organic compounds, such as humic acids, may also be required to mitigate membrane fouling.

Beach or shallow wells are sometimes used to avoid direct intakes of surface water. The quality of the surface water supply source can be monitored for many years to assess needed changes in a treatment facility's design.

Fresh water. Intakes for most fresh surface water treatment facilities, regardless of the treatment process, are submerged pipes in rivers, lakes, or reservoirs. A fixed-position intake pipe is commonly found where sufficient data are available to determine that the pipe will always be submerged regardless of climatic conditions. However, many utilities prefer multiple-depth openings to optimize source water quality.

The elevation of the intake pipe should be at least a few feet below the water surface to avoid inflow of floating debris and higher concentrations of aquatic plants, which tend to stay in the photic zone (i.e., those areas of water that are penetrated by light). The intake pipe must also be placed as far from the bottom as possible to avoid collection of sediments. Intakes possessing the ability to withdraw water from multiple depths are recommended in waterways that experience seasonal anaerobic conditions in the benthic region to avoid membrane fouling resulting from increased manganese and iron concentrations. Additional details are contained in *Water Treatment Plant Design* 4th ed. (AWWA/ASCE 2005) and *Water Quality and Treatment* (AWWA 1999).

The end of the intake should be screened to avoid the entrainment of large debris. The diameter of the intake pipe should be sized to adequately to permit the required flow, while maintaining acceptable approach velocities to prevent sediment entrainment and the scouring of vegetative growth from the pipe. The presence of zebra mussels in many waterways in North America also requires additional considerations in the design of intake systems. Provision must be provided for the maintenance of the intake screens and pipe work, including disinfection (zebra mussel kill) and physical removal of zebra mussels from the facilities. In many cases, provision of two parallel intake facilities is recommended.

Seawater or brackish water. Intakes from tidal surface water bodies feeding RO water treatment facilities share many common problems with freshwater systems. However, a number of other issues, such as the susceptibility of a facility to corrosion, storm damage, and marine organism growth, must be considered.

A number of existing seawater membrane treatment facilities use surface intake systems. Many of these systems are located in the Middle East or on islands, both natural and artificial (i.e., oil platforms). Most large-scale membrane facilities using direct surface water intakes are located adjacent to large tidal water bodies, such as the Atlantic Ocean or the Arabian (Persian) Gulf. Some critical problems in the design of intakes in these areas are how far offshore and how deep the intake should be placed and what type of terminal should be used.

Oceanographic investigations for intakes are required to assess storm impact potential, potential growth rates of attaching benthic marine organisms (such as corals and sponges), and near-shore water quality fluctuations. The terminal must be below a water depth affected by damaging orbital storm wave motion and yet far enough offshore to avoid the near-shore sediment transport area where storms can cause suspension of large quantities of sediment. Water quality changes must also be considered in the establishment of the intake point. In the Arabian Gulf, water quality and temperature vary significantly. In some instances, the final intake point may lie several miles offshore. Alternative designs should be considered before a surface intake is installed into any tidal water body.

Similar to fresh water surface sources, the end of the intake should be designed to limit entrainment and impingement. Marine growth may also require additional considerations in the design of the intake system. Provisions for intake screen and pipework must be provided, including disinfection and physical removal of marine growth from the facilities. In many cases, provision of two parallel intake facilities is recommended.

Groundwater

Under steady-state conditions, groundwater normally provides a chemically stable, low turbidity source of water over a long time. However, in coastal areas with high groundwater withdrawal quantities, groundwater quality can vary dramatically. Overpumping can cause saltwater intrusion, which in turn may cause a membrane treatment plant to have problems unless it is designed to accommodate the increased concentration of dissolved solids.

In the development of a groundwater source, the aquifer must be carefully tested and modeled to determine the anticipated short- and long-term changes in water quality. Groundwater quality can change depending on the nature of the aquifer used or the presence of overpumping. The potential for significant water quality changes over time should be considered in the design of the membrane treatment system.

PRETREATMENT

Preserving membrane integrity through proper pretreatment of source water is essential to maximize the efficiency and longevity of an RO or NF membrane system. This section provides a discussion of the various methods of pretreatment that prevent chemical alteration of the membrane polymer and foulant accumulation and scaling on the membrane surface.

Prevent Membrane Damage

If an RO or NF membrane is chemically altered by substances in the source water, the membrane performance efficiency will decrease (such as a decline in salt rejection or loss of productivity). Chemical attacks on membranes generally occur via oxidation or hydrolysis, both of which are easily controlled. The susceptibility to chemical attack is a function of the chemical composition of the membrane polymer.

Cellulose acetate polymers are subject to a loss of rejection properties because of a gradual hydrolysis of the acetyl groups on the polysaccharide backbone. The rate of hydrolysis is a function of pH. Mineral acid is generally required to adjust the pH of most source waters into the 5.5 to 6 range to maximize cellulosic membrane life. Polyamide membranes are capable of operating over a rather broad pH range: from pH 2 to 11 on a continuous basis and up to pH 12 for short-term cleaning. When a polyamide membrane is used for processing water at the higher pH (>8) range, careful consideration must be given to controlling calcium carbonate scaling, as discussed in greater detail in this section.

Although polyamide membranes are not particularly pH sensitive, all varieties of these membranes are intolerant of chlorine and certain other strong oxidizing agents to some extent. Dechlorination through the addition of sodium metabisulfite in excess of stoichiometric requirements should protect the more tolerant polyamide membranes from chlorine attack. For the most susceptible polyamide compositions, chlorine should be totally avoided as a part of pretreatment. Cellulosic membranes, on the other hand, will tolerate chlorine at levels used to provide disinfection of potable water supplies, typically 1 mg/L Cl_2 or less. However, over long membrane service life, the chlorine will facilitate oxidation of the membrane material. In some cases, such as municipal wastewater tertiary treatment, chloramines have been successfully used with composite polyamide membranes for biological control.

Mitigate Membrane Fouling

An accumulation of one or more foreign substances on the surface of a membrane will result in a loss of productivity. Higher operating pressures will then be required to maintain water production (flux) and quality. Membrane fouling generally occurs by one of the following mechanisms:

- Deposition of silt or other suspended solids that were inadequately removed by the pretreatment
- Inorganic scale deposits formed because of precipitation of sparingly soluble salts or silica
- Biological fouling caused by excessive microbial growth
- Interaction of organics with the membrane

In some instances, pretreatment is required to remove algae; certain metals, such as iron and manganese; or other particulate matter. The need for such treatment is dictated by the source water quality, the permeate standards, and the need to protect the membranes. Only the most commonly encountered contaminants are discussed in this manual.

Particulate removal. Designers must take great care to minimize the amount of suspended solids fed to the membrane systems. Most RO and NF membranes used today are spiral-wound elements. Suspended solids can negatively impact a spiral-wound membrane in several ways. As discussed in chapter 1, spiral-wound membranes are fabricated with a feed spacer separating the individual membrane leaves. Suspended solids will plug the feed spacer, resulting in increased pressure drop. The increased feed–concentrate flow stream pressure drop necessitates increased feed pressure to maintain permeate flow rate and, if the pressure drop is too great, the membrane element can be physically damaged. Ensuring adequate removal of suspended solids is a top priority of membrane system designers.

The performance of pretreatment system particle removal is characterized using turbidity and SDI. In some surface water applications, zeta potential is also measured. It is recommended that the zeta potential be greater than –30 mV.

Membrane manufacturers of spiral-wound elements require the feedwater turbidity to not exceed 1 ntu and the SDI to not exceed 4 or 5. However, it is recommended the following guidelines for suspended solids be met:

- Turbidity less than 0.3 ntu
- SDI of 3 (hollow fiber) and 4 or 5 (spiral-wound)

Turbidity is best measured by an in-line continuous monitor. SDI, as described in ASTM method D4189, is based on the rate of plugging a standard 0.45-μm membrane filter. The procedure is shown in appendix C. Zeta potential, used for fresh and brackish surface water, measures a colloid's electrical stability with a meter that can also be installed for continuous monitoring.

SDI values of 3 for hollow fiber membranes and 4 or 5 (depending on manufacturer) for spiral-wound membranes are upper limits recommended by various manufacturers. If these levels are exceeded, pretreatment is required; at lower levels, pretreatment may be recommended to reduce cleaning cycles. The minimum

Table 2-4   Pretreatment techniques (listed in decreasing order of effectiveness) for reducing silt and colloidal material

Method	Comments
Low-pressure membrane filtration (MF or UF)	Operates at low pressures and requires periodic chemical cleaning and frequent backwashing. Removes particulates but essential no organics (unless a precoagulant is fed). High solids loads may require additional pretreatment to be cost effective.
Precoat filtration	Precoat media must be added to replace losses in the backwash step. Does not remove dissolved organics. High solids loads may require additional pretreatment to be cost effective.
Coagulation/flocculation/sedimentation/ filtration	Provides the most process flexibility of all methods. Process is able to remove appreciable organics using coagulation. Highly tolerant of variable suspended solids loads.
Multimedia and pressure filtration	Pilot testing may be required to determine the best media for SDI reduction. May be used in conjunction with coagulants– flocculants, with and without settling.
Rapid sand filters and ultrahigh-rate filters	Coagulants are generally required to achieve acceptable SDI reduction, most through inline coagulation. Can handle limited high turbidity events.

pretreatment for suspended solids, regardless of the SDI, typically is a 5-μm cartridge filter located immediately upstream of the membrane feed pump. If the SDI exceeds the manufacturer's recommendations, it may be possible to achieve sufficient reductions by other treatment techniques listed in Table 2-4. The treatment techniques include a wide range of processes, depending on the concentrations of various contaminants.

For those cases where contaminant particle size is so small that filtration alone is not sufficient, or the suspended solids load exceeds the ability of filtration to operate effectively, adding chemicals to coagulate the colloidal particles is necessary. These chemicals destabilize the colloidal particles by neutralizing the electrostatic charge that surrounds the particles. Once neutralized, the particles are readily agglomerated and removed by sedimentation and/or filtration. Pretreatment techniques can involve relatively complex systems, such as coagulation/flocculation/ sedimentation/filtration, for applications where high concentrations of suspended solids occur in the source water. *AWWA Water Quality and Treatment* and *AWWA/ ASCE Water Treatment Plant Design* describe conventional treatment processes.

The use of coagulation in a pretreatment system prior to RO or NF must be approached with caution. Properly applied, these chemicals are very effective. When overdosed or dosed at the wrong pH, their use can cause more problems than it solves. It is not possible to predict the feed rate based on chemical or physical parameters of the source water. Jar testing or pilot plants are essential to determine the optimal chemical treatment and level of application. With surface waters, the level of suspended solids can vary widely depending on a host of environmental factors. This necessitates frequent checks to determine the proper feed rate to maintain the required turbidity and SDI. Online instruments, such as streaming current detectors, can be applied to control chemical dosing rates.

Common coagulant–flocculant chemicals are listed in Table 2-5. Ferric and aluminum salts can be used effectively provided the pH is properly controlled, sufficient time is allowed to fully precipitate the metallic hydroxide, and the precipitates are completely removed by the media filter. Otherwise, the downstream membrane system can be fouled by aluminum or iron hydroxides. In case of an upset, both of these inorganic coagulants can be removed from the membrane by cleaning, with iron being somewhat easier to dissolve than aluminum. Cationic polyelectrolytes are excellent coagulants but, if overdosed, will foul membranes rapidly and sometimes irreversibly. Polymer use should be approached with caution; the least likely to react with the membrane are the anionic or nonionic polymers. Cationic polymers can also react with anionic scale inhibitors to form insoluble organic deposits that can be very difficult to remove by cleaning. Many RO and NF membrane manufacturers state that cationic polymers should not be used in membrane pretreatment processes and essentially all manufacturers prefer no polymer be used in pretreatment as long as turbidity and SDI criteria are met.

Although the cautionary information in the preceding discussion is important, silt or colloidal fouling is not an issue with most groundwater sources. Most plants drawing water from brackish aquifers or hard groundwaters in Florida operate successfully using only a 5-μm filter for protection against particulate fouling. Certain large seawater RO plants have been able to avoid pretreatment for colloidal fouling problems by drawing the water from a beach well rather than from a surface intake.

Scale control. As product water that is relatively low in solutes passes through the membrane, the remaining feedwater becomes increasingly concentrated in dissolved solids. At certain degrees of concentration, the solubility of various salts can be exceeded, which causes salts to precipitate onto the membrane surface. This process is called *scaling*. Scaling can severely reduce the flow or flux of permeate and can irreversibly damage the membrane. Calcium sulfate is particularly notorious for its ability to damage membranes.

For a large proportion of mineralized source waters, the concentration of salts in the concentrate stream (and conversely the degree of permeate recovery) is limited to the point at which the membrane process becomes uneconomical without pretreatment. This situation is particularly true for water with high concentrations of calcium, barium, strontium, sulfates, or carbonates. With silica precipitation, however, a certain degree of oversaturation is generally tolerated because the chemical reaction is relatively slow and feedwater leaves the system before the precipitate forms. However, membrane manufacturers or system suppliers should always be consulted before silica oversaturation is allowed for a membrane system, particularly when multivalent cations such as iron are present. Lime softening at a pH greater than 11 can be used to reduce silica. Inhibitors to prevent silica deposition also are used to address this problem. Table 2-6 provides a list of common limiting salts or compounds.

Limiting salt calculations are normally performed with computer software. Appendix C illustrates the general steps used to determine the limiting salt and calculate allowable permeate recoveries. The results of those calculations show that, for the hypothetical feedwater, the solubility of calcium carbonate is exceeded and calcium carbonate will precipitate. The results also show that a recovery rate of 84 percent is possible before the solubility limit of strontium sulfate is exceeded. The examples in appendix C are illustrative and do not take the ionic strength of the solution into account.

Table 2-5   Common coagulant–flocculants

Chemical	Comments
Inorganics	
Aluminum sulfate or alum, $[Al_2(SO_4)_3]$	Minimum solubility is achieved at pH 5.7 to 6.5 in freshwater and brackish water applications. Lower values are reported for seawater.
	Must allow sufficient time for complete precipitation or aluminum salts may deposit on membrane.
Aluminum chlorohydrate (ACH) and Polyaluminum chloride (PACl)	Highly effective coagulant results in minimal membrane fouling, effective over wide pH range (pH 5 to 8).
Ferrous sulfate, $(FeSO_4)$	Oxidation to ferric form of iron is required to be effective. Optimal pH is >8.4 for freshwater for particulate removal. Lower pH is optimal for organics reduction.
Ferric sulfate, $[Fe_2(SO_4)_3]$	Works best at ambient pH in freshwater for particulate removal. Lower pH is optimal for organics reduction.
Ferric chloride, $(FeCl_3)$	Works best at pH 6.0 to 7.0 for freshwater. Chemical is widely used for membrane pretreatment of surface water.
Organic polyelectrolytes	
Cationic	Will interact with many scale inhibitors. Can irreversibly foul many spiral-wound membranes. Consult manufacturer.
Anionic and nonionic	Will not react with most scale inhibitors. May foul certain membranes. Consult manufacturer. Generally less effective than cationic as a coagulant–flocculant.

Table 2-6   Common limiting salts

Salt	Solubility Product of Salt, pK_{sp} at 25°C
Calcium carbonate $(CaCO_3)$	8.30
Calcium fluoride (CaF_2)	8.27
Calcium phosphate $(CaPO_4)$	25.00
Calcium sulfate $(CaSO_4)$	4.70
Barium sulfate $(BaSO_4)$	9.70
Strontium sulfate $(SrSO_4)$	6.20
Silica (SiO_2)	2.70

An increase up to a certain point in ionic strength of the solution will make the salt more soluble and, in effect, increase the allowable permeate recovery rate. Design software that membrane manufacturers use takes into account the impacts of ionic strength in determining allowable recovery rates.

To increase the permeate recovery rate, feedwater may be chemically altered to reduce the concentration of cations or anions of the limiting salt. One method to prevent the formation of calcium carbonate scales is to add an acid to convert carbonate ions ($CO_3{}^{2-}$) to bicarbonate ions ($HCO_3{}^-$). Bicarbonate ions can also be converted to carbonic acid (H_2CO_3) and subsequently carbon dioxide during acidification. Appendix C gives an example of adding sulfuric acid to control calcium carbonate scaling.

Scale inhibitors are often added to the feedwater stream to allow the membrane system to operate at permeate recovery rates in excess of limiting salt constraints. Scale inhibitors work by one of several mechanisms including mitigation of scale formation by inhibiting the rate of formation of crystalline precipitates under supersaturated conditions, chelation of metal ions permitting them to stay in solution at higher concentrations, or dispersion, which maintains colloids in suspension until discharged from the membranes in the concentrate stream.

Several different chemicals have been historically used as scale inhibitors including polyphosphates (potassium pyrophosphate and sodium hexametaphosphate). Sodium hexametaphosphate, used in conjunction with acid, was the scale inhibitor of choice for many years in RO systems. One disadvantage of sodium hexametaphosphate is the tendency of the polyphosphates to hydrolyze over time, reducing its effectiveness. Another disadvantage of sodium hexametaphosphate is its ineffectiveness in inhibiting the precipitation of other sparingly soluble salts.

The development of synthetic polymers (polyacrylates) in the 1970s provided significant progress in scale control. The synthetic polymers provided good calcium carbonate and calcium sulfate control while providing limited metal ion stabilization and dispersant activity. Scale inhibitors currently utilized evolved from these early synthetic polymers with the development of proprietary copolymers that provide excellent scale inhibition, enhanced metal ion stabilization, and colloidal dispersant properties. Many scale inhibitors marketed are formulated to provide optimum performance on one or more sparingly soluble salt.

Scale inhibitor dosage calculations are too complex to be presented in this manual. There exist issues regarding compatibility with coagulant and flocculant aids, and membrane materials that must be considered. Chemical dosage and efficacy information for specific membranes is available from scale inhibitor manufacturers, and membrane manufacturers provide information on the compatibility of scale inhibitors with their membranes.

Methods other than acids or scale inhibitors used to control scaling or colloidal fouling include:

- Ion exchange softening to reduce multivalent cations (Ca^{2+}, Mg^{2+})

- Lime softening to reduce multivalent cations and silica

- Aeration and chemical oxidation and filtration to reduce iron and manganese

- *Greensand* or oxidation filtration to reduce iron and manganese

- Coagulation and filtration to reduce colloidal and particulate matter

Scale with crystalline morphology. Scale forms on a membrane surface when naturally occurring, sparingly soluble salts are concentrated beyond their solubility limit by the membrane process. Table 2-7 lists the commonly encountered scales and the methods for preventing precipitation on a membrane. The methods will be discussed in greater detail later in this chapter.

The solubility limit of a sparingly soluble salt is defined by the salt's solubility product constant K_{sp}, which is discussed in more detail in appendix C. Membrane manufacturers have design software that performs complex calculations to yield values of K_{sp}. For ease of discussion and preliminary analysis, most chemists and engineers prefer to simplify the mathematics by defining a conditional solubility product constant (K_{sp}) that specifies solubility as a function of ionic strength (I). The ionic strength of a solution may be defined as follows:

$$I = \frac{1}{2}\sum m_i z_i^2 = \frac{1}{2}\left(m_1 z_1^2 + m_2 z_2^2 + m_3 z_3^2 + ... + m_n z_n^2\right) \qquad \text{(Eq 2-1)}$$

Where:

m_i = molar concentration of the ith species

Z_i = ionic charge of the ith species

n = total number of ionic species in the solution

An example of an ionic strength calculation is given in Table 2-8. In addition, Figures 2-2 and 2-3 illustrate how the solubility product of the sulfate salts of calcium, barium, and strontium vary with the ionic strength of the solution. Figure 2-4 illustrates how the solubility product of calcium fluoride salts vary with the ionic strength of the solution. Figure 2-5 illustrates how the solubility of calcium phosphate varies with respect to pH.

Whenever the ratio of the ion product to the K'_{sp} exceeds 1.0, there is a potential for scale deposition on the RO or NF membrane and pretreatment is essential. Calculation of an ion product is also discussed in appendix C. For spiral-wound

Table 2-7   Common scales and other inorganic foulants and methods for controlling them

Species	Method of Control	
	Primary	Secondary
Calcium carbonate ($CaCO_3$)	Mineral acid Threshold inhibitor	Soften
Calcium sulfate ($CaSO_4$)	Threshold inhibitor Soften	Limit recovery
Barium sulfate ($BaSO_4$)	Threshold inhibitor Soften	Limit recovery
Strontium sulfate ($SrSO_4$)	Threshold inhibitor Soften	Limit recovery
Calcium fluoride (CaF_2)	Threshold inhibitor Soften	Limit recovery
Calcium phosphate ($CaPO_4$)	Mineral acid Threshold inhibitor	Limit recovery
Silica (SiO_2)	Threshold inhibitor Limit recovery	Raise pH to greater than 8.5 (if carbonate scale is not an issue) or increase temperature
Ferric hydroxide [$Fe(OH)_3$]	Precipitation and filtration Chelating agent	Soften
Aluminum hydroxide [$Al(OH)_3$]	Precipitation and filtration at pH of minimum solubility Chelating agent	—
Sulfur (S) (from hydrogen sulfide)	Exclude air and other oxidants prior to membranes	—

Table 2-8   Example of an ionic strength calculation

Species	Assumed Concentration, mg/L	Number of Milligrams per Mole	m_i*	z_i^2	$m_i z_i$[3]
Calcium (Ca^{2+})	409	40,000	0.0102	4	0.0408
Magnesium (Mg^{2+})	169	24,300	0.00695	4	0.0278
Sodium (Na^+)	314	23,000	0.0137	1	0.0137
Bicarbonate (HCO_3^-)	150	61,000	0.00246	1	0.00246
Sulfate (SO_4^{2-})	1,510	96,100	0.0157	4	0.0628
Chloride (Cl^-)	500	35,500	0.0141	1	0.0141

$$\sum m_i z_i^2 \qquad = 0.1617$$

$$I = \frac{1}{2}\sum m_i z_i^2 \qquad = 0.0808$$

*Determined by dividing the value in column 2 by the value in column 3.

membranes, because of concentration polarization at the membrane surface and occasional water quality variation, pretreatment is recommended whenever the ratio of the ion product to K'_{sp} is greater than 0.8.

In theory, supersaturation of all insoluble salts can be evaluated in this manner. However, when examining calcium carbonate solubility, engineers prefer to evaluate scaling potential in terms of either the Langelier saturation index (LSI) or, in the case of seawater, the Stiff-and-Davis stability index (S&DSI). Both indexes are explained further in appendix D. For either index, a positive value indicates a scale-forming condition. For most brackish waters, the LSI has proven to be an adequate predictor. For seawater, which has a much higher ionic strength, the S&DSI has become the preferred index. Nomographs have been widely published to allow one to calculate either index without having access to logarithm tables or a calculator that has scientific functions. Membrane manufacturers, consulting engineers, and technical service departments of chemical suppliers have computer programs that can either be made available or accessed on request to evaluate the supersaturation of sparingly soluble salts at various levels of recovery from a source water of known composition. Results from one such program are given in Figure 2-6.

The following are some methods for preventing scale (as briefly mentioned in Table 2-7):

- Acidify to remove carbonate or bicarbonate ions

- Limit recovery to prevent salts and/or silica from concentrating in excess of solubility limits

- Soften the source water to remove calcium ions

- Use threshold scale inhibitors, which are effective for calcium sulfate and calcium carbonate

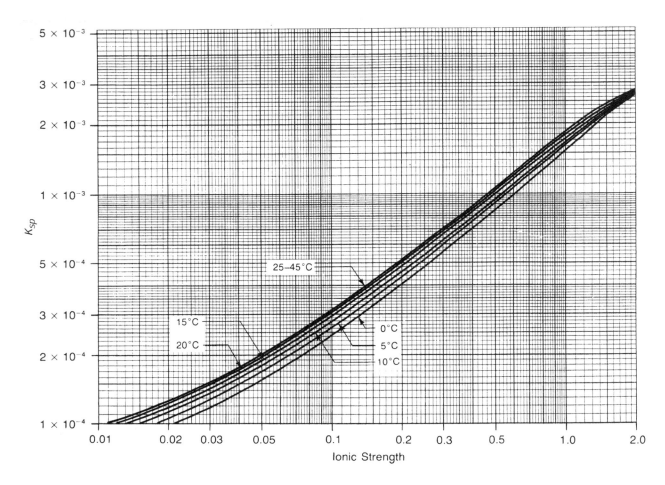

Figure 2-2 Calcium sulfate solubility product versus ionic strength

Acidification is effective in preventing calcium carbonate scaling, provides a small benefit in terms of increased silica solubility, and is usually required to prevent hydrolysis of cellulose acetate membranes. The obvious safety hazards associated with handling strong mineral acids necessitate appropriate operator training and conscientious attention to safe handling practices. Cation exchange softening is impractical on most brackish waters because of the high levels of hardness in the water; it is not feasible with seawater. Lime softening is practiced occasionally for brackish waters with exceptionally high hardness, but the costs of capital, labor, chemicals, and sludge disposal are high. Limiting recovery to ensure solubility limits are not exceeded should be viewed as a last-resort method for dealing with crystalline scales because the practice wastes a substantial portion of the source water resource. The addition of a threshold scale inhibitor is the most practical and widely used method to prevent crystalline scale from forming on membranes.

Threshold scale inhibitors have often been incorrectly referred to in desalination literature as sequestrants. These chemicals do not sequester by being in exact proportions for interaction with calcium, barium, or strontium. Instead, they react with the surfaces of ion clusters to prevent the orderly growth needed to form the scale crystal or allow it to grow to a harmful size. Because of this unique property,

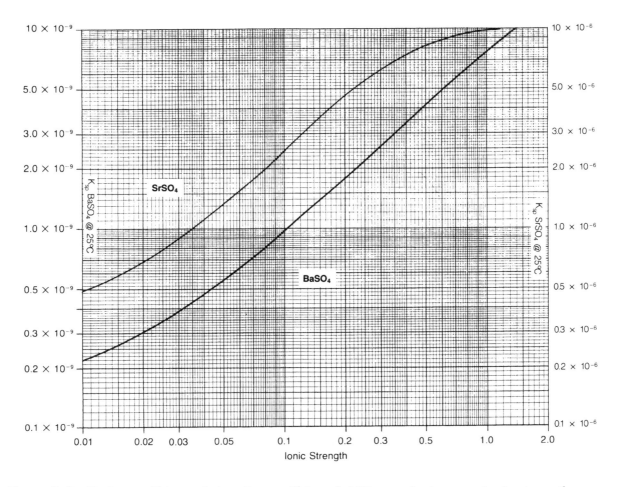

Figure 2-3 Barium sulfate and strontium sulfate solubility product versus ionic strength

scale inhibitors can be added at very low levels, usually less than 5 mg/L, into the membrane source water to prevent scale from forming at multiple levels of supersaturation. Two types of chemical scale inhibitors that have achieved widespread usage in the production of potable water are polyphosphates and high-performance polymeric scale inhibitors, most typically polyacrylates.

Before the development of polymeric scale inhibitors, sodium hexametaphosphate (SHMP) was widely used in membrane systems to prevent sulfate scales from precipitating in a membrane system. However, SHMP has several potential drawbacks:

- It is less effective than the new polymeric scale inhibitors, so higher doses of SHMP are normally required.

- The solid form of SHMP has to be diluted for injection. Once diluted in water, it starts to hydrolyze to the orthophosphate, which is ineffective as a scale inhibitor and contributes to calcium phosphate scaling.

- Discharging the concentrate stream, which contains phosphates, can contribute to environmental problems.

- It can contribute to biological growth within the membrane element.

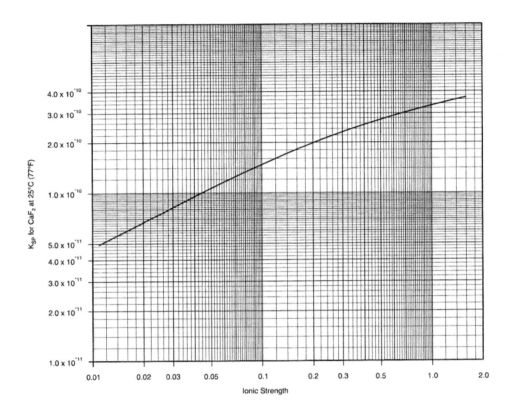

Figure 2-4   Calcium fluoride solubility product versus ionic strength

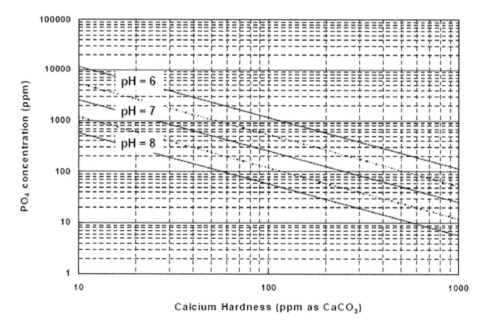

Figure 2-5   Calcium phosphate solubility versus pH

RO system	Plant Name
Percent recovery	80

Feedwater Analysis

Cations	mg/L	Anions	mg/L
Ca	100	HCO_3	189.9
Mg	140	SO_4	350
Na	870	Cl	1,600
K	40	F	1.6
Ba	0.1	NO_3	0
Sr	20	PO_4	0
Fe	0	CO_3	0.28
Silica	14	CO_2	13.53
Temperature	25°C	Pressure	300 psi

Parameter	Value
Ionic strength, feedwater	6.800001E-02
Total cation as $CaCO_3$	2,743 mg/L
Total anion as $CaCO_3$	2,780 mg/L
Total dissolved solids, feedwater	3,096 mg/L
pH, feedwater	7.2
Total dissolved solids, concentrate	15,479 mg/L
pH, concentrate	7.91

Polymeric Antiscalant Dosage*

Constituent	Minimum Dose, mg/L	Recommended Dose, mg/L
$CaCO_3$	3	5
$SrSO_4$	2	4
$BaSO_4$	3	5
CaF_2	—	5

Degree of Saturation of Potential Scales

$CaCO_3$	1.94%	$SrSO_4$	250%
$CaSO_4$	29%	$BaSO_4$	2,375%

Ion Product

Constituent	Ionic Strength
$CaCO_3$	2.903823E-07
$SrSO_4$	2.078944E-05
CaF_2	2.211644E-09
$CaSO_4$	2.272678E-04
$BaSO_4$	6.630918E-08

* To ensure scale-free operation, polymeric antiscalant should be dosed consistent with the greatest scale potential in the system as indicated by the highest dosage given.

Figure 2-6 Sample computerized evaluation of the supersaturation of sparingly soluble salts for a given source water, with a polymeric scale-inhibitor dose projection

High-performance polymeric scale inhibitors were developed to offset the deficiencies attributable to SHMP and to provide a dependable, cost-effective pretreatment alternative. Operating data found in Figures 2-7 and 2-8 demonstrate the scale control efficacy of a polymeric inhibitor.

The data in Figure 2-7 are from a pilot test conducted at the Island Water Association in Sanibel, Fla. Operating without mineral acid to reduce the feed pH, a 3 mg/L dose of polymer provided effective control of calcium carbonate scaling at an LSI of +2 in the concentrate stream. The concentrate stream was also supersaturated in strontium and barium sulfates. After the test had concluded, the utility switched the entire plant to the polymeric scale inhibitor to save the expense of adding acid. The plant continues to operate without any scaling problems.

Figure 2-8 presents data collected from a pilot RO system operating on a highly supersaturated calcium sulfate water at Venice, Fla. Again, the stability of the normalized data indicates effective inhibition of the sulfate scales of calcium, barium, and strontium, as well as of calcium carbonate. This plant was constructed in two sections; about half of the membranes at the time were cellulosic. The plant continued to operate with a combination of sulfuric acid and polymeric scale inhibitor.

Amorphous deposits.   Many groundwaters contain hydrogen sulfide, which can be oxidized to elemental sulfur if air or other oxidants are introduced into the membrane system. If such an air leak occurs before the pretreatment filters, a certain portion of the colloidal sulfur may be removed by the filters and membrane damage can be minimized. However, a significant proportion of the colloidal sulfur is smaller than the 5- to 25-μm effective retention size of the filters and will pass through to the membrane elements. It is especially important to ensure that air is not allowed to enter the module from the reject or product side of the system on shutdown. If it does, colloidal sulfur fouling, which is difficult to remove by cleaning, will be inevitable. No chemical pretreatment can prevent colloidal sulfur fouling; good system design is the best prevention.

Silica (SiO_2) is another example of a substance that, if its solubility is exceeded, can form an amorphous, inorganic deposit on a membrane. Because silica is a polymer rather than having a crystalline ionic lattice, threshold scale inhibitors (scale inhibitors) have not been very effective in stabilizing supersaturated silica solutions. However, there are commercially available dispersants that have good success in controlling silica deposition. Silica deposition may also be controlled by limiting the RO or NF recovery. Nonetheless, the slow kinetics of silica polymerization permits some well-designed membrane systems to operate at above the theoretical solubility. Figure 2-9 shows the theoretical silica solubility in the pH range of 7 to 7.7 as a function of water temperature; the values in this figure also indicate maximum levels of silica in the brine stream that have been achieved without precipitation on the membrane.

Silica solubility can be altered by pH adjustment as shown in Figure 2-10. The effect is less dramatic at low pHs than at the high end of the pH scale.

Another amorphous foulant occasionally appearing in membrane plants is iron hydroxide. When found in groundwater, iron is usually in the form of soluble ferrous bicarbonate. Provided the system is maintained in an anaerobic condition, ferrous iron is unlikely to cause problems. However, if allowed to oxidize, ferric iron will precipitate as the hydroxide in the pH range in which most waters are processed. Some membrane manufacturers specify maximum levels of iron permissible in the source water.

Location: Sanibel, Fla.
RO Feed: 3,700 mg/L TDS

Membrane: Thin-film composite spiral wound
Recovery: 80 percent

Scaling Potential:
LSI: +2.0
Strontium Sulfate: 156 percent of Saturation
Barium Sulfate: 226 percent of Saturation

Antiscalant Dose: 3 mg/L

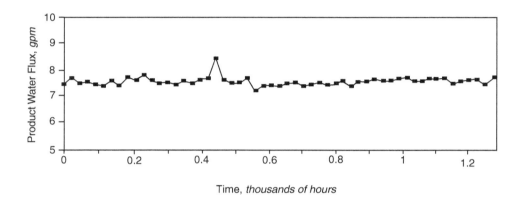

Time, *thousands of hours*

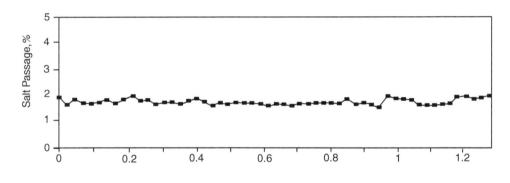

Time, *thousands of hours*

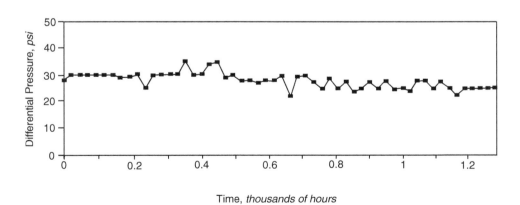

Time, *thousands of hours*

Figure 2-7   Scale inhibition study, Sanibel, Fla.

Location: Venice, Fla.   Membrane: Hollow Fiber
RO feed: 2,600 mg/L TDS   Recovery: 57 percent

Scaling Potential:
LSI: +1.3
Calcium Sulfate :   157 percent of Saturation
Strontium Sulfate :   271 percent of Saturation
Barium Sulfate :   1,816 percent of Saturation

Antiscalant Dose: 5 mg/L

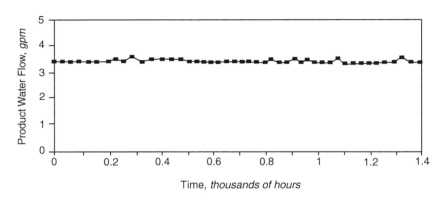

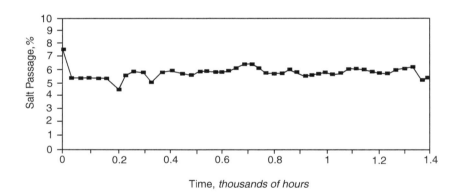

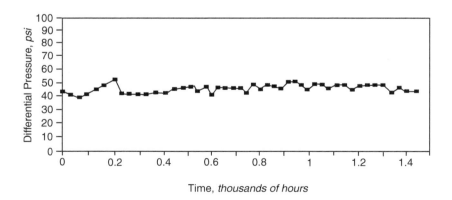

Figure 2-8   Scale inhibition study, Venice, Fla.

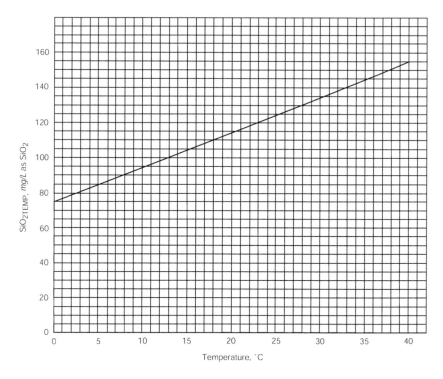

Figure 2-9   Effect of temperature on theoretical SiO_2 solubility, pH 7.7

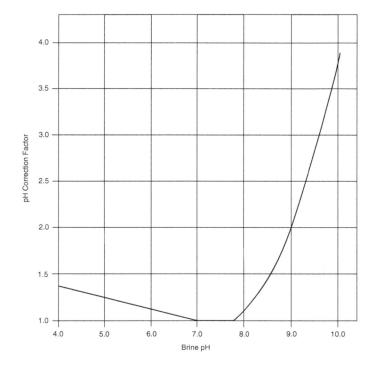

Figure 2-10 SiO_2 pH correction factors

If removal is needed to meet operating guidelines under the manufacturer's warranty, iron is usually removed by oxidation followed by filtration. Manganese greensand filtration is one method of providing both iron removal and filtration (Figure 2-11). Care should be taken to prevent excess oxidant, such as potassium permanganate, from contacting membranes. Air oxidation or chlorine addition followed by filtering through appropriate filter media is another option, provided the same precautions are taken to minimize residual iron as when used as a coagulant–flocculant. Feedwater with a free chlorine residual should not contact thin-film composite membranes. For source water with high ferrous and low ferric iron levels, precipitates can be held in suspension by lowering the pH to 6.0 or less and adding dispersants and chelants. MF and UF have also been effectively used to remove undissolved iron, and iron dispersants are now available commercially.

Iron fouling may also occur by deposition of corrosion products from mild steel or cast-iron components in the raw water system. Such fouling is generally found in older, often smaller systems where existing materials have not been replaced. Proper selection of construction materials is the best insurance against this type of iron fouling. Precipitation of other metal hydroxides is rare with groundwater sources but occurs occasionally when alum-pretreated surface water is processed by membranes. No matter what the source of the alum, if a source water is treated with alum for removal of suspended solids before membrane processing, precautions must be taken with regard to pH and reaction time to ensure as complete a precipitation of the aluminum hydroxide as possible. Filtration systems must be maintained in optimal condition to prevent aluminum precipitates from getting into the membrane feedwater; otherwise, membrane fouling is likely to occur.

Figure 2-11   Greensand horizontal filters (from a 9.6 mgd membrane softening plant, Dunedin, Fla.)

Biological fouling. Control of biological fouling is essential if a membrane system is to perform at design levels on a consistent basis. Because the interior of a membrane element is wet and possesses a large surface area, it is an ideal place for microorganisms to grow. Once established on the membrane, microbes can adhere to the polymer tenaciously. More harmful than the organisms themselves is the polysaccharide they secrete into the biofilm. This biofilm uniformly covers the membrane, causing a deterioration in flux and salt rejection. The population of microorganisms in most brackish groundwater sources is small enough that pretreatment for biological fouling is not required, provided the membrane system is used on a fairly continuous basis. For surface waters, microbial fouling control must be considered in design and operation.

One of the best steps toward eliminating biological fouling is to size the membrane system capacity to meet the need for water. Any membrane that is allowed to sit out of service for more than a day or two should be flushed with pretreated water or permeate on a daily basis to prevent a tolerably small bacteria population from growing to an intolerable level. If the system is to be out of service for extended periods of time (such as a week or more), it is necessary to flush the membranes with permeate and add a sanitizer or membrane preservative recommended by the manufacturer. Formaldehyde and sodium bisulfite solutions are effective in preventing microbes from proliferating in the membrane elements during storage, but the use of formaldehyde is highly restricted because of its potential carcinogenic properties.

Surface waters are more likely to need some type of pretreatment to prevent biofouling. For the most highly contaminated waters, continuous chlorination is necessary for membranes that can tolerate free chlorine. For less severe problems, periodic shock treatments or intermittent chlorination/dechlorination may be the only treatment sufficient to prevent biofouling. Table 2-9 summarizes current methods used to control biological fouling in membrane systems. Only approved products should be used. Many states require that chemical additives be NSF-60 certified for potable water applications.

Table 2-9   Pretreatment for control of biological activity*

Treatment	Comments
Chlorination	Dechlorination required for polyamide membranes.
Copper sulfate	Effective for algae. Generally limited to seawater systems.
Chloramines	Some polyamide membranes not affected, but these chemicals are not as efficient as other disinfectants. Long contact time may be required.

Shock Treatment	Comments
Sodium bisulfite	Minimum dose of 500 mg/L for at least 30 minutes. Time between treatments depends on bacteria counts. Will not affect most membranes.
Iodine	Effective, but life of polyamide membrane will be shortened. Maximum dose is 15 mg/L.
Hydrogen peroxide	Same as for iodine. Presence of metals on membrane surface should be minimized during use.

*Biological control methods should be approved by the membrane manufacturer in order not to void membrane warranties.

RO systems treating seawater from open intakes are particularly prone to biological fouling. Several methods of mitigating biofouling have been practiced, including shock chlorination of intake pipework (followed by dechlorination). In other cases, parallel raw water pipework has been supplied. Alternating raw water pipework on an intermittent basis results in the formation of anaerobic conditions and mitigation of biogrowth in the pipe line. Pretreatment technologies that are capable of mitigating biofouling include MF, UF, and biological filtration.

Membranes used to process tertiary sewage effluent (the most notable being Water Factory 21 in the Orange County, Calif., Water District) were noted for having severe but manageable biofouling problems following conventional lime softening and media filtration. Lengthy piloting of MF and UF indicated that these technologies significantly mitigate biofouling. The successor to Water Factory 21, dubbed the Groundwater Replenishment System, utilizes MF as pretreatment to thin-film composite membranes.

Biological treatment of water was first implemented in France and other western European countries nearly 20 years ago. Biological filters typically consist of granular activated carbon (GAC) beds that are optimized for microbial utilization of a portion of the NOM in the water. The surfaces of the filter media act as a support for microbial attachment and growth, resulting in a biofilm adapted to using the organic matter found in that particular water. Bouwer and Crowe (1988) found that removal of TOC in these filters range from 5 to 75 percent.

Recent research performed indicates that biofouling of seawater RO units can be aggravated by prechlorinating/dechlorinating seawater as a result of increased concentrations of AOC in the water. Preoxidation, commonly practiced in membrane treatment, can result in increased membrane fouling. Goel et al. (1995) reported that the fraction of assimiable organic matter (AOM) in water was increased after preoxidation, but the numerical value varied from site to site. USBR (2003) examined the use of biological filtration, filtration, and prechlorination as mitigation strategies for membrane treatment. The authors found that chlorination of feedwater had no beneficial effect in mitigating RO biofouling. They found that biological treatment followed by filtration substantially reduced the rate of biological fouling in the system. The authors determined that utilizing biological treatment to reduce assimiable organic carbon (AOC) could result in substantial cost reductions in a large surface-water membrane desalination plant.

Control of biological fouling is of particular concern with the use of cellulose acetate membranes. Theoretically, cellulose membranes can be biologically degraded by cellulose-producing bacteria. Consequently, feedwaters to cellulose membranes are typically chlorinated. Documented biological degradation has rarely been reported.

Organic fouling. There are several different sources of organic fouling that exist. A major cause of organic fouling is overdosing of high molecular-weight cationic polymers used for coagulation. Oils, grease, and other water-immiscible organics must also be kept away from the membranes; otherwise, irreversible fouling can occur. Groundwaters rarely contain such foulants, but careful selection and application of activated carbon prefiltration is advised if these foulants are present. High molecular-weight, weakly charged, dissolved organics, such as the humic and fulvic acids naturally found in many water supplies, can foul RO and NF membranes alone or in combination with other feedwater contaminants.

Mitigation of organic fouling may require additional pretreatment, including such technologies as GAC filtration coagulation/flocculation/ sedimentation/filtration, ozone/biological activated carbon, or biofiltration (i.e., slow sand) to remove organics associated with fouling.

Empirical data from operating membrane treatment plants indicate that algal blooms in the raw water source result in accelerated membrane fouling. Additionally, the release of AOM into water by algae through secretions and on cell lyses is of concern.

Her et al. (2002) examined fouling at the Mery-sur-Oise (France) NF plant. The Mery-sur-Oise plant uses conventional surface water treatment followed by ozonation. Two pilot units (one using sand-filtered water, the other using ozonated, filtered water) were operated in parallel. Ozonation was observed to result in greater fouling as a result of a change in NOM characteristics and increasing AOM concentrations. The researchers concluded that humic substances were not found to be major foulants and that significant fouling from proteins and polysaccharides occurred.

USBR (2002) conducted NOM fractionation studies on natural surface waters examining the effect of molecular weight fractionation and hydrophobicity on membrane fouling. They found that fouling of a polyethersulfone NF membrane was dependent on NF membrane characteristics, NOM polarity, NOM molecular weight, and feed solution chemistry. Solutions possessing higher ionic strength exhibited more membrane fouling and reduced NOM rejection, predominantly due to hydrophobic interactions. At low ionic strength, fouling occurred predominantly due to hydrophilic interactions. The authors found that modification of the membrane surface (more hydrophilic) through ultraviolet (UV) irradiation and UV-assisted graft polymerization could be used to modify the rate of fouling dependent on the specific feedwater chemistry.

MEMBRANE PROCESS THEORY

Many types of membranes and processes with different performance characteristics are available. Selection of a specific membrane depends on the process the membrane uses to separate the components of the feedwater (e.g., RO/NF and ED/EDR membranes use different processes).

- The efficiency of the membrane process in separating the feedwater components, and

- The stability of the membrane, as well as the compatibility with the feedwater components to be separated.

In general, feedwater component separation is accomplished based on one of the following:

- Molecular size differences between the components and the membrane polymer structure, as in MF, UF, NF, or RO,

- Electrical charge, as in ED/EDR, and

- Solubility of the different components in the membrane phase, as in dialysis.

The RO process can remove more than 99 percent of all dissolved minerals and more than 95 percent of organic compounds, as well as biological and colloidal suspended matter, including turbidity, from water. The NF process is primarily used for organic removal and water softening, and it can remove 5 to 95 percent of TDS.

In any membrane process, flow characteristics are unique functions of the membrane polymer. For example, product flow or solute (salt) passage for a polyamide polymer is different from that of a cellulose acetate polymer, which is different from that of a polysulfone polymer. If the membrane area in a device is twice that of another device using the same polymer, the water flow will be double. Similarly, a thicker membrane will give less water flow than a thinner membrane of the same polymer. The pressure applied in the system and the concentration differential across the membrane can be adjusted by an end user. Other factors, such as the membrane material, membrane area in a device, and membrane thickness, are set and controlled only by the membrane manufacturers and system suppliers. The following paragraphs discuss the adjustable variables for RO and NF.

In natural osmosis, a semipermeable membrane separates pure water (solvent) from a salt (solute) solution, as shown in Figure 2-12. Pure water naturally passes through the membrane to dilute the salt solution; the driving force for the flow is the difference in chemical potential between the two solutions. Chemical potential is directly proportional to changes in temperature and pressure and inversely proportional to changes in solute concentration. Water flow continues until the pressure created by the hydraulic head equals the osmotic pressure of the salt solution. At this point the two liquids are said to be at *osmotic equilibrium* (Figure 2-13).

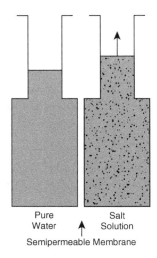

Figure 2-12   Osmotic flow

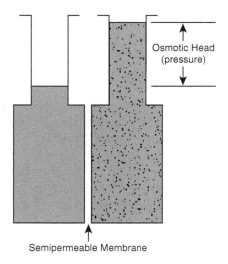

Figure 2-13   Osmotic equilibrium

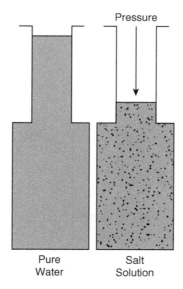

Figure 2-14   Reverse osmosis

In RO, applying external pressure on the salt solution allows the net natural flow of water to be reversed (Figure 2-14), hence the term *reverse osmosis*. NF is a similar process to RO, but NF's "looser" membranes require a lower driving force to move water through the membrane.

Design Equations

This section describes the fundamentals associated with diffusion-controlled membrane processes, such as RO and NF. In such processes, water is forced through the membrane by a pressure differential (a type of motion called *convection*), and dissolved salts pass through the membrane because of a concentration differential (a type of motion called *diffusion*). Because the membrane is semipermeable, both dissolved salts and water are transported to differing degrees through the molecular structure of the active surface layer of the membrane. The osmotic pressure for a salt solution can be estimated as 1 psi per 100 mg/L TDS for fresh and brackish waters. At saline salt concentrations (i.e., 35,000 mg/L TDS), the ratio of pounds per square inch to milligrams per liter TDS is greater than 1.0 (Weber 1972).

The standard model for describing the RO and NF processes is the homogenous solution diffusion (HSD) model, which illustrates the effects of feed concentration, membrane characteristics, recovery, and pressure on permeate concentration. The HSD model incorporates operational parameters (water quality, water recovery, and membrane-specific coefficients) to determine system performance. The HSD model does not consider the effects of certain chemical and physical constraints, and it makes certain simplifying assumptions. However, the equations are superior to using percent rejection as a means of predicting permeate water quality.

Figure 2-15 shows a single membrane element, as well as the terminology used to describe flow, concentration, and pressure. The following equations are used for RO and NF membrane processes to determine system efficiency.

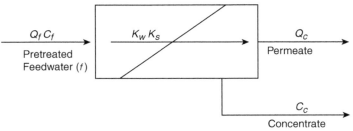

Q = Flow
C = Concentration
K_w = Water mass transfer coefficient
K_s = Solute mass transfer coefficient

Figure 2-15   Schematic diagram of an RO membrane element

Mass balance for water flow:

$$Q_f = Q_p + Q_c \qquad \text{(Eq 2-2)}$$

Where:

Q_f = feedwater flow rate, units of volume per time, e.g., gpd
Q_p = permeate flow rate, units of volume per time, e.g., gpd
Q_c = concentrate flow rate, units of volume per time, e.g., gpd

Mass balance for solute flux:

$$Q_f C_f = Q_p C_p + Q_c C_c \qquad \text{(Eq 2-3)}$$

Where:

C_f = feedwater solute concentration, units of mass per volume, e.g., mg/L
C_p = permeate solute concentration, units of mass per volume, e.g., mg/L
C_c = concentrate solute concentration, units of mass per volume, e.g., mg/L

Product recovery rate:

$$R = \frac{Q_p}{Q_f} \qquad \text{(Eq 2-4)}$$

Where:
R = decimal fraction of product water recovered from feedwater

Water flux:

$$F_w = K_w(\Delta P - \Delta \pi) = \frac{Q_p}{A} \qquad \text{(Eq 2-5)}$$

Where:

F_w = water flux, units of flow rate per unit area, e.g., gpd/ft^2

K_w = water mass transfer coefficient (see Eq 2-5), units of flux per pressure, e.g., gpd/ft^2/psi

ΔP = transmembrane pressure differential, units of pressure, e.g., psi

$\Delta \pi$ = transmembrane osmotic pressure differential, units of pressure, e.g., psi

A = effective membrane area

NOTE: $\Delta P - \Delta \pi$ = net applied pressure (NAP).

Dissolved solute flux:

$$\begin{aligned} F_s &= K_s(C_m - C_p) \\ &= K_s\left[\left(\frac{C_f + C_c}{2}\right) - C_p\right] = \frac{Q_p C_p}{A} \end{aligned} \qquad \text{(Eq 2-6)}$$

Where:

F_s = solute flux, units of mass per time per area, e.g., lb/ft^2/d

K_s = solute mass transfer coefficient (see Eq 2-6), units of length per time, e.g., ft/d

C_m = concentration at the membrane surface

NOTE: The use of average feed-side solute concentration disregards concentration polarization and film theory effects.

Water mass transfer coefficient:

$$K_w = \frac{Q_p}{A(\Delta P - \Delta \pi)} = \frac{Q_p}{A(NAP)} \qquad \text{(Eq 2-7)}$$

Solute mass transfer coefficient:

$$K_s = \frac{Q_p C_p}{A \Delta C} \qquad \text{(Eq 2-8)}$$

Where:

ΔC = concentration differential (see Eq 2-8)

Concentration differential:

$$\Delta C = (C_m - C_p) = \left(\frac{C_f + C_c}{2}\right) - C_p \qquad \text{(Eq 2-9)}$$

Equation 2-10 describes the effects of each of the five independent variables (K, C_r, K_w, ΔP, and R) on the permeate concentration:

Permeate concentration:

$$C_p = \frac{K_s C_f}{K_w \Delta P + \Delta \pi \left(\frac{2 - 2R}{2R}\right) + K_s} \qquad \text{(Eq 2-10)}$$

Each of these variables may be changed independently while the other four remain constant. For example, the feedwater may be altered by source selection or pretreatment. The membrane's salt rejection (SR) varies inversely with feedwater concentration (Figure 2-16). Thus, C_p will increase if C_f increases and decrease if C_f decreases. The mass transfer coefficients K_w and K_s depend on the membrane. Different membranes have different mass transfer characteristics, a fact that highlights the value of pilot testing membranes before designing a membrane system. Permeate concentration will increase as K_s increases and decrease as K_s decreases. In contrast, C_p will decrease as K_w increases and increase as K_w decreases. Thus, to produce low TDS water inexpensively, the best choice is a membrane with a very high K_w and a very low K_s.

Variations in pressure, recovery, and temperature also affect permeate concentration. As pressure increases, the HSD model predicts that permeate concentration will decrease; as pressure decreases, permeate concentration will increase (Figure 2-17). Mass transfer of solutes is diffusion controlled (i.e., independent of pressure) and will progress through the membrane at a constant rate. Pressure can be increased or decreased to affect permeate concentration and recovery. As pressure is increased, more water will be forced through the membrane and the permeate will be diluted. The opposite is true for decreasing pressure.

Recovery variations have the opposite effect on C_p when compared to pressure changes. As recovery increases or decreases, the permeate concentration increases or decreases, respectively (Figure 2-18). If temperature increases and all other parameters are constant, the permeate flux and passage of salt increase (i.e., there is a lower SR), as shown in Figure 2-19. *Percent salt passage* refers to the percentage of source water TDS or other dissolved solutes of interest that pass through the membranes into the product water. Table 2-10 summarizes the effects of increasing pressure, temperature, recovery, and feed salt concentration on permeate flow and salt passage.

Organics, such as high molecular-weight DBP precursors, are usually removed by sieving. One method of determining the rejection mechanism is to vary pressure and recovery and observe solute rejection. If the percent solute rejection does not vary with pressure and recovery, sieving is the likely rejection mechanism. If percent

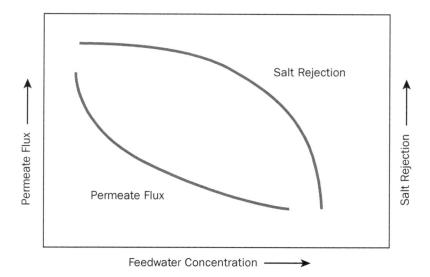

Figure 2-16 Effect of increasing salt concentration on flux and salt rejection

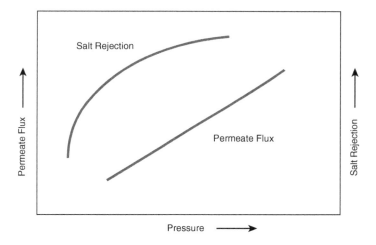

Figure 2-17 Effect of feedwater pressure on flux and salt rejection

rejection varies with pressure and recovery as described in the HSD model, diffusion is the rejection mechanism. Optimizing the process for rejection is easier if the mass transport mechanism is identified.

RATING RO AND NF ELEMENTS

All RO and NF devices are rated in terms of initial capacity and SR under a set of standard conditions that are defined by the individual membrane manufacturers. Table 2-11 gives standard conditions for a number of RO devices.

The differences in standard conditions make it difficult to compare competitive devices. Valid comparisons can be made only when competitive membranes are evaluated for a common set of operating conditions. Evaluations of RO membranes become feasible only when each device's performance is rated at an equivalent feedwater concentration, temperature, pressure, and recovery (conversion). The RO

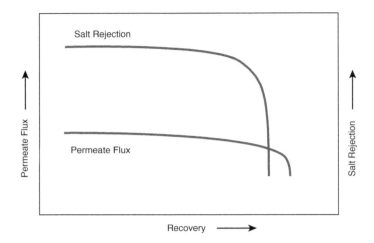

Figure 2-18   Effect of increased recovery on flux and salt rejection

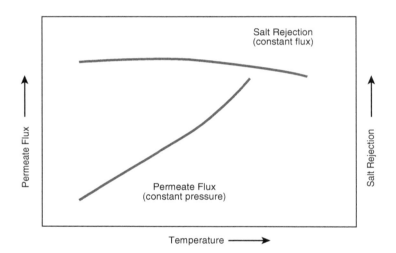

Figure 2-19   Effect of feedwater temperature on flux and salt rejection

Table 2-10   Factors influencing RO and NF performance

Factor	Permeate Flow	Salt Passage
Increasing effective pressure	Increases	Decreases
Increasing temperature	Increases	Increases
Increasing recovery	Decreases	Increases
Increasing source water salt concentration	Decreases	Increases

Table 2-11   Typical standardized test conditions for various RO devices (8-in.-diameter modules)

Water Source	Brackish				Seawater		
Configuration	Composite Spiral	Spiral	Hollow Fiber	Hollow Fiber	Composite Spiral	Hollow Fiber	Hollow Fiber
Membrane*	PA	CA	PA	PA	PA	PA	CA
Feedwater composition, mg/L NaCl	2,000	2,000	1,500	1,500	32,000	35,000	35,000
Pressure, psi	225	420	400	225	800	1,000	780
Temperature, °C	25	25	25	25	25	25	25
Conversion, %	15	10	75	50	8	35	30

*Membrane types: PA, polyamide; CA, cellulose acetate.

and NF manufacturer's standard conditions should be adjusted to site-specific operating criteria. Because the interrelationships of the equations in this chapter are complicated and time-consuming to calculate, membrane manufacturers use computer software to accomplish the task rapidly. These computer programs define the number and design of RO or NF elements required to deliver a specific quantity of water in a given time under site-specific operating parameters. These programs also predict the average permeate quality obtained from a grouping of RO devices, whether this grouping is the entire plant or a stage in a multistage facility.

In a given system, the number of RO modules needed to produce a specified flow and permeate quality differs for each supplier. The difference in quality is relevant only to the product water specifications of the end user. Appendix C provides information on converting from a manufacturer's standard conditions to site-specific conditions.

Membrane Array Design

The term *membrane array* refers to a series of membrane elements, usually arranged in stages with a decreasing number of membrane elements in each succeeding stage. An example is a three-stage system with the number of elements in a ratio of 4:2:1 going from stage 1 to stage 2 to stage 3. Figure 2-20 illustrates a three-stage array. (The purpose of the stages will be discussed later in this chapter.) When the feedwater and finished water characteristics have been measured or otherwise determined, the actual membrane system or array can be designed. The reader should consult appendix B for more information. The design process involves the following steps:

1. Determine the appropriate membrane process (NF, RO, etc.).

2. Set maximum flux rates and recovery rates (total and per membrane element or pressure vessel).

3. Determine the net applied pressure limits.

4. Determine the solute rejection requirements.

5. Select the membrane type.

6. Reassess and set design flux, pressure, and recovery rates for optimum treatment and cost.

7. Determine the preferred membrane train number and size.

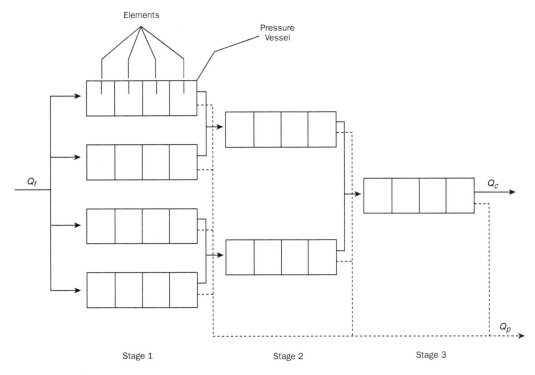

Figure 2-20   Schematic diagram of an RO membrane device

8. Establish the amount of necessary membrane area (spiral-wound membranes only).

9. Select the membrane element diameter and length.

10. Select the number of elements per pressure vessel (spiral-wound membranes only).

11. Determine the number of stages consistent with selected per element recovery rate.

12. Calculate the array size consistent with membrane train as well as number of elements and pressure vessels.

13. Calculate the predicted permeate solute concentration and assess against target value.

14. Consider interstage pressure boosting or first stage permeate throttling to balance flux.

15. Evaluate the potential ability to blend feedwater with source water and repeat steps 6 through 13, as necessary.

The following discussion provides an overview of these membrane array designs.

Membrane behavior. A number of variables determine the overall water production and permeate quality. The important design equations can be found in the membrane process theory section of this chapter. These equations are used to calculate permeate recovery rate, water mass balance, solute mass balance, water flux, solute flux, and permeate solute concentration.

Recovery. The permeate recovery rate R is the ratio of the permeate flow rate to the feedwater flow rate. Generally, the permeate recovery rate is set at the highest possible rate consistent with the desired water quality concerns, feedwater scaling limits, and lowest capital and operating costs. Incorporating solute concentration with each flow stream allows a mass balance to be established for the membrane system.

Water flux. The water flux is controlled by the water permeation coefficient (K_w, also called the *water mass transfer coefficient*), the water temperature, and the net driving pressure (NDP). The water permeation coefficient is inherent to a particular membrane and is based on the materials and conditions of construction. NAP is the difference between the feed-side pressure and permeate-side pressure. NDP is equal to the net applied pressure minus the average or mean osmotic pressure. The difference between the feed-side and permeate-side applied pressure selected by the designer can vary over a relatively wide range within the mechanical constraints of the membranes. The water flux increases by about 3 percent per degree Fahrenheit temperature increase.

Solute flux. Solute flux depends on the concentration difference across the membrane and the solute permeation coefficient (K_s, also called the *solute mass transfer coefficient*). The solute permeation coefficient is inherent to the membrane material and condition of construction. The concentration difference can be selected by altering the permeate recovery rate or by using a different source water.

Permeate solute concentration. Equation 2-10 is used to predict permeate solute concentration. The equation incorporates the basic equations for solute and water flux and is based on five independent variables: feedwater solute concentration, solute permeation coefficient, water permeation coefficient, permeate recovery rate, and NAP. The feedwater solute concentration is inherent to the selected supply source. The solute and water permeation coefficients are inherent to a particular membrane. Both the permeate recovery rate and NAP can be set by the designer or operator.

To illustrate the impacts of changes in the variables on permeate solute concentration, the example presented here uses the design parameters in Table 2-12.

Impact of varying permeate recovery rate. Table 2-13 shows how varying the permeate recovery rate significantly changes the permeate (C_p) and concentrate (C_c) solute concentration. The table also shows the significant decrease in feedwater flow rate with increasing permeate recovery rates.

Impact of varying feedwater pressure. Table 2-14 shows the variation in C_p with a change in NAP. Comparing Tables 2-12 and 2-13 demonstrates that a 50 percent increase in permeate recovery rate (from 50 percent to 75 percent) results in a 67 percent increase in C_p, while a 50 percent decrease in NAP (from 500 psi to 250 psi) results in a 93 percent increase in C_p. Thus, NAP has a greater impact per unit change on C_p than permeate recovery rate. Figure 2-21 illustrates how permeate solute concentration can vary with NAP and permeate recovery rate. A sharp rise in the solute concentration occurs with low applied pressure and high permeate recovery rate.

Table 2-12   Assumptions for the permeate solute concentration example

Parameter	Value
Permeate design flow	1.0 mgd
Membrane element area	80 ft^2
Feedwater TDS concentration	1,000 mg/L
Water flux values	8 gpd/ft^2, 12 gpd/ft^2, and 16 gpd/ft^2
NAP	100 psi, 250 psi, and 500 psi
Water permeation coefficients	0.005 day^{-1}, 0.05 day^{-1}, and 0.5 day^{-1}
Solute permeation coefficients	0.1 ft/d, 1.0 ft/d, and 10.0 ft/d
Permeate recovery rates	50%, 75%, and 90%

Table 2-13   Impact of varying permeate recovery rate[*]

Permeate Recovery Rate, %	Feedwater TDS Concentration, mg/L	Concentrate Water TDS Concentration, C_c, mg/L	Average Feedwater Side, mg/L	Permeate TDS Concentration, C_p, mg/L	Required Feedwater Flow Rate, mgd
50	1,000	1,951	1,475	49	2.00
75	1,000	3,762	2,381	79	1.33
90	1,000	8,566	4,783	159	1.11

*These values assume C_p = 1.00 mgd, K_w = 0.05 day^{-1}, K_s = 1.0 ft/d, ΔP = 250 psi.

Table 2-14   Impact of varying NAP[*]

NAP, psi	Permeate TDS Concentration, C_p, mg/L
100	177
250	79
500	41

*These values assume C_f = 1,000 mg/L TDS, K_w = 0.05 day^{-1}, K_s = 1.00 ft/d, R = 75%.

Impact of varying membrane characteristics. Table 2-15 shows the relative impact of varying the membrane's water and solute permeation characteristics (K_w and K_s, respectively). Extreme differences in permeate solute concentrations can be realized by using different membrane materials and construction methods.

Water flux rate. Permeate flow can be varied by changing the water permeation coefficient and NAP. Based on the assumed design parameters in Table 2-11, the relative impacts on water flux (F_w) achieved by manipulating these variables can be demonstrated.

Impact of NAP. Table 2-16 demonstrates the relative impact of varying NAP on water flux. The response of flux to net applied pressure is directly proportional in a linear fashion.

Impact of varying water permeation coefficient. Table 2-17 demonstrates the variation in water flux achievable by selecting membranes with differing water permeation coefficients. Again, the impact is directly proportional in a linear fashion.

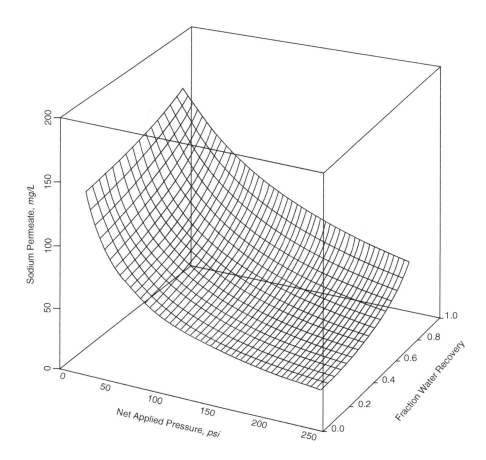

Figure 2-21 Three-dimensional plot of permeate sodium concentration as a function of NAP and permeate recovery rate

Table 2-15 Impact of varying membrane characteristics on C_p *

K_s Value, ft/day	C_p, mg/L		
	$K_w = 0.005$ day^{-1}	$K_w = 0.05$ day^{-1}	$K_w = 0.5$ day^{-1}
0.1	79	9	0.9
1.0	463	79	9
10.0	896	463	79

*These values assume $R = 75\%$, $\Delta P = 250$ psi, $C_f = 1,000$ mg/L TDS.

Table 2-16   Impact of varying NAP on water flux[*]

NAP, psi	Water Flux (F_w), ft/d
100	11.6
250	29.0
500	58.1

*These values assume $K_w = 0.05$ day^{-1}.

Table 2-17   Impact of varying water permeation coefficient on water flux[*]

Water Permeation Coefficient (K_w), day^{-1}	Water Flux (F_w), ft/d
0.005	2.90
0.05	29.0
0.5	290

*These values assume $\Delta P = 250$ psi.

Membrane array configuration. Typically, an assumed maximum flux is set during the design process to prevent undue fouling rates. This assumed maximum system water flux ranges up to approximately 16 gpd/ft^2 (gfd) for spiral-wound membrane elements for fresh and brackish sources. Hollow fiber membrane element flux are typically less than 1 gpd/ft^2. Train sizes are generally limited to 3 mgd, though larger train sizes have been used for very large plants. Membrane arrays are generally one to three stages with multiple membrane elements connected in series with each stage (refer to Figure 2-20). Generally, the permeate recovery rates for a one-, two-, or three-stage array with six 40-in.-long membrane elements per pressure vessel assembly are as follows:

- One stage: ~50 percent

- Two stages: ~50 percent to ~75 percent

- Three stages: ~75 percent to ~85 percent

For spiral-wound membranes, depending on feedwater quality, two-stage arrays can achieve recoveries of more than 75 percent by using seven elements per pressure vessel (i.e., more membranes) or by recycling a portion of the concentrate to a point before the first stage. The number of membrane elements (and associated vessels) in a second or third stage is usually about one-half the number of elements in the preceding stage. This decrease in elements is necessary because the preceding stage removes approximately 50 percent of the feedwater entering that stage as permeate. Appendix B provides an example of the process used to arrive at a selected membrane array and train size.

Staging of concentrate, as previously described, is utilized to increase the overall recovery while maintaining adequate cross-flow in the membrane elements. In cases where increased water quality is required, permeate staging may be practiced. Systems utilizing permeate staging are referred to as *multipass systems*. In a multipass system, two RO or NF units are installed in series, where the permeate from the first unit is the feedwater for the second unit. In potable water treatment, a two-pass or partial two-pass system might be considered for one of the following reasons:

- Improve the permeate quality (TDS, boron)

- Increase rejection of bacteria, pyrogens, and organic matter

- Increase system reliability

The most frequent application of multipass systems in potable water treatment is in seawater desalination. Because permeate quality degrades over time, most seawater desalination systems are designed with a second-pass desalination system capable of treating between 10 percent and 25 percent of the first-pass permeate flow. The second-pass permeate is then blended with the first-pass permeate to reduce water quality parameters of concern to below the target level. Partial second-pass systems benefit from the excellent quality of the feedwater and can typically be operated at very high fluxes (~20 gfd) and recovery (~90 percent). Partial second-pass systems for seawater desalination systems are most frequently applied to address TDS concerns, though regulatory actions are driving its implementation for reducing boron concentrations.

Flux balancing.   The fouling rate of individual membrane systems is a function of the permeate recovery in the element. It is typical that the first several elements in a pressure vessel produce the largest percentage of permeate because these membranes experience both the lowest TDS water and the highest applied pressure. With the increasing application of low-pressure RO membranes and NF membranes, the effect of pressure drop across the membrane system can have substantial impacts on productivity of membranes located in the second and third stages (for concentrate staged systems). To improve the productivity of the second and third stages and reduce fouling in the first stage, flux balancing is frequently implemented. Flux balancing can be used to limit the first-stage flux and increase the flux of later stages. Flux balancing is applied using one of two methods. In the first method, permeate backpressure is applied to the first stage using a backpressure valve. The backpressure effectively reduces the NDP of the first stage, resulting in a reduction in flux. The energy is conserved in the concentrate of the first stage, resulting in higher feed pressures and therefore, higher productivity in the second and third stages. One disadvantage of utilizing first-stage backpressure is the higher energy consumption resulting from throttling the first-stage permeate. To address this disadvantage, large systems employing flux balancing will use an interstage feed pump to raise the feed pressure to the second stage. This permits the feed pressure of the first stage to be reduced, saving energy. More novel designs use energy recovery devices to recover energy from the final-stage brine and transfer this energy to either the second or third stage.

POSTTREATMENT

Posttreatment of an RO or NF system permeate is typically required to ensure that adequate disinfection is provided to comply with drinking water regulations and to mitigate corrosion in the distribution system.

Disinfection

Chlorine is generally used for disinfection because of its recognized efficiency as a disinfectant and because there is a reduced level of DBP precursors in the permeate. However, other final disinfectants could be used depending on a utility's specific practices.

Stabilization

Permeate leaving the membrane system is low pH water with excessive dissolved gases and high corrosion potential. This condition results from the acid used to minimize carbonate and from the significant reduction of calcium, magnesium, and bicarbonate ions. Acid converts bicarbonates to carbon dioxide, which easily passes through the membranes into the permeate, while the remaining bicarbonate ions are readily rejected, especially for the RO process. If it is not removed, carbon dioxide will redissolve to form carbonic acid. In addition, any dissolved gases in the feedwater, such as hydrogen sulfide, also pass through the membrane into the permeate. Thus, the corrosivity of the water is caused by a combination of low pH, excessive carbon dioxide, and a lack of buffering capacity (bicarbonates). Generally, water treated with NF will reject a smaller fraction of calcium and bicarbonate and will require less chemical addition to achieve stabilization.

Using sodium hydroxide or another base to raise the pH and convert carbonic acid to bicarbonate and adding corrosion inhibitors will reduce the corrosivity of the permeate. In certain instances, a portion of disinfected and/or filtered source water can be blended with permeate to increase the alkalinity of finished water.

REFERENCES

AWWA/ASCE. 2005. *Water Treatment Plant Design,* 4th ed., New York: McGraw-Hill.

AWWA 1999. *Water Quality and Treatment: A Community Handbook* 5th ed., New York: McGraw-Hill.

Campbell, M.D., and J.H. Lehr. 1973. *Water Well Technology.* New York: McGraw-Hill.

Bouwer, E.J., and P.B. Crowe. 1988. Biological processes in drinking water treatment. *Jour. AWWA.* 80(9): 82.

Driscoll, F.D. 1986. *Groundwater and Wells.* St. Paul, Minn.: Johnson Division.

Filmtec Corp. Filmtec Technical Manual. 2004. Filmtec Corp., Minneapolis, Minn.

Goel, S., R.M. Hozalski, and E.J. Bouwer. 1995. Biodegradation of NOM: Effect of NOM source and ozone dose. *Jour. AWWA.* 87(1): 90–105.

Konikow, L.F., and J.D. Bredehoeft. 1978. Computer Model of Two-Dimensional Solute Transport and Dispersion in Groundwater. *Techniques of Water Resources: Investigations of the US Geological Survey.* Reston, Va.: US Geological Survey.

McDonald, M.G., and A.W. Harbaugh. 1988. *A Modular Three-Dimensional Finite-Difference Groundwater Flow Model.* US Geological Survey Techniques of Water Resources Investigations, Book 6. Reston, Va.: US Geological Survey.

Mickley, M., R. Hamilton, L. Gallegos, and J. Truesdall. 1993. *Membrane Concentrate Disposal.* Denver, Colo.: American Water Works Association.

Missimer, T.M. 1994. *Water Supply Development for Membrane Water Treatment Facilities.* Boca Raton, Fla.: Lewis Publishers.

Morin, O.J., and P.J. Malaxos. 1988. In *Proc. from Surface Water Discharge of Reverse Osmosis Concentrates.* National Water Supply Improvement Association. November 18–19, Davis, Calif.

National Water Well Association and the Plastics Pipe Institute. 1980. *Manual on the Selection and Installation of Thermoplastic Water Well Casing.* Worthington, Ohio: The National Water Well Association.

Reeves, M., D.S. Ward, N.O. Johns, and R.M. Cranwell. 1986. *Theory and Implementation for SWIFT II, the Sandia Waste-Isolation Flow and Transport Model for Fractured Media.* NUREG/CR-3328, SAND 83-1159. Albuquerque, N.Mex.: Sandia National Laboratories.

Ridgway, H.F., C.A. Justice, C.W. Whittaker, D.G. Argo, and B.H. Olson. 1984. Biofilm fouling of RO membrane: Its nature and effect on treatment of water for reuse. *Jour. AWWA,* 76(6): 94–102.

USBR. 2002. Membrane Fouling: Influence of Natural Organic Matter Properties and Membrane Surface Treatment on Nanofiltration Treatment, Desalination Research and Development Program Report No. 83. Washington, D.C.

USBR. 2003. Biological Pretreatment for Membrane Systems, Desalination Research and Development Program Report No. 79. Washington, D.C.

Volk, C.A., C.B. Volk, and L.A. Kaplan. 1997. Chemical composition of biodegradable dissolved organic matter in streamwater. *Limnol. Oceanogr.* 42: 39–44.

Weber, W.A. 1972. *Physicochemical Processes for Water Quality Control.* New York: John Wiley and Sons.

This page intentionally blank.

Chapter **3**

Facility Design and Construction

Revision Authors: Nikolay Voutchkov and Robert Bergman

RO and NF systems require specialized equipment not found in conventional treatment facilities. This chapter presents design and construction fundamentals of all key elements of the NF and RO plants, including intake facilities, pretreatment equipment, membrane systems, and facilities for posttreatment of membrane plant product water and waste streams (concentrate and residuals). Conventional technologies for pretreatment and posttreatment will only be discussed relative to RO and NF systems. Additional information on conventional technologies can be found in *AWWA Water Quality and Treatment*, AWWA/ASCE *Water Treatment Plant Design*, and other references.

Custom-engineered and standard prepackaged RO and NF treatment components are available from various membrane and equipment manufacturers. Raw water characteristics, hydraulic capacity, recovery, salt rejection, water flux decline, corrosion potential, and membrane type determine the necessary equipment specifications. Components include pretreatment equipment, the membrane process unit, permeate and concentrate posttreatment equipment, and auxiliary system equipment, such as equipment for membrane cleaning, chemical feed and storage, instrumentation and control, and flushing systems. Figures 3-1, 3-2, and 3-3 show examples of different sizes of membrane units ready for installation.

RAW WATER INTAKE FACILITIES

The raw water intake facilities are among the key components of every NF and RO plant. Adequate and consistent flow and quality of raw water over the entire useful life of the

Figure 3-1   5,500 gpd RO system

Figure 3-2   40,000 gpd RO system

Figure 3-3   86,000,000 gpd RO system (Ashkelon, Israel)

plant must be assured. Feed water for NF and RO plants comes from groundwater, surface water, or treated wastewater (for reuse and water reclamation applications). For potable water plants, the intake facilities can be divided in two main groups: open surface water intakes and subsurface intakes. Key design considerations and fundamentals for each of the two groups of intakes are discussed in the following sections.

Subsurface Raw Water Intake Facilities

Most NF and brackish RO plants utilize subsurface intakes, primarily vertical wells tapping groundwater aquifers. Subsurface intakes are widely used for small- and medium-size seawater desalination plants. Large seawater desalination plants are most commonly constructed with open ocean intakes. Key considerations for the development of subsurface intakes for brackish water and seawater desalination plants are discussed elsewhere (Hunt 1996; Missimer 1994; Schwartz 2000; Voutchkov 2004).

Subsurface water intake systems include raw water collection facilities (vertical or horizontal intake wells, infiltration galleries, and riverbed or seabed filtration systems [collectively defined as bank filtration]), and associated intake pumping and electrical components. These facilities are used for collection of groundwater for NF and brackish water RO systems (brackish water wells) and ocean water for seawater RO plants (beach wells and seabed filtration systems). The subsurface intake facilities are relatively simple to build and the raw water that is collected is pretreated via slow filtration through the subsurface sand/seabed formations in the area of raw water extraction. Therefore, raw water collected using subsurface intake facilities is usually of better quality in terms of solids, silt, oil and grease, natural organic contamination, and aquatic microorganisms, as compared to surface water intakes. Under normal, steady-state conditions, subsurface intakes provide chemically stable water over a long period of time. However, groundwater quality can change depending on the nature of the aquifer or due to aquifer overpumping. Therefore, the subsurface water source aquifer should be tested and modeled to determine the anticipated short- and long-term changes in water quality.

General design considerations for subsurface intakes. Detailed hydrogeologic information is needed before a well field for a subsurface water intake can be designed and constructed. The level of sophistication of the test program and subsequent modeling depends on the size of the system and the local hydrogeology. The following questions must be answered before a well field is designed:

- Is a groundwater source available?

- How much water will the groundwater source produce (safe yield)?

- Will the water quality remain stable during pumping?

- How many production wells must be constructed to safely obtain the desired yield?

- What are the optimal well locations and pumping rates?

- If water quality changes, what will be the changes in concentration of key chemical parameters?

The hydrogeological investigation includes several key steps.

1. Complete a preliminary geological survey to identify if the selected site is generally suitable for the construction of subsurface water intake.

2. Drill test holes to collect samples of the aquifer formation deposits for visual classification and grain-size distribution analysis.

3. Install one or more test wells and observation wells, and conduct a pumping test to determine the site-specific hydraulic characteristics of the aquifer necessary for subsurface system design and determination of the intake system yield.

4. Collect adequate samples of the raw water and analyze sample water quality. If the brackish or seawater source water quality is under the influence of a fresh water source, in which quality and quantity varies seasonally, perform year-around intake water quality sampling to determine seasonal fluctuations of source water quality.

5. If the subsurface intake system would require the installation of multiple collection facilities (wells, or infiltration galleries/bank filtration facilities), complete a computer model analysis to establish the response of the production aquifer to pumping and the potential impact of groundwater collection on adjacent fresh or saline water aquifers, which may interact with the aquifer used for source water for the NF or RO plant.

Some key factors that determine if the use of subsurface intake is practical or/and economical for a seawater desalination plant are: the transmissivity/productivity of the geological formation/aquifer; the thickness of the production aquifer deposits; and the existence of nearby fresh water source aquifers, which could be negatively impacted by the beach well operations or have measurable effect on beach well water quality.

Considerations for selection of subsurface intake site for NF and brackish water RO plants. In addition to the permeability, productivity, and safe yield of the source water aquifer, the key factor that determines the location and feasibility of the intake for an NF or brackish water RO plant is the raw water quality. Plant failure can be caused by large changes of intake water salinity, and variations or elevated concentration of water quality contaminants, such as silica, manganese, iron, radionuclides, or scaling compounds that may create fouling or operational problems, which increase treatment costs or limit the available options for concentrate disposal. Subsurface geologic conditions determine to great extent the quantity and quality of the raw water. Confined or semiconfined aquifers yield the most suitable source of water for brackish water NF or RO systems (Missimer 1994).

Whenever groundwater is pumped from an aquifer, there is always some modification of the natural flow in this aquifer. Many brackish water aquifers are density stratified and when water is pumped from the top portion of the aquifer, higher salinity groundwater propagates upward, increasing source water salinity over time. Many brackish water aquifers are semiconfined, and they may have a common boundary with other aquifers of different water quality. When the production aquifer is pumped, a certain portion of the recharge volume may be supplied from the adjacent bounding aquifers, thus causing a change of source water quality from that of the original aquifer to the water quality of the bounding aquifers over time. These changes in source water quality may not only affect the intake water salinity but also the overall ion make-up of the source water for the NF or RO plant, which may affect the systems allowable recovery and may also affect concentrate disposal permitting. Therefore, it is essential to conduct predesign hydrogeologic investigation that includes predictive modeling of the potential long-term changes in source water quality that could occur over the useful life of the subsurface intake system.

Considerations for selection of subsurface intake site for brackish or seawater RO plants. The geological conditions that favor the construction of subsurface water intakes are permeable sand formations in which transmissivity exceeds 0.088 mgd/ft (1,000 m³/day/m) (Schwartz 2000) and with depth extending 45 ft (15 m) or more.

Beaches on shallow bays or banks on slowly flowing portions of a river that contain significant amount of mud/alluvial deposits and have limited natural flushing do not favor the use of subsurface intakes. High content of fine solids in the bay seawater or river water in combination with low frequency of bay/riverbank flushing and low transmissivity of the beach deposits may render these areas less desirable or unsuitable for construction of NF/RO plant subsurface intakes.

Both beach wells and near-shore surface intakes (riverbank/beach well intake systems) use the same water as a source. In desalination plants with surface intakes, the solids contained in the source water are removed in the desalination plant pretreatment filtration system. In desalination plants with riverbank/beach well intakes, the same amount of solids is retained on the river/ocean floor in the area of well source water collection while the filtered water is slowly conveyed through the river/ocean floor and the beach subterrain formation until it reaches the well collectors. The natural river flow/ocean wave action near the river/ocean floor is the force that allows the solids to separate from the beach well source water to be dissipated in the river/ocean. If the bay area is not well flushed and the naturally occurring wave movement is inadequate to transport the solids away from the beach well collection area at a rate higher than the rate of solids deposition, these solids would begin to accumulate on the river/ocean floor and would ultimately reduce the well capacity and negatively impact source water quality over time.

Intake wells. Intake wells are vertical or horizontal water collectors drilled in the source water aquifer. The vertical intake wells are less costly than the horizontal wells but their yield may be relatively small (0.1 to 1.0 mgd [400 to 4,000 m^3/day])—although some wells can produce much more than 1 mgd. The most widely used type of horizontal collector well are often referred to as *radial collector wells* or *Ranney wells*. Another type of horizontal collector well gaining popularity for seawater applications is the *horizontal directionally drilled (HDD) collector*.

Vertical intake wells. These intake wells should consist of a nonmetallic casing (typically, fiberglass reinforced plastic [FRP] or polyvinyl chloride pipe), proper-grade stainless steel well screen (if needed), and a stainless steel submersible or vertical turbine pump (Figure 3-4).

Horizontal collector intake wells. These intake wells are not as commonly used for NF and RO source water supply as vertical wells because of their relatively high installation costs. However, they may be the best choice for some applications. They consist of a caisson that extends below the ground surface with water well collector screens (laterals) projected horizontally from inside the caisson into the surrounding aquifer (Figure 3-5). Because the well screens in the collector wells are placed horizontally, a higher rate of source water collection is possible than with most vertical wells. This allows the same intake water quantity to be collected with fewer wells.

Individual horizontal intake wells are designed to collect between 0.5 mgd and 5.0 mgd (2,000 and 20,000 m^3/day) of source water. The caisson is constructed of reinforced concrete that may be between 9 ft to more than 20 ft (2.7 m to 6.0 m) inside diameter with a wall thickness from approximately 1.5 to 3.0 ft (0.5 to 1.0 m) depending on the depth (Hunt 1996). The caisson depth varies according to site-specific geologic conditions, ranging from approximately 30 ft to more than 150 ft (10 to 45 m).

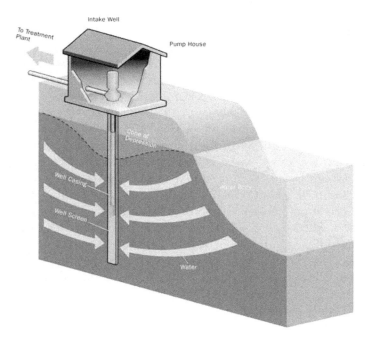

Figure 3-4   Vertical intake well

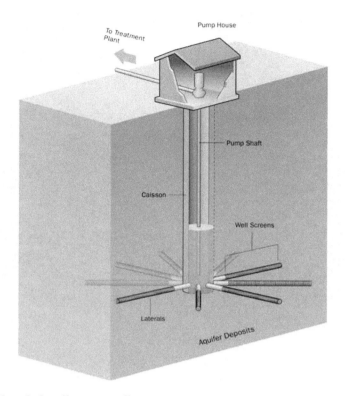

Figure 3-5   Horizontal radial collector well

The number, length, and location of the horizontal laterals are determined based on a detailed hydrogeological investigation. Typically, the diameter of the laterals ranges from 8 to 12 in. (0.2 to 0.3 m), and their length extends to 200 ft (60 m). The size of the lateral screens is selected to accommodate the grain size of the underground soil formation. If necessary, an artificial gravel-pack filter can be installed around the screen to suit finer-grained deposits.

When horizontal radial collector wells are used for fresh or brackish groundwater intake, the caisson is extended above the flood plain elevation for this location to protect the pumping equipment, electrical, and instrumentation and control equipment from flooding. When used as seawater beach wells, especially for smaller size applications, the radial or HDD collector-type wells can be constructed water tight at or below grade to minimize their visual impact on the shoreline. In large capacity applications, the horizontal beach wells are coupled with the intake pump station installed above the well caisson. The well intake pump station can be designed with submersible pumps to minimize noise levels. However, for mid- and larger-size wells, vertical turbine pumps most frequently are used because these pumps have higher energy efficiency.

Infiltration galleries. Infiltration galleries are riverbank or beach filtration systems, which may be considered when conventional horizontal or vertical intake wells cannot be used due to unfavorable hydrogeological conditions. For example, they are suitable for intakes where the permeability of the underground soil formation is relatively low, or in the case of river or seashore filtration, where the thickness of the beach or the onshore sediments is insufficient to develop conventional intake wells. The infiltration galleries consist of an excavation trench,

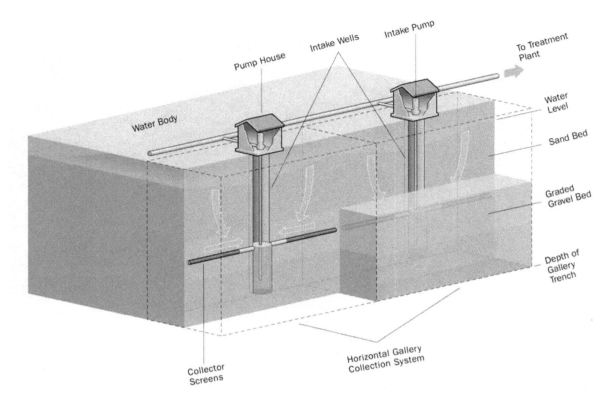

Figure 3-6   Infiltration gallery

which is filled with filtration media of size and depth similar to that of the granular media filters used for conventional water treatment plants. Vertical or horizontal collector wells are installed equidistant (usually 100 to 200 ft [30 to 60 m]) inside the filter media. Typically, the capacity of a single collection well is 0.2 to 2.0 mgd (750 to 7,500 m³/d).

The most common type of infiltration gallery is a horizontal well collection system with a single trench (Figure 3-6). The media in the wells is configured in three distinctive layers: a bottom layer of sand media of approximately 6 to 10 ft (2 to 3.5 m), followed by a 4 to 6 ft (1.2 to 2 m) layer of graded gravel pack surrounding the horizontal well collector screens; topped by a 20-ft to 30-ft (6-m to 9-m) layer of sand. The horizontal well collector screens are designed for inflow velocity of 0.1 ft/sec (3 cm/sec) or less.

The infiltration galleries could be designed either similar to conventional rapid sand filters (if the natural source water movement, such as ocean water wave or riverbed motion, can provide adequate backflushing of the infiltration gallery media); or the infiltration galleries could be constructed as slow sand filtration systems, which have at least a 30-ft (9-m) layer of sand overlying the collection well screens. Infiltration galleries are usually 15 to 20 percent more costly to construct than conventional intake wells, and therefore, their use is warranted only when the hydrogeological conditions of the intake site are not suitable for conventional vertical or horizontal intake wells. Infiltration galleries have found a very limited application

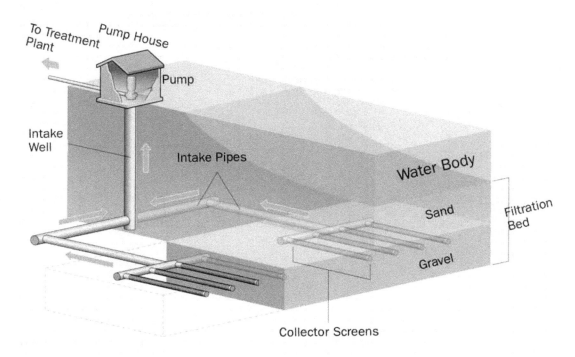

Figure 3-7   Riverbed/seabed filtration system

for NF and RO plant intakes to date. Currently, worldwide there are no NF or RO plants of capacity larger than 5 mgd (20,000 m³/d) using infiltration gallery intakes.

Riverbed/seabed filtration systems. These subsurface intake (bank filtration) systems consist of a submerged slow sand media filtration system located at the bottom of the intake water source (ocean, lake, or river floor), which is connected to a series of intake wells located on the shore (see Figure 3-7). As such, river or sea filter beds are sized and configured using the same design criteria as slow sand filters.

The design surface loading rate of the filter media is 0.05 to 0.10 gpm/ft² (0.12 to 0.24 m³/m² hr). Approximately 1 in. (2.54 cm) of sand is removed from the surface of the filter bed every 6 to 12 months, for a period of 3 years, after which the removed sand is replaced with new sand to its original depth. Typically, riverbed/seabed filtration systems are the costliest subsurface intake systems. Their construction costs are approximately 1.2 to 2.3 times higher than those of the conventional intake wells. In terms of overall cost of water (including both the capital and O&M components), the riverbed/seabed filtration systems are usually more costly than any of the other types of subsurface intakes.

The largest seawater desalination plant with a seabed intake system is the 13.2 mgd (50,000 m³/day) Fukuoka District RO facility in Japan (Figure 3-8). The Fukuoka seawater desalination plant seabed intake area is 312,000 ft² (29,000 m²).

HDD collector wells are simplified versions of the riverbed/seabed filtration intake systems. The main difference is that the HDD collector wells use the natural riverbed or seabed as a filtration system, when this is viable. When the riverbed or seabed at the particular intake location is unsuitable to provide adequate intake flowrate, a manmade riverbed/seabed filtration system has to be used.

Equipment for sand removal from subsurface source water. If the source water from subsurface intakes contains a significant amount of sand that

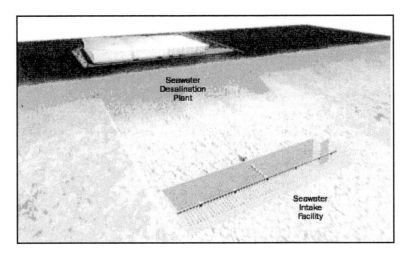

Figure 3-8   Seabed filtration system of Fukuoka District RO facility, Japan

should be removed before processing through the downstream treatment facilities, strainers and cyclones are sometimes used.

Strainers. Sand strainers operate by physically straining the sand on a metallic or plastic mesh screen. Strainers can achieve up to 95 percent removal of sand using a 150-mesh screen size. For larger membrane treatment plants, self-cleaning strainers are used. These units use a portion of the source water flow to wash the screen surface and remove the accumulated sand.

Disk filters. This prefiltration equipment operates using specially designed thin plastic disks that are diagonally grooved on both sides to a precise micron size. The disks are between 20-µm and 400-µm size. The disks are stacked and compressed by a spring on a specially designed spine. When stacked, the top grooves run opposite to the bottom grooves, thereby creating a depth filtration element with a significant number of intersecting grooves that trap the source water solids. The disk stack is housed in a corrosion-proof and pressure-resistant chamber. During the filtration mode, the disks are tightly compressed together by the spring and the differential pressure. Filtration occurs when water percolates from the outer diameter to the inner diameter of the element. During backwash, the disks are released by reducing the inlet hydraulic pressure. Multijet nozzles provide tangential spray on the loosened disks, causing them to spin and release the retained solids, which are flushed to the drain. The disk filter technology has a proven track record for freshwater applications.

Cyclones. Cyclones operate using the greater inertia of sand particles in the water stream in cyclonic motion to separate the sand from the source water stream. While cyclones can achieve up to 98.5 percent sand removal, the resulting pressure loss of 14 to 18 psi (1 to 1.3 bars) yields a high energy cost (Thompson et al. 2001). Cyclones may be used at individual wells; however, a combined source water stream can be treated using one or more large cyclones in parallel.

Surface Water Intake Facilities

Surface water delivery systems include the following key components: off-shore intake structure; intake pipeline; intake chamber; trash racks; fine screens; source water intake pump station; electrical and instrumentation and control equipment;

and chemical feed equipment. The proper design of surface water intakes requires the collection of detailed source water quality data from the proposed site of the intake, characterization of aquatic life in the vicinity of the intake, and completion of a detailed sanitary survey assessing the potential sources of contamination in the vicinity of the intake location (such as waste discharges of industrial and municipal wastewater plants, storm drain discharges, or large port or marina activities, which may result in oil and gasoline spills and other ocean water contamination).

Surface water intakes are constructed for large brackish or seawater desalination plants. Surface water (such as tidally influenced brackish river water or brackish lake water) is occasionally used for some brackish water RO facilities, because of the extensive pretreatment facilities that are needed and the potential large diurnal and seasonal water quality fluctuations for many of these source waters.

Off-shore ocean intake structure. The off-shore intake structure is usually a vertical concrete or steel well (vault) or pipe located at the river or ocean floor and submerged below the water surface. The off-shore intake structure is designed to reliably collect an adequate amount of source water that has a minimum content of debris and aquatic organisms. The exact location and depth of the off-shore intake structure is determined based on a hydrological study to ensure that the intake is adequately submerged at minimum water level (low tide), protected from the damaging orbital storm wave motion, and far enough off-shore to avoid the near-shore sediment transport zone where storms can cause suspension of large quantities of sediment that can ultimately damage the intake structure and interconnecting piping. Diurnal and seasonal source water quality fluctuations should also be considered when determining the location of the intake structure. At minimum river water level (low tide) conditions, the inlet mouth should be submerged at least 10 ft (3 m) below the water surface. In addition, the distance between the inlet mouth and the river/ocean floor should be no less than 10 ft (3 m) to prevent excessive sand carryover into the downstream intake facilities. The intake water supply can be protected against large aquatic organisms and large floating debris by installing wire net across the intake mouth. A picture of the Larnaca, Cyprus, seawater desalination plant intake structure is shown in Figure 3-9.

For large membrane plant intakes located at riverbed/ocean floor depth of 30 ft (10 m) or higher, a velocity cap structure, supported several feet above the intake box opening, can be installed to reduce the intake source water entrance velocity to less than 0.5 ft/sec (0.15 m/sec) and thereby minimize the entrainment of aquatic organisms and suspended solids in the intake source water (Figure 3-9). Shallow intakes for small- or medium-size plants (capacity less than 5 mgd [20,000 m^3/day]) are often equipped only with screens attached to the end of the intake pipe to prevent large objects from entering the pipe and pump system.

Typically, the surface water intake structure is located several hundred to several thousand feet off-shore. The best location of the intake structure in terms of intake water quality is at riverbed/ocean floor depths of 100 ft (30 m) or higher (deep water intake). Debris load in the source water at such depths is 20 times less than that in the surface water or the shallow waters of the tidally influenced near-shore area (Gille 2003). Depending on the plant location and riverbed/ocean floor formation, installing the intake structure at 100 ft (30 m) depth may require an intake pipeline that is between 30 ft (10 m) and 6,000 ft (1,800 m) long. Because the construction cost for an intake pipeline located on the riverbed/ocean floor is very high (between 4 to 10 times higher than the cost of the same size pipe installed inland in the ground), the intake water quality benefits of locating the off-shore intake structure in deep waters have to be compared against the costs for construction of the intake structure and pipeline. The best location for a surface water intake from a life-cycle cost point

Figure 3-9   Off-shore intake structure, Larnaca, Cyprus

of view is typically a site where riverbed/ocean floor depth of 100 ft (30 m) can be reached within 1,500 ft (460 m) or less from the shore line. If such a riverbed/ocean floor location is not available within a reasonably close vicinity of the desalination plant, it is more cost-effective to collect source water of inferior water quality and build a more elaborate pretreatment system, than to install a costly off-shore intake structure and a long intake pipeline.

Because of the high costs of deep intake structures and long pipelines, most of the existing desalination plants with open intakes are located in shallow near-shore areas where the riverbed/ocean floor depth is typically between 10 to 30 ft (3 to 10 m). As a result, plants with surface water intakes have source water with high content of debris, solids, and aquatic organisms, requiring elaborate pretreatment prior to membrane separation.

Intake pipeline.   The intake pipeline connects the intake structure to the source water pump station. This pipeline is usually located on the riverbed/ocean floor. Pipeline material is typically high density polyethylene (HDPE), concrete, or steel. A high-grade stainless steel is recommended for seawater applications. Because HDPE piping is available only in sizes of up to 64 in. (1,600 mm), larger diameter intake lines are constructed using concrete pipe. Due to lower costs, often it is more cost-effective to use two separate, smaller size HDPE intake lines rather than one larger diameter concrete or steel pipe. Stainless steel is used less frequently, especially for large plants, because of the high cost of the pipeline material and the potential for corrosion. Carbon-steel or cast-iron intake piping can also be used for fresh water applications. Intake pipelines are designed for velocity of 4 to 6 ft/sec (1.2 to 1.8 m/sec) to minimize the growth of aquatic organisms on the inner walls of the pipes. Velocities lower than 3 ft/sec (1.0 m/sec) would result in a relatively slow intake flow stream that creates an opportunity for excessive growth of aquatic organisms and reduction of the intake pipeline conveyance capacity over time. Very high intake velocities may result in excessive impingement and entrainment of aquatic organisms.

Intake screens. A typical surface water intake system for medium and large membrane plants includes a set of manually cleaned bar racks followed by automated traveling fine bar screens and/or fine-mesh screens. The bar racks usually have a 3 to 4 in. (75 to 100 mm) distance between the bars, and their purpose is to retain large-size debris and aquatic life in the source water. Fine self-cleaning bar screens typically have $\frac{1}{8}$ to $\frac{3}{8}$ in. (3 to 10 mm) openings between the bars. Because the main function of these screens is to protect the intake pumps from damage, the actual distance between the bars has to be smaller than the distance between the intake pump impellers. Fine bar screens are used if the downstream pretreatment system consists of conventional granular media filters. If the pretreatment system selected for the NF or RO plant is of membrane type (MF or UF), bar screens do not provide sufficiently effective removal of source water particles to protect the integrity of the MF/UF pretreatment system. One of the key issues of using a MF/UF pretreatment is that the MF/UF membrane fibers can be punctured by sharp objects in the source water, such as broken shells. Pilot testing experience at several locations indicates that if MF/UF pretreatment is used, the surface intake system should include fine-mesh screens of 120 μm or smaller ahead of the pretreatment filter to protect the membrane elements from damage and premature loss of integrity. Typically, microscreens (Figure 3-10) or disk filters can be used for this application. The use of microscreens, if combined with an aquatic organism retrieval system, also has environmental benefits. Most fish larvae and other phyto- and zooplankton are larger than 120 μm, and if microscreens are used, more than 80 percent of these organisms can be retained on the screens and returned back to the ocean using a low-pressure pump station—thereby minimizing the impact of the plant intake system on the aquatic environment. The main disadvantage of the use of microscreens is that they add to the plant construction and O&M costs. Usually, they are 20 to 50 percent more costly than conventional fine bar screens. Use of conventional granular media pretreatment filters does not require the installation of microscreens ahead of the filters because the granular media is not susceptible to damage by sharp objects in the source water and effectively retains these objects.

Smaller size desalination plants use strainers instead of bar screens to protect the downstream intake pumps and pretreatment systems. For plants that have conventional granular media pretreatment systems, 500- to 900-μm strainers are adequate prescreening devices. Plants equipped with membrane pretreatment filters would require the use of 80- to 120-μm strainers. Figure 3-11 shows a 500-μm strainer system.

Intake pump station. The plant intake pump station is usually installed downstream of the screening facilities. The suction level of the intake pumps should be designed below the inlet mouth of the off-shore intake structure. The intake pump station service facilities should also be located above the 100-year flood elevation.

The pump station should be engineered for a very high level of reliability and provided with adequate standby units following good engineering practices. Intake pump stations are designed with a minimum of two duty and one standby pumps. If the number of duty units exceeds five, the on-site availability of two standby pumps is often recommended. One of these pumps should be installed in the pump station, and the other pump may be an uninstalled spare that is available on site. If the plant has to have guaranteed production availability over 95 percent of the time, then

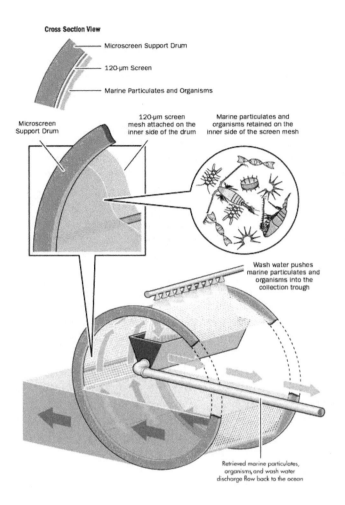

Cross Section View

Microscreen Support Drum

120-μm Screen

Marine Particulates and Organisms

Microscreen
Support Drum

120-μm screen
mesh attached on the
inner side of the drum

Marine particulates and
organisms retained on the
inner side of the screen mesh

Wash water pushes
marine particulates and
organisms into the
collection trough

Retrieved marine particulates,
organisms, and wash water
discharge flow back to the ocean

Figure 3-10   Microscreens

when five or more duty pumps are used, two standby pumps should be installed in the pump station. The use of more than five duty pumps is not recommended because of the increased O&M complexity, unless the NF or RO plant configuration favors the dedication of an individual intake pump to each RO treatment train.

Vertical turbine pumps are used for RO or NF membrane plants because these pumps have relatively high energy efficiency as compared to other types of pumps. These pumps can be installed in a wet well or in a can connected directly to the intake pipeline. Canned pumps are preferred in the case of space constraints because their use eliminates the need for a large-size wet well. Installation of variable frequency drives on at least some of the intake pumps is recommended at NF or RO plants that operate under varying recovery rates or large salinity swings.

The intake pump station may be equipped with chlorination equipment for control of biogrowth on the intake facilities and pipelines, although the use of chlorine will necessitate other special design considerations because chlorine can

Figure 3-11   500-µm source water pretreatment strainers

damage most types of NF and RO membranes and chlorination–dechlorination systems may actually increase microbial fouling of membrane systems.

When the intake pump station is located far (more than 2,000 ft [600 m]) from the desalination plant site, it is usually more cost-effective to use an on-site sodium hypochlorite system for chlorination rather than to run a long chlorine feed line from the main plant site. Currently, there are a number of commercially available on-site hypochlorite generation systems that generate hypochlorite solution using seawater, as long as the disinfection by-products formed are within acceptable limits. These systems are very reliable and do not require any additional chemicals to generate sodium hypochlorite.

Seawater desalination plant intake co-location with power generation station discharge. Co-location of desalination plants with large power generation stations may yield significant cost savings and further reduce the cost of desalinated water. This alternative intake approach includes direct connection of the RO plant intake piping to the discharge outfall of a nearby power plant (see Figure 3-12).

DISCHARGE

Power plants use large volumes of seawater for cooling purposes. Because the power plant intake seawater passes through the small diameter (typically $^7/_8$-in. [20 mm]) tubes of the plant condensers to cool them, power plant discharge cooling water, used as a source water for the desalination plant, is already screened through bar racks and fine screens similar to those used at surface water intake desalination plants. Therefore, a desalination plant intake connected to the discharge outfall of a power plant does not require the construction of a separate intake structure and intake pipeline. Because the cost of a new surface water intake for a desalination plant is typically 10 to 20 percent of the total plant construction expenditure, power plant co-location allows achieving significant construction cost savings.

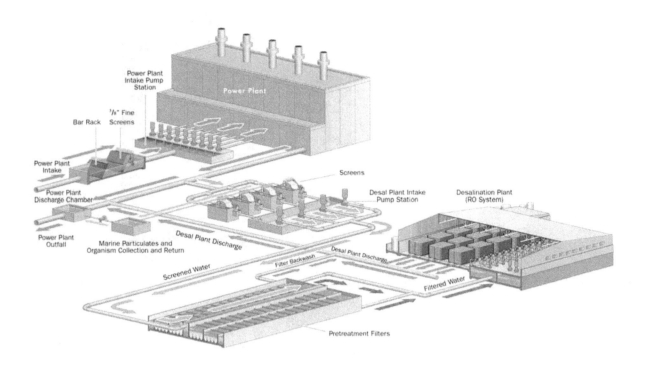

Figure 3-12   Desalination plant intake and discharge connection to power plant

The use of the intake–discharge co-location approach will include the construction of a separate new desalination plant intake pump station. The power plant discharge is under slight pressure (3 to 10 psi [0.2 to 0.7 bars]) within several hundred feet from the beginning of the cooling water discharge outfall. However, this pressure is insufficient to convey the source water from the point of interconnection with the power plant outfall to the desalination plant pretreatment facilities.

According to the power plant–desalination plant co-location approach, the desalination plant concentrate discharge line is connected downstream of the point of RO plant intake. The distance between the desalination plant intake and discharge points of interconnection on the power plant discharge outfall has to be designed long enough to prevent short-circuiting of plant concentrate to the plant intake under any operational conditions of the power plant. This distance will depend on the power plant discharge flow and pressure under various operational scenarios and on the volume of the desalination plant intake and discharge. The point of interconnection of the desalination plant discharge is also determined by the hydraulics of the power plant discharge. If not located appropriately, the desalination plant concentrate discharge pipeline, which is designed to protrude into the power plant outfall line to achieve better mixing, may create local head losses in the power plant discharge line and result in backpressure to the power plant condensers, which in turn may yield reduction of power plant generation capacity. In addition, the desalination plant discharge location has to be selected in such a way that it yields a complete mixing between the heavier desalination plant concentrate and the warmer power plant discharge, before the blend of the two discharge streams reaches the ocean to minimize potential environmental impacts of the elevated salinity at the point of discharge. Because the desalination plant uses the power plant outfall for disposal of plant concentrate, the construction of a separate outfall for the desalination plant is not required. This provides an additional cost advantage of the co-location of the desalination plant intake and discharge with the power plant discharge. Summary of the key advantages and disadvantages of the co-location approach is presented in Table 3-1 (discussed in detail elsewhere [AWWA Water Desalting Committee 2004, Voutchkov 2004]).

General Design Considerations for Surface Water Intakes

Surface water intakes are susceptible to direct physical damage by storms, corrosion, freezing and thawing in temperate climates, and human activities. The intake water quality could also be affected by natural seasonal variations of the surface water and its temperature. Table 3-2 summarizes surface intake system components and related general design considerations. Source water investigations are recommended to assess storm impact potential, potential growth rates of attaching benthic aquatic organisms (such as zebra mussels, corals, and sponges), and near-shore water quality fluctuations.

Pretreatment Systems

The membrane pretreatment system is located downstream of the plant intake facilities. As discussed in chapter 2, NF and RO systems treating groundwater often require minimal pretreatment—just cartridge filtration (as a safety filtration device to remove suspended solids that can plug, foul, or damage membranes) and chemical addition (acid and/or scale inhibitor). For plants with shallow subsurface intakes or surface water intake facilities, pretreatment facilities are much more extensive. Considering that a surface water membrane plant intake system has equipment (bar racks, fine traveling screens, microscreens, and strainers) to prescreen large debris, floating materials, most large aquatic organisms, coarse sand, and stringy materials from the source water, the key groups of membrane foulants that should be removed by the pretreatment system are:

- Colloidal and particulate foulants (suspended solids and silt)

- Inorganic compounds that may precipitate and scale or foul the membranes (such as iron and manganese, calcium carbonate, calcium sulfate, strontium sulfate, barium sulfate, or silica)

- Organic foulants (organics, microorganisms, and soluble organic compounds that can serve as food to the microorganisms in the source water)

Design fundamentals of the pretreatment systems used for removal of these foulants are provided in the following section.

Table 3-1   Advantages and disadvantages of co-location of desalination and power plants

Advantages	Disadvantages
• Capital cost savings by avoiding the construction of separate intake pipeline and structure and new discharge outfall.	• Use of warmer seawater may accelerate membrane biofouling, especially if the source water is rich in organics.
• Decrease of the required RO system feed pressure and power cost savings as a result of using warmer water.	• RO membranes may be exposed to iron or nickel fouling if the power plant condensers and piping are built of low quality materials.
• Reduction of unit power cost by connecting directly to power plant generation facilities and avoiding power transmission charges.	• Source seawater has to be cooled if its temperature increases above 40°C in order to protect RO membrane integrity and useful life.
• Accelerated permitting process as a result of avoidance of construction of new intake and discharge outfalls in the ocean.	• Permeate water quality diminishes slightly with the increase of source water temperature.
• Reduction of marine organism impingement and entrainment because the desalination plant does not take additional seawater from the ocean.	• Use of warmer water may result in lower boron rejection and require feed water pH adjustment to meet stringent boron water quality targets.
• Reduction of the impact on marine environment as a result of faster dissipation of thermal plume and concentrate.	• RO plant source water screening may be required if the power plant disposes its screenings through their outfall and the point of disposal is upstream of the desalination plant intake.
• Reduction of the power plant thermal discharge to the ocean because a portion of this discharge is converted to potable water.	• Desalination plant operations may need to be discontinued during periods of heat treatment of the power plant facilities.
• Use of already disturbed land at the power plant minimizes environmental impact.	• Coordination between desalination plant and power station operations is needed.

SUSPENDED SOLIDS AND SILT REMOVAL FACILITIES

Pretreatment System Configurations

The most suitable pretreatment facility configuration for a given source water depends on how high the source water turbidity and silt content are above the acceptable feedwater turbidity and SDI levels. Most spiral-wound NF and RO membrane manufacturers require membrane feedwater turbidity not to exceed 1.0 ntu, and SDI not to exceed 4 or 5, depending on the membrane product. It is usually recommended that the feedwater turbidity and SDI be less than 0.5 ntu and 3, respectively.

Table 3-3 provides a guideline for a combination of treatment processes recommended to be used for effective pretreatment of the source water as a function of source water turbidity and SDI levels. The pretreatment configurations shown in this table should be used as a guideline only. Thorough water quality analysis and pilot testing are recommended to define an optimum pretreatment system for the site-specific source water quality of a given project.

Table 3-2   Surface water intake design elements and considerations

Intake Component	Related Design Considerations
Intake structure	
Elevation	Inflow during low water or drought conditions
	Inflow during floods or high water
	Protection from damage, such as erosion or ice damage
	Minimization of sediment inflow
	Minimization of floating debris and plant debris inflow
Location (offshore)	Water depth
	Water quality variation
	Storm damage
	Damage from ship collision
Intake pipeline	
Material	Corrosion
	Maintenance access
Intake screens	Clogging and maintenance
	Corrosion
Intake pumps	Corrosion
	Backup
	Power failure
	Damage potential (based on location)

A basic description and key design criteria for the pretreatment facilities included in Table 3-3 are presented in the following sections. A more detailed reference for design of these pretreatment facilities can be found in the AWWA/ASCE book *Water Treatment Plant Design*, as well as numerous other sources.

Coagulation and Flocculation

The coagulants most frequently used for membrane plant source water coagulation are ferric salts (ferric sulfate and ferric chloride). Aluminum salts (such as alum or polyaluminum chloride) are not used because it is difficult to maintain aluminum concentrations at low levels and in the dissolved form because aluminum solubility is very pH dependent.

Coagulant dosage for a given source water is determined based on jar and/or pilot testing. The optimum coagulant dosage is pH dependent and has to be established based on on-site jar or pilot testing for the site-specific conditions of a given application. The target coagulation pH may be achieved by the coagulant addition alone, in other cases an acid (e.g., sulfuric acid) or base (e.g., caustic soda) may need to be added. Sulfuric acid is also often added as in pretreatment for calcium carbonate control, and caustic soda is often used in permeate posttreatment for pH adjustment and finished water corrosion control.

Table 3-3   Recommended pretreatment system configuration for suspended solids and silt removal based on source water SDI and turbidity

Process Recommended to be Included in the Pretreatment Configuration	SDI <4		SDI ≥4			
			Turbidity, ntu			
	<0.5	≥0.5 & <2	≥2 & <20	≥20 & <40	≥40 & ≤100	≥100
Coagulation and flocculation		X	X	X	X	X
Conventional sedimentation or dissolved air flotation				X	X	X
Enhanced sedimentation					X	X
Single-stage granular media or membrane filtration	X	X				
Two-stage granular media or single-stage membrane filtration			X	X	X	X

In general, it is best not to use polymers in NF and RO pretreatment. However, if used, only nonionic or anionic polymers are considered because most NF and RO membrane elements carry a negative surface charge. Use of a cationic polymer is likely to form a polymer film on the membrane surface, which will foul the membrane elements. The type and dosage of polymer (nonionic or anionic) that is most suitable for a given application has to be determined by jar and/or pilot testing. Polymer is added at a very low dosage (less than 0.2 mg/L). Adding elevated polymer dosages should be avoided because it usually results in high content of unused polymer in the filter effluent, which in turn plugs the cartridge filters and deposits on the membrane elements—thereby shortening the cartridge filter useful life and expediting the need for membrane cleaning. There also is a significant risk that the polymer fouling will be irreversible, resulting in permanent membrane performance decline.

Conventional and Enhanced Sedimentation

Sedimentation is used upstream of granular media filters when the membrane plant source water has daily average turbidity higher than about 20 ntu (see Table 3-3). The sedimentation basins should be designed to produce settled source water of less than approximately 2.0 ntu and measurable SDI (15-min SDI below 6). To achieve this level of turbidity removal, the sedimentation basin is equipped with a coagulant (most frequently iron salt) and flocculant (polymer) feed systems. The design coagulant and flocculent dosages should be established based on jar and/or pilot testing.

Conventional sedimentation basins are designed for a surface loading rate of 800 to 1,200 gpd/ft² (32.6 to 48.8 m³/m² d), a weir loading rate of 20,000 gpd/linear ft (250 m³/m d) and a hydraulic detention time of 2 to 4 hr. Surface loading rate is used to calculate the surface area requirements of the sedimentation basin.

Detention time is used in conjunction with the surface loading rate to calculate the volume and the side depth of the sedimentation basin.

If the source water turbidity exceeds 100 ntu, conventional sedimentation basins are often inadequate to produce turbidity of the desired target level of 1.0 to 2.0 ntu. Under these conditions, the sedimentation basin has to be designed for enhanced solids removal by installing lamella plates or using sedimentation technologies that combine lamella and fine granular media for enhanced solids removal.

The use of enhanced sedimentation technologies is needed for treating source water from a brackish or seawater surface water intake that is under a strong influence of river water with elevated turbidity. This condition occurs when a seawater or brackish desalination plant intake is located in a river delta area or is strongly influenced by a seasonal surface water runoff. For example, during the rainy season, the intake of the Point Lisas seawater desalination plant in Trinidad is under the influence of the Orinoco River, which carries a large amount of alluvial solids and is under the river water influence. The desalination plant intake turbidity could exceed 200 ntu (Irwin and Thompson 2003). To handle this high solids load, the plant source water is settled in a lamella sedimentation tank prior to conventional single-stage dual media filtration.

Granular Media Filters

Granular media filtration is the most commonly used source water pretreatment process for surface water NF and RO plants (other than cartridge filtration). This process includes the filtration of the source water through one or more layers of granular media (e.g., anthracite coal, silica sand, garnet).

General Design Considerations for Granular Media Filtration Systems

Because the purpose of the pretreatment filters for NF and RO plants is to not only remove more than 99 percent of all suspended solids in the source water but to also reduce the content of the much finer silt particles by several orders of magnitude, the design of these pretreatment facilities is governed by the filter effluent turbidity and SDI target levels. The filter efficiency of removing suspended solids (reducing turbidity) of the source water is not directly related to its silt removal efficiency (SDI reduction capability). Dissolved organics and coagulant (iron salts) can absorb on/in the filter test pad and result in increased SDI values. Full-scale experience at many granular media pretreatment filter installations indicates that many filters can consistently reduce source water turbidity to less than 0.1 ntu, while at the same time have effluent SDI values frequently exceeding 4. In many cases, granular media filters at NF/RO membrane plants need to be designed more conservatively than similar filters in a conventional surface water treatment plant. Taking into consideration that the key function of the pretreatment filters is to effectively remove more than 99.9 percent of the silt particles in the water that have sizes of less than 50 μm, the filtration system should be designed for

- Relatively lower surface loading rates (2–4 gpm/ft^2);

- The use of deeper filter media bed for the removal of silt-size particles;

- If the pretreatment facility is designed as a direct filtration system, it is important to have close control of the coagulant dosage and to achieve complete mixing of the coagulant with the filter feed water. Although overdosing of coagulant may have little to no effect on the filter effluent turbidity, it often can have a profound negative effect on the SDI level and ultimately on the useful life of the downstream cartridge filters and potential fouling of RO/NF membranes. Even small residual amounts of unreacted/unused and/or unfiltered coagulant are retained on the cartridge filters, resulting in their premature plugging. The effect of overdosing of coagulant (iron salt) on the SDI level can be recognized by visually inspecting the SDI test filter paper. In this situation, a significant improvement of the source water SDI can be attained by reducing coagulant feed dosage or in case of poor mixing, modifying the coagulant mixing to minimize/eliminate the unreacted chemical.

If the filter influent source water has nonmeasurable SDI (i.e., higher than 6.6 using the standard 15-min SDI test procedure [described in appendix D]), the construction of a two-stage filtration system is often used. The first stage filter is designed as dual-media filter with a layer of anthracite coal on the top of a layer of sand, and the second-stage filter is made up of three layers (anthracite coal over silica sand over garnet). The layers have progressively smaller grain size from top to bottom (1.1 mm anthracite to 0.2 mm garnet) and higher specific gravity (1.5 for anthracite to 4.2 for garnet). The minimum filter bed depth should be 3 ft (1 m).

The filters are backwashed using filtered water or, if acceptable, concentrate from the NF or RO membrane system. The backwash rate should provide 30 to 50 percent media bed expansion. The number of filters should allow full flow operation with one filter out of service in backwash and one out of service for maintenance.

The two types of media filters most widely used for pretreatment of NF and RO membrane plants are pressure and gravity filters. The major differences between pressure and gravity filters are the head required to convey the water through the media bed and the type of vessel used to contain the filter unit. Gravity filters usually require 6 to 10 ft (2 to 3 m) of head and are housed in open concrete or steel tanks. Pressure filters have greater driving pressure and are contained in enclosed vessels. Because of the cost of constructing large pressure vessels with the proper wetted surfaces for corrosion resistance, pressure filters are used for small- and medium-size capacity NF and RO plants. Gravity pretreatment filters are used both on small and large membrane plants.

MF and UF Membrane Filters

The most common membrane pretreatment process uses hollow-fiber MF or UF membranes to separate suspended solids and particles (including microbes) from the source water. MF and UF membrane systems have been shown to be very effective for turbidity and silt removal. Turbidity can be lowered consistently below 0.1 ntu, and filter effluent has SDI levels below 3 more than 90 percent of the time.

It is recommended that pilot testing be used in developing design criteria for the site-specific conditions and MF/UF product selection. Both pressure-type MF/UF systems, where the membranes are encased in pressure vessel or vacuum-type systems, where the membranes are immersed or submerged in tanks open to atmospheric pressure and use filtrate/permeate pumps to create the driving force, may be used. Detailed design guidelines for MF and UF filtration systems are presented elsewhere (AWWA 2004, 2005; USEPA 2003).

Comparison of Conventional and Membrane Pretreatment Filtration Systems

Membrane filtration technologies have a number of advantages as compared to conventional granular (sand/anthracite) media filtration systems. Granular media filtration, however, is a well understood and widely used pretreatment technology with a proven track record and has a number of features that may render it cost competitive under specific circumstances. Therefore, the selection of filtration technology for membrane pretreatment has to be based on a thorough life-cycle cost–benefit analysis. Side-by-side pilot testing of the two types of systems is also highly recommended to develop background system performance information for an objective technology selection. The following issues have to be considered when selecting between granular media and membrane pretreatment filtration for a specific application.

Effect of influent water quality. MF and UF systems have a wider spectrum of particle removal capabilities than conventional media filtration. Single- or dual-media filters have lesser removal efficiency in terms of source water organics, DBP precursors, fine particles, silt, and pathogens. Membrane filtration technologies are also less prone to complications caused by seasonal changes in source water temperature, pH, turbidity, color, microbial contamination, and size and type of water particles, because their primary treatment mechanism is mechanical particle removal through fine-pore membranes. Therefore, the upstream chemical coagulation and flocculation of the influent water particles is of lesser importance for their consistent and efficient performance. In contrast, the pretreatment efficiency of the conventional media filtration technologies is very dependent on how efficient chemical coagulation and flocculation of the water is ahead of the filtration process. Coagulation and flocculation water chemistry is more sensitive to changes in seasonal water quality than the mechanically driven membrane particle separation processes.

Therefore, for applications where intake water quality experiences significant seasonal variations and presents a challenge in terms of high microbial, fine particle, and organic contamination, membrane filtration technologies are likely to be the technology of choice, assuming it is cost-effective for the specific application. However, for influent water sources of high quality and limited seasonal variations, sand media filtration may offer an efficient and cost-effective pretreatment alternative to membrane filtration.

Another condition under which the sand media filtration may offer certain benefits is for a source of water that is very likely to be exposed to sudden and unpredictable changes of water quality such as very high or low pH chemical spills; large oil and grease spills; frequent exposures to very high water temperature; or other contaminants that may damage the MF/UF pretreatment membranes or RO/NF membranes irreversibly, if they are used for this application. If the membrane elements are permanently damaged, the cost of their replacement could be significant, especially for large membrane NF/RO treatment plants. Granular filter media can handle a wider range of extreme intake water quality conditions before irreversible damage, and the cost of media replacement is significantly lower than that for replacing all membrane elements for the same size plant.

This issue is of a very significant importance for pretreatment systems for seawater desalination plants with surface intakes. Often the source seawater contains small sharp objects (such as shell particles), which can easily puncture the pretreatment membranes and result in a very quick loss of their integrity, unless the damaging particles are removed upstream of the membrane pretreatment system. To remove sharp seawater particles that can damage the membranes from the source water, the NF/RO plant intake system has to incorporate a microscreening system.

The installation and operation of a microscreening system is significantly more costly than the use of conventional traveling fine screens, and therefore its cost has to be taken under consideration when comparing conventional and membrane filtration pretreatment. The performance and reliability of the conventional pretreatment systems are not sensitive to the content of sharp objects in the seawater and do not require more elaborate and costly screening ahead of the filters. Fine traveling screens of $1/8$ to $3/8$-in. (3 to 10 mm) openings provide adequate protection of conventional granular media pretreatment systems.

Footprint. Membrane technologies are very space efficient as compared to granular media filtration. The smaller footprint benefits of membrane filtration are of greater importance when upgrading existing water treatment plants of limited site area availability or where the cost of new land acquisition is significant.

Depending on the type and size of the membrane modules and the intake water quality characteristics, the membrane filtration system may have a 20 to 60 percent smaller footprint than a conventional filtration system. The space benefits of membrane filtration are more significant for high-turbidity waters where two-stage granular media filtration may be required to achieve performance comparable to a single-stage membrane system. As a rule of thumb, under typical surface-water quality conditions, the footprint of granular media filters, designed at a surface loading rate of 4.5 to 5 gpm/ft^2 (11 to 12 m^3/m^2 hr), is approximately 50 percent larger than that of MF or UF systems producing similar filtered water quality. For better-than-average influent water quality where granular media filters can perform adequately at a 6 to 8 gpm/ft^2 (15 to 20 m^3/m^2 hr) of hydraulic surface loading rate, the footprint difference is usually 20 to 40 percent in the benefit of membrane filtration.

Waste stream quantity and quality. Conventional and membrane pretreatment systems differ significantly by the type, quality, and amount of the generated waste streams. Conventional media filtration systems generate only one waste stream—waste filter backwash. The volume of this stream in a well designed plant varies between 2 to 6 percent of the total plant intake source water volume. In addition to the solids that were originally in the source water, this waste stream also contains coagulant (typically iron salt) and polymer (if used). Often the pretreatment filter waste backwash water is treated, blended with the NF/RO plant concentrate, and discharged to a surface water source.

The membrane pretreatment systems generate two large volume waste streams: waste membrane wash water and membrane cleaning solution. The volume of the membrane wash water stream is 5 to 10 percent of the plant intake source volume— i.e., approximately two times larger than the waste filter backwash generated by conventional pretreatment systems. The waste stream difference is even larger, taking into account that the microscreens required to be installed to protect the pretreatment membrane filters will generate additional waste discharge for their cleaning. While conventional traveling fine bar screens use less than 0.5 percent of the intake source water for cleaning, the microscreens would require wash volume that equals 2 to 3 percent of the intake flow. The relatively larger waste stream volume of the membrane pretreatment system would require proportionally larger intake source volume, which in turn would result in increased size and construction costs for the NF/RO membrane plant intake facilities, and higher operation and maintenance costs for source water pumping to the pretreatment facilities. In addition to daily membrane washing and monthly membrane cleaning, cost competitive design and operation of membrane pretreatment systems often require short daily chemically enhanced membrane backwash (CEB), using a high dosage of chlorine and base and acid over a short period of time. This performance enhancing CEB wastewater is discharged to the wastewater collection system and adds to the volume of the waste streams generated at the NF/RO membrane plant and to the overall cost of source water pretreatment.

One advantage of the main membrane waste wash stream is that it does not contain source water conditioning chemicals (coagulant and polymer) and therefore, it is more environmentally friendly—i.e., containing only solids that already were in the source water. However, the other two waste streams generated during the CEB and monthly pretreatment membrane cleaning are not suitable for surface water discharge and have to be pretreated on site in a neutralization tank prior to their discharge to the sanitary sewer. The additional treatment and disposal costs of the waste membrane cleaning chemicals have to be taken into consideration when selecting the use of membrane pretreatment systems over conventional granular media filtration.

Chemical use. Conventional granular media pretreatment systems use source water conditioning chemicals for effective solids separation. This adds to the plant chemical costs. However, they do not use any chemicals for media cleaning (outside of occasional addition of chlorine). The membrane pretreatment systems use significant amounts of membrane cleaning chemicals. The cost of these cleaning chemicals has to be considered in the cost–benefit analysis of the plant pretreatment system. Another factor that has to be accounted for in the overall plant chemical use and cost analysis is that the NF/RO system cleaning frequency, and therefore the NF/RO membrane cleaning costs, may be reduced by using membrane pretreatment because of the better solids and silt removal capabilities of this type of pretreatment.

Power use. Conventional pretreatment systems use a limited amount of power to separate particulates in the source water. As previously mentioned, large NF/RO plants use gravity granular media filtration for pretreatment, which has minimum power requirements. On the other hand, depending on the type of membrane system (pressure or vacuum-driven), the membrane systems will consume a greater amount of power. More power is not only used to create a flow-driving pressure through the membranes but also for membrane backwash and feedwater pumping. The total power use has to be taken into consideration when completing a life-cycle cost comparison of conventional versus membrane pretreatment systems for a given application.

Economy of scale. MF/UF membrane and granular media pretreatment systems may yield different economies of scale depending on the water treatment plant capacity. Both processes have a comparable economy-of-scale for plant capacity of up to 10 mgd (40,000 m³/day). For larger NF/RO plants, the single-stage gravity-type granular media filtration systems yield more favorable economy-of-scale benefits—however, this may be changing as MF/UF systems and products are further optimized for large capacity treatment plants.

Frequency of filtration media replacement. Properly operating granular media filters lose less than 5 percent of filter media per year, which needs to be replaced periodically to maintain consistent performance. The costs of granular media replacement are usually predictable and relatively low. At present, a properly designed and operated MF/UF facility can have membrane life greater than 5 years. Assuming 5 years of useful life, approximately 20 percent of the membrane elements would need to be replaced per year to maintain system production capacity and performance.

Diversity of membrane elements and configurations. Currently, all MF and UF membrane manufacturers offer their own design, size, and configuration of membrane elements and systems. The membrane systems differ by the type of filtration driving force (pressure versus vacuum); the size of the individual membrane elements; the size of the membrane vessels; the configuration of the membrane modules; the type of membrane element backwash; the type of membrane integrity testing method; and other factors.

The current diversity of membrane element sizes and configurations, and lack of standardization and commoditization may have a number of disadvantages for the membrane plant owner. For example, if an existing membrane manufacturer discontinues the production of membrane elements or a given type of membrane system or goes out of business, the plant owner would incur additional costs if suitable membrane replacements were not available and a new pretreatment system needed to be acquired.

Cartridge filters.   As indicated previously, the cartridge filter functions as a guard or safety filter to protect the downstream RO/NF system from damage caused by particulate matter. Cartridge filters are designed to remove at least 90 percent of particles larger than their nominal rated size. For all but the smallest capacity RO/NF systems, many filter cartridges are installed in stainless-steel or FRP pressure housing vessels (see Figure 3-13).

The cartridge filters used in municipal membrane treatment plants are 40-in. (1 m) long. The pressure vessels may be oriented vertically or horizontally. Cartridges are rated for removal of particle sizes of 1, 2, 5, 10, and 25 μm, with the most frequently used size being 5 μm. Polypropylene wound cartridges are commonly used, although other types, such as melt-blown or pleated cartridges, are also in use. The differential pressure across the cartridge filter(s) should be monitored to aid in determining when filter cartridges should be replaced. In addition, valved sample ports should be installed immediately upstream and downstream of the cartridge filter vessel(s) for water quality sampling and testing (including SDI field testing).

Figure 3-13   Cartridge filters located horizontally in vessel

Often systems are designed with average hydraulic loading rates of less than 4 gpm (0.25 L/sec) per 10 in. (250 mm) length. Additional filtration capacity is provided to allow cartridges to be replaced without the need to interrupt production. Pressure vessels are typically constructed of 316-L stainless steel for NF and brackish RO installations and duplex stainless steel for seawater RO installations.

The clean cartridge filter pressure drop is specified as less than 3 psi (0.2 bars). Generally, cartridges are replaced when the filter differential pressure reaches 10 or 15 psi (0.7 or 1 bar). The operational time before replacement depends on source water quality and the degree of pretreatment. A cartridge filter replacement is needed once every 6 to 8 weeks. Particles are disposed of with the filters as solids waste.

For NF or RO systems where sand in the feedwater might be anticipated, rigid melt-blown cartridges or cartridge filters with single open ends and dual O-rings on the insertion nipple (rather than conventional dual open-end cartridges) are commonly used. The single open-end insertion filters have positive seating and an insertion plate, which do not allow deformation of the filter cartridge under pressure caused by sand packing. Double open-end cartridge filters are held in place by a spring-loaded pressure plate. Under pressure from packed sand, wound-type cartridge filters can bend, causing the ends of the filter to unseat and allow direct entry of sand into the NF/RO system feed line.

Inorganic Foulant Control Facilities

Facilities for iron and manganese removal. Iron is found in groundwater and deep surface water low in dissolved oxygen. It may be either in soluble ferrous state (Fe^{2+}); in ferric state (Fe^{3+}); in inorganic complexes with silicates, phosphates, polyphosphates, sulfates, and other species; or in organic complexes. Groundwater usually contains iron as ferrous bicarbonate. When dissolved ferrous bicarbonate is exposed to air, the iron is oxidized to the ferric state, and it forms an insoluble hydroxide that is difficult to remove from NF and RO membrane surfaces. Manganese is usually found with iron and behaves similarly. Although iron and manganese can be removed by lime softening or biological assimilation, the most widely used treatment is a combination of oxidation and filtration by a granular media containing manganese oxide, such as greensand. If the iron and manganese can be kept in the dissolved state in the membrane system and product water goals can be met, their removal is not necessary as they are rejected by the NF/RO membranes similarly to other divalent ions. In fact, because most NF and RO membranes cannot tolerate strong oxidants, there is a process risk of using iron or manganese removal with chemical oxidant addition, and pretreatment for iron and manganese removal is avoided unless necessary.

Scaling control facilities. Scaling is caused by the precipitation of low solubility salts such as carbonate, calcium sulfate, barium sulfate, strontium sulfate, and silica within the membrane system. Stability of these compounds depends on their concentration in the concentrate flow stream, water temperature, pH, and other factors. For example, higher temperatures and pH facilitate the precipitation of calcium carbonate. Scaling control can be achieved by lowering recovery, adjusting pH (acidification), addition of scale inhibitor chemicals (antiscalants), or by removing scaling ions in pretreatment facilities.

Acidification. Acid addition is used for calcium carbonate control and minimize hydrolysis in cellulosic membranes. The addition of sulfuric (or, in rare cases hydrochloric) acid lowers the carbonate concentration by converting bicarbonate to carbon dioxide. The carbon dioxide passes through the membrane and is removed in the posttreatment system. Sulfuric acid is preferred over hydrochloric acid because of cost and safety reasons. However, hydrochloric acid may be used if the sulfate added by sulfuric acid significantly affects the system design and cost. In some cases, the additional sulfate increases the risk of scale (i.e., barium sulfate or calcium sulfate) and thereby lowers the achievable recovery. Acid feed systems include positive displacement metering pumps (or centrifugal pumps for large systems) drawing from a day tank. In some cases, where allowed by the permitting agency and desired by the owner, acid metering pumps that pump directly from bulk chemical storage have been installed.

Some of the compounds of intake surface water (such as humic acid) serve as natural chelating agents and antiscalants. It is prudent to pilot test to assess if acidification can be avoided. The elimination of acid addition also avoids the use of permeate posttreatment degasifiers for carbon dioxide stripping and avoids costs associated with their construction and operation.

Scale inhibitor addition.   Scale inhibitors (antiscalants) are commonly fed in NF/RO pretreatment to protect against membrane scaling from precipitation of sparingly soluble salts and silica. Some scale inhibitors prevent the formation of seed crystals and others deform the seed crystals so they cannot grow and cause problems in the membrane system. In some cases, dispersants are added to the scale inhibitor formulations to aid in preventing colloidal material deposition.

Sodium hexametaphosphate is used in many plants around the world although in the United States (and many other locations where available), proprietary chemical formulations are more commonly used because of their improved effectiveness, long storage life without losing strength, microbial growth resistance while in the feed tank, ease of handling, or other reasons. It is important to select the correct scale inhibitor for the specific application. For example, the presence of iron in the source water can cause precipitation and membrane fouling with some types of antiscalants. Additionally, it is now believed that some scale inhibitors can act as coagulants and facilitate the deposition of organic carbon onto membrane surfaces. Pilot testing in southwest Florida has shown that the elimination of antiscalant feed has resulted in lower rates of fouling in highly organic waters (Thompson et al. 2001).

Organic Foulant Control Facilities

Organic foulants are of two key types: biological matter (microorganisms and their biological waste products), and organic compounds that naturally occur in the source water or are of man-made origin.

Facilities for control of microbiological fouling.   Microorganisms that naturally occur in the source water and their biological waste products deposited on the surface of the membrane elements can foul membranes and decrease their productivity over time. Microbiological fouling can be effectively controlled by reduction of source water constituents that accelerate microorganism growth: food (nutrients) and oxygen. The concentration of the microorganisms in the source water can be effectively reduced by their exposure to strong oxidants (e.g., disinfectants); by physical removal (i.e., filtration); by removal of soluble organic compounds that serve as food to the microorganisms; or by depriving the microorganisms oxygen by applying strong reducing agents such as sodium bisulfite. These methods are briefly described in the following sections.

Biological inactivation by oxidation and UV disinfection.   Several oxidants, such as chlorine, chlorine dioxide, and chloramines, can be used for surface source water microbiological growth control. Microbial control is an area of controversy and focus of research at this time. This is because there have been some membrane plants that have had serious microbial fouling problems after chlorination or other means of microbial control—possibly worse than if no chemical disinfectants were used. It has been shown that continuous chlorination and dechlorination (before the RO membranes) can increase bioactivity by increasing the assimilable organic compounds in the source water. Some membrane plants have suffered permanent damage of the NF/RO membranes by exposure to the chemical oxidant when the dechlorination chemical system failed.

Chlorination is the most popular disinfection process. Chlorine can be added continuously at relatively low dosages (typically 1 to 2 mg/L) or intermittently for 3 to 5 hr per day, several days at a time as needed at dosages of 3 to 5 mg/L. The actual dose required depends on project-specific chlorine demand. When chlorine is used for microbiological control, the source water has to be dechlorinated (using sodium bisulfite or sulfur dioxide) to protect the NF/RO membrane elements from chemical oxidation and failure. In the case of low-bromide feedwater, such as wastewater treated for reuse, continuous low concentrations of chloramines can effectively control microbial fouling and not damage oxidant intolerant membranes. For example, the water reuse facility Water Factory 21 in Orange County, Calif., which processes wastewater effluent for reuse, has successfully applied a continuous chloramine residual for years without damage to their chlorine-sensitive polyamide RO membranes by adding chlorine, which reacts with the natural ammonia in the wastewater treatment plant effluent. However, chloramination of seawater is not recommended, because this water contains large amount of bromides, which when exposed to ammonia, form bromamines. Although chloramines are relatively weak oxidants that do not result in measurable membrane damage, bromamines have an order-of-magnitude higher oxidation strength and their contact with the membrane material will cause irreversible damage, as shown during testing completed at the West Basin pilot seawater desalination plant in Carson, Calif. The seawater RO membranes at this pilot facility were irreversibly damaged within a week from the initiation of seawater chloramination. Exposure of polyamide membrane to chlorine or chloramines may void the membrane warranty provided by the manufacturer—therefore use of these or any oxidants in pretreatment should be considered very carefully and, if used, designed with a highly reliable dechlorination step ahead of the RO/NF.

UV disinfection is an alternative method for microbiological control. However, in some facilities, microbial regrowth after UV treatment negated the benefits, so its use should be evaluated carefully. UV disinfection method is power intensive and, therefore less cost-effective than chlorination–dechlorination. The cost-effectiveness of UV disinfection is dependent on the source water quality. If the source water has high levels of turbidity, the UV dosage could be relatively high. For optimum performance, it is recommended that the total suspended solids (TSS) of the source water fed to the UV unit not exceed 10 mg/L. The best location of the UV system would be between the cartridge filter and the RO membranes. Because of space constraints, however, that is not possible, so as an alternative, just prior to the cartridge filter is acceptable. Full-scale experience at a 600-gpm power plant RO facility using an adjacent river as a water source, indicates that the UV dosage required for effective microbiological growth control was $30 \text{mW} \cdot \text{sec/cm}^2$ (Zahnow 2002).

Media filtration. Granular media filtration is a well-known and very effective process in removing some bacteria. MF and UF membrane filtration provides higher efficiency in removing bacteria and the waste products of their metabolism. Design of granular and membrane pretreatment filtration systems is discussed elsewhere in this chapter.

Facilities for control of organic fouling.   Organic compounds are a diverse group of source water contaminants that come from a variety of sources: humic and fulvic acids from natural breakdown of organic matter, oil and grease, phenols, pesticides, surfactants, tannins, fertilizers from agricultural runoff, industrial wastes, endocrine disruptors, and so forth. Many organics, such as those indicated by oil and grease measurement, may damage RO/NF systems as a result of chemical interaction with the membrane material or fouling of the membrane surface.

One of the key parameters for measuring the content of organic compounds in the source water is the TOC concentration. DOC and AOC, parameters that indicate the availability of organic substances in the source water to serve as a food source for biogrowth, also can indicate potential for organic fouling. If the TOC of the intake water is less than 0.5 mg/L, then the source water is generally considered to be of low organic content and is not expected to pose significant organic fouling problems or to be a measurable source of food for the microorganisms in the source water. If the source water TOC concentration is below about 4 mg/L, and the membrane plant pretreatment includes a chlorination–dechlorination system and granular media filters with coagulation–flocculation provisions or MF/UF membrane filtration with provisions for coagulant addition, organic fouling of NF/RO membranes is not very likely. These treatment facilities provide 20 to 50 percent of TOC reduction and minimize organic or microbiological fouling, but jar or other types of tests need to be conducted on the specific water. However, if the TOC concentration of the source water exceeds 4 mg/L, the risk of organic biofouling should be thoroughly investigated.

Depending on the nature of the organic compounds, the potential treatment methods are oxidation via chlorination–dechlorination; enhanced coagulation followed by sedimentation and filtration using elevated dosages of coagulant for increased TOC removal; MF/UF membrane filtration with coagulation; air stripping (if the organic compounds are volatile); GAC adsorption/filtration; UV disinfection; and dissolved air flotation (if the main organic compounds are oil and grease or algae). The design of these processes can be found elsewhere in the chapter or in other sources (such as the AWWA/ASCE *Water Treatment Plant Design*).

RO AND NF SYSTEMS

The membrane unit is composed of RO or NF membrane elements, pressure vessels and support racks, feedwater pumps, valves and piping, sample panels, instrumentation and controls, and energy recovery devices (as applicable). As discussed in chapter 2, system pressure often determines the types of components used in a membrane system.

Membrane Elements

Many types of RO and NF membranes are commercially available. Most RO and NF products currently installed are spiral-wound configuration, although some hollow fiber and other products are also available. The membranes include those formulated with polyamide, polyamide derivatives, cellulose acetate, cellulose triacetate, or cellulose acetate blends, and other organic polymer materials. Standard size elements commonly used in public water supply systems are 4 or 8 in. (100 or 200 mm) diameter and 40 in. (1,020 mm) long, although 60-in. (1,520-mm)-long elements are also available. Larger diameter elements are being developed to improve economy of scale (USBR et al. 2004). Currently, 16-in. (400-mm) and 18-in. (460-mm)-diameter spiral-wound membrane elements are available.

Membrane Pressure Vessels

Fiberglass-reinforced plastic is often used for pressure vessel modules. Membrane pressure vessels and modules are usually installed on welded steel or fiberglass-reinforced plastic support racks. Pressure vessels for spiral-wound elements are manufactured to hold up to 8 (40-in.-long) elements in series, although 6 or 7 elements per vessel are more common, even for large systems. Hollow fiber membrane pressure vessels contain 1 or 2 elements.

Spiral-wound pressure vessels have feed and concentrate connections from the end or side (called *side-port*). Newer multiport pressure vessels with two side ports near each end are available that can minimize the need for manifold piping. The permeate connection is on the end, in the center of the end cap, in all spiral-wound pressure vessels. Figure 3-14 shows examples of end- and side-port pressure vessels.

Membrane Process Trains

Membrane systems with more than one individually controlled membrane skid (or rack) are arranged in parallel process trains. Each process train contains one or more membrane stages. In cases where the design includes one feed pump and other pretreatment components dedicated to specific membrane skids and controlled as a unit, the entire grouping of components is referred to as a *process train*. Another type of design used less often is where each membrane stage of a multistage system is separated into individual control blocks made up of membrane skids.

The number of membrane trains or control blocks depends on the overall capacity of the facility, the degree of production flexibility needed, and the percent production loss that is acceptable when one train or block is out of service for membrane cleaning or other maintenance.

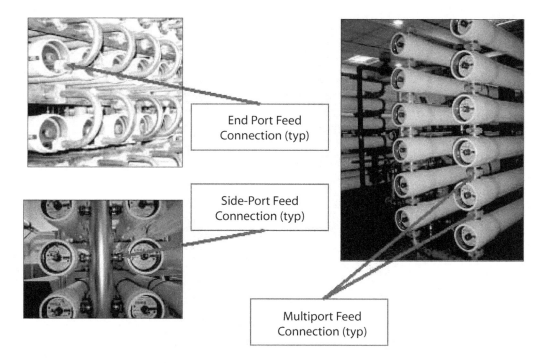

End Port Feed Connection (typ)

Side-Port Feed Connection (typ)

Multiport Feed Connection (typ)

Figure 3-14   End-, side-, and multiport pressure vessels

Membrane System Pumps

Horizontal centrifugal or vertical turbine can-type pumps are typically used for RO and NF systems. Smaller capacity seawater RO systems often use positive displacement pumps with suction and discharge accumulators or pulsation dampeners to minimize pressure fluctuations. Variable speed pumps are used in small systems that do not employ energy recovery systems, although seawater systems may employ both variable speed pumps and energy recovery. Larger systems use multistage centrifugal pumps. In some cases, an energy recovery turbopump is used for membrane feed pumping, as discussed in the following sections.

Energy Recovery Systems

Many seawater RO and higher pressure brackish RO systems employ energy recovery (ER) devices to minimize power costs. Additionally, some NF and RO systems use hydraulic turbochargers to boost the interstage pressure to the second or third stage of a multistage system to improve flux balancing. Energy is recovered by using the residual high pressures present in the concentrate water stream. Common ER devices include integrated turbopumps, with reverse-running impellers (for the concentrate flow stream) on a shaft common with feedwater pumping impellers, impulse turbines (such as Pelton wheels) coupled to the feedwater pump motors, hydraulic turbochargers often used to boost pressure to the first or second stage of a membrane system, and pressure exchangers. ER is not economically justified for all systems. Systems with relatively low recovery and relatively high concentrate flow rates and pressures are more likely to justify ER devices. All seawater RO systems can justify the use of ER because of the high pressures used and the relatively low hydraulic recovery of the systems. The amount of energy recovered should be based on water-to-water hydraulic energy transfer efficiencies to account for all losses, including belts and gearing losses in some cases. The decision on using an ER system should be based on life-cycle cost analysis.

Integrated Turbopumps

Figures 3-15 and 3-16 present a typical can-type turbopump and process flow diagram. The motor, reverse-running impellers, and pumping impellers are on the same shaft. Energy from the concentrate stream flowing through the reverse-running impeller section is transferred to the common motor and pumping shaft, thus saving energy. The energy savings can be calculated as follows:

$$\Delta KW = KW_{in} - KW_{out} \qquad \text{(Eq 3-1)}$$

Where:

KW_{in} = Kilowatt energy to pump =

$$\left[\frac{Q_f \times TDH_{pump} \times SG_f}{(3,960 \times Pump_{Eff} \times Motor_{Eff})} \right] \times 0.7457$$

KW_{out} = Kilowatt energy recovered =

$$\left[\frac{Q_c \times TDH_{Turbine} \times SG_c \times Turbine_{Eff}}{3,960}\right] \times 0.7457$$

Q_f = Feed flow rate, gpm

Q_c = Concentrate flow rate (to the ER device), gpm

TDH_{pump} or $TDH_{turbine}$ = Total dynamic head for pump or across recovery turbine, ft of water

SG_f or SG_c = Specific gravity of feed flow or concentrate flow

$Pump_{Eff}$, $Pump_{Turbine}$, $Motor_{Eff}$ = Efficiency of pump, energy recovery turbine, and motor, %

For example:

Q_f = 500 gpm
Q_c = 175 gpm (65% recovery)
TDH_{pump} = 690 ft (300 psi)
$TDH_{Turbine}$ = 600 ft (260 psi)
SG_f or SG_c = 1.0
$Pump_{Eff}$ = 76%
$Pump_{Turbine}$ = 55%
$Motor_{Eff}$ = 92%

$$KW_{in} = \left[\frac{500 \text{ gpm} \ 690 \quad \text{ft} \ \times \ .0}{(3,690 \times 0.76 \times 0.92)}\right] \times 0.7457 = 93 \text{ KW}$$

$$KW_{out} = \left[\frac{125 \text{ gpm} \times 600 \text{ ft} \times 1.0 \times 0.55}{3,960}\right] \times 0.7457 = 8 \text{ KW}$$

ΔKW = 85 KW

Impulse Turbines

Impulse turbines use the Pelton wheel principles to transfer energy from the pressurized concentrate flow stream to a pump device. The impulse turbine may be coupled to the shaft of a motor that drives a horizontal or vertical centrifugal or a positive displacement pump, such as a quintiplex pump sometimes used for seawater RO systems. Figure 3-17 presents a photograph of an impulse turbine for a centrifugal pump.

HYDRAULIC TURBOCHARGERS

Hydraulic turbochargers are used primarily to recover energy in brackish water RO systems or for flux balancing in low pressure RO or NF systems. The device is basically two impellers on a common shaft (with no motor). Figure 3-18 presents a

Figure 3-15   Integrated turbopump (Englewood, Fla.)

typical turbocharger, and Figure 3-19 shows how it often is placed in a two-stage membrane system. The pressure boost can be calculated as follows:

$$\Delta P_{tc} = HT_{\text{Eff}} \times Q_c/Q_f \times (Pc_{\text{turbo-in}} - Pc_{\text{turbo-out}}) \qquad \text{(Eq 3-2)}$$

Where:

ΔP_{tc}	=	Pressure boost to the feed flow through the turbocharger
HT_{Eff}	=	Hydraulic transfer efficiency
Q_c	=	Concentrate flow rate (to the energy recovery device)
Q_f	=	Feed flow rate (through the energy recovery pumping section)
$Pc_{\text{turbo-in}} - Pc_{\text{turbo-out}}$	=	Concentrate stream pressure in and out of the hydraulic turbocharger

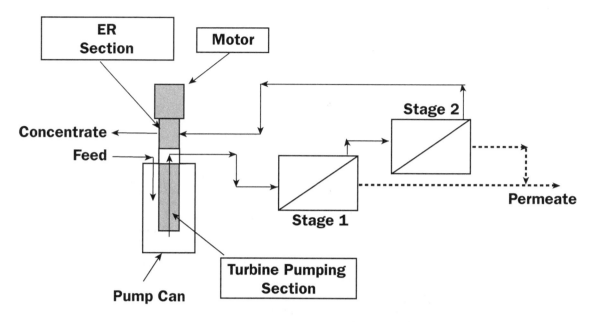

Figure 3-16   Integrated turbopump for feed pumping

Figure 3-17   ER impulse turbine (Calder AG)

For example:

$$
\begin{array}{rcl}
Q_f &=& 500 \text{ gpm} \\
Q_c &=& 275 \text{ gpm (45\% recovery)} \\
HT_{\text{Eff}} &=& 62\% \\
Pc_{\text{turbo-in}} &=& 975 \text{ psi} \\
Pc_{\text{turbo-out}} &=& 10 \text{ psi} \\
\Delta P_{tc} &=& 0.62 \times (275 \text{ gpm}/500 \text{ gpm}) \times (975 \text{ psi} - 10 \text{ psi}) = 329 \text{ psi}
\end{array}
$$

Figure 3-18   PEI hydraulic turbocharger (Pump Engineering Inc.)

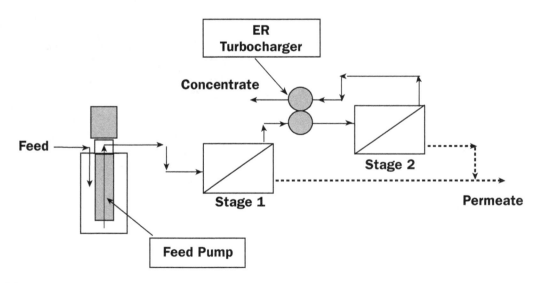

Figure 3-19   Hydraulic turbocharger for interstage pressure boost

Pressure/Work Exchanger Type

Isobaric ER devices, such as pressure exchangers and work exchangers, which approximate positive displacement type devices (rather than centrifugal type devices), are used on seawater RO systems and have the highest efficiency of all the currently available ER devices (up to about 94 percent). Figure 3-20 shows two types, one especially well suited for smaller seawater RO systems and another primarily targeting large capacity seawater RO plants. In RO systems using pressure exchanger type ER devices, the feed pump must pump flow approximately equal to the permeate flow rate plus losses, and another pump is used to boost the feed flow from the pressure exchanger outlet to the required membrane feed pressure (see Figure 3-21).

Piping and Valves Materials of Construction

Proper selection of materials of construction is critical for NF and RO systems because the corrosive process streams can severely limit useful life of the components, and also, for components located upstream of the membranes, these corrosive process streams may release corrosion by-products that could scale or damage the membranes.

Brackish water RO and some NF systems typically use 316-L stainless steel for high pressure piping, or higher grades of stainless steel, depending on the feed and concentrate water quality. Some NF or low salinity RO systems use type 304-L stainless steel for feed and concentrate piping. Seawater RO systems often use 254SMO or AL6XN (6 percent molybdenum) duplex stainless steel or super duplex stainless steel for high pressure piping. Nonmetallic piping (PVC, CPVC, FRP, and HDPE) is commonly used for low pressure piping.

A variety of valves are used in a membrane unit process. The grades of materials used for valves depend on the required pressure ratings and the corrosivity of the contacting liquid. Typically, PVC valves are used for low pressure systems and proper-grade stainless-steel valves for high pressure applications.

Valves designed for a high pressure drop are used for concentrate throttling to minimize cavitation and operational noise. Butterfly and ball valves are used to isolate individual headers, manifolds, and membrane trains. Check valves are used on pump discharge lines and on permeate and concentrate lines from each membrane train. Pressure relief valves or rupture disks are included on the permeate piping between the membranes and isolation valves, depending on the system staging and the header and manifold configurations. Air-relief valves are sometimes installed at high points on concentrate and permeate manifolds to remove air during startup. Vacuum breakers are included to prevent unwanted draining or siphoning while the unit is off. Most systems employ multiple sample valves located in the membrane array for water quality monitoring.

Alternative Membrane System General Layouts

Many different general layouts can be used for membrane systems depending on the size of the facility, the number of membrane process trains, personal preferences of the designer, and other factors.

For small skid-mounted systems, it is common to have the pretreatment chemical injection points, cartridge filter, feed pump, and membranes and pressure vessels on the skid. For larger systems, the pretreatment components and feed pumps are not located on the rack supporting the membranes and pressure vessels. Designs involve decisions regarding components being dedicated to individual trains or grouped such that they are common to all of the trains. Many larger systems have a common source- or feedwater header that receives pretreatment chemical addition and a common cartridge filtration system (consisting of several parallel cartridge filters).

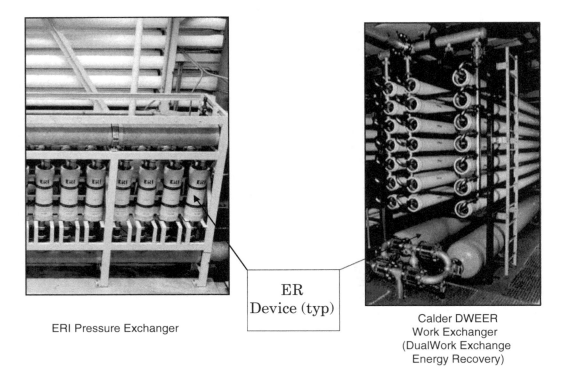

ERI Pressure Exchanger

ER Device (typ)

Calder DWEER
Work Exchanger
(DualWork Exchange
Energy Recovery)

Courtesy of Energy Recovery Inc. and Calder AG

Figure 3-20   Pressure/work exchangers

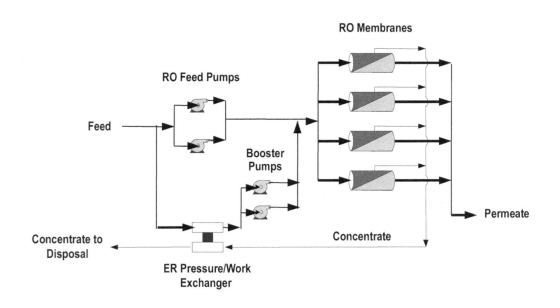

Figure 3-21   RO system with isobaric pressure/work exchangers and boost pumps

Typically, large systems will have feed pumps configured in one of two arrangements: (1) dedicated feed pump for each train, possibly with a common spare pump or (2) all feed pumps located in a pumping center in parallel with a discharge header that supplies multiple trains. A major advantage of the dedicated feed pump concept is that it is a simple system and, for each train, no more feed pressure needs to be generated than needed for that particular train. The pumping center concept is more complex but has the advantage that fewer pumps are needed than the number of trains (lowering pump facility costs). A disadvantage of the pumping center is that each train uses a throttling (control) valve from the supply line from a common feed header, and the header pressure must be at least as high as the greatest pressure required considering all the trains supplied by the header. This results in a greater energy consumption than a dedicated system with variable speed drives.

For systems using energy recovery devices on concentrate streams, most often the energy recovery devices are dedicated to individual trains. In some designs, energy recovery units have been combined in a location that receives combined concentrate from all trains. The system arrangement used for a particular project should consider the degree of control desired, reliability and redundancy issues, costs, and other factors.

POSTTREATMENT SYSTEMS

Treatment facilities downstream of the RO or NF system are posttreatment processes. As discussed in chapter 2, posttreatment of both permeate and concentrate varies depending on specific applications and regulatory requirements. For municipal water systems, posttreatment is always required for the permeate flow stream before distribution to the utility customers. In some plants, the concentrate flow stream also receives posttreatment before disposal.

Permeate posttreatment processes include a PVC or FRP degasifier (decarbonator) for removing carbon dioxide and hydrogen sulfide (if present), as well as chemical addition for stabilization. In a degasifier, the water falls by gravity through packing material and air from a blower or fan moves upward (countercurrent to the water), allowing the efficient gas stripping to occur. Often, the degasified water discharges to a clearwell beneath the degasifier and product transfer pumps transport the product water to finished water storage, or in some cases, the degasified water may be piped directly to finished water storage. Chemical addition includes a disinfectant (chlorine or chlorine plus ammonia forming chloramines); an alkaline chemical (caustic soda, soda ash, lime); and, sometimes, a corrosion inhibitor (polyphosphate, orthophosphate, or a blend) and/or fluoride. The use of lime and soda ash may result in an unacceptable turbidity increase and caustic may be preferred.

Corrosion Control

Permeate water from NF/RO treatment processes poses unique challenges to engineers and water suppliers because of the fact that it contains few minerals and little to no alkalinity. The result is aggressive water that may be prone to wide variations in pH, which can further complicate corrosion.

Table 3-4 provides a summary of the water quality characteristics for a model seawater, brackish water, and their respective RO permeates. As indicated by the indices presented in Table 3-4, the source seawater, brackish water, and permeate waters are aggressive and high corrosion potential may be inferred. Posttreatment concepts should be developed to reduce the corrosion potential of these waters by producing water that is slightly depositing with respect to calcium carbonate and has a Larson ratio of less than 5 (Larson 1970).

Table 3-4   Model water quality

Parameter	Unit	Seawater		Brackish Water	
		Raw Water	Permeate	Raw Water	Permeate
Temperature	°C	10	10	25	25
pH	S.U.	7.9	6.1	6.8	5.5
Alkalinity	mg/L as $CaCO_3$	116	3	183	6
TDS	mg/L	35,000	251	10,339	216
Calcium	mg/L	408	0.6	232	1.0
Magnesium	mg/L	1,298	1.9	331	1.5
Sodium	mg/L	10,767	92	3,116	78.8
Potassium	mg/L	387	4.28	93	3.0
Barium	mg/L	NA	NA	0.0	0.0
Strontium	mg/L	NA	NA	0.02	0.0
Carbon dioxide	mg/L	4.0	4.0	33.8	33.8
Carbonate	mg/L	0.1	0.0	0.7	0.0
Bicarbonate	mg/L	142	2.2	166	6.1
Sulfate	mg/L	2,710	3.5	1,087	4.5
Chloride	mg/L	19,360	148	5,382	124
Fluoride	mg/L	1.3	0.0	0.99	0.01
Silica	mg/L	0.02	0.0	14	0.3
LSI	+/–	NA	–5.9	–0.3	–5.4
Stiff & Davis Stability Index	+/–	–0.31	NA	NA	NA
CCPP	mg/L (as $CaCO_3$)	NA	–17	–9.6	–73
Aggressivity Index		NA	6.8	11.8	6.7
Larson ratio		270	118	68	36

NOTES: NA: Not applicable; Stiff and Davis Stability Index: Similar to the LSI, used to qualitatively assess carbonate scale formation for high TDS waters.

Corrosion Control Approaches

To develop posttreatment concepts for corrosion control following RO treatment, it is first necessary to have treatment goals. The following goals are used as a guide for developing posttreatment concepts:

- Alkalinity ≥40 mg/L as $CaCO_3$
- Calcium carbonate precipitation potential (CCPP) = 4 to 10 mg/L as $CaCO_3$
- Larson ratio <5
- Calcium plus alkalinity >50 mg/L as $CaCO_3$

Alkalinity greater than or equal to 40 mg/L as $CaCO_3$ was chosen as a goal because it has been suggested by others that alkalinity less than this value is considered low and may result in poor buffering and pH variations in distribution systems (Schock 1991).

The following provides a summary of typical posttreatment techniques used in RO treatment processes. Their application to the model permeate water quality presented in Table 3-4 is discussed.

Decarbonation

Decarbonation may be required because of the presence of high concentrations of carbonic acid that is typically accompanied by low pH. Excess presence of hydrogen ion (i.e., low pH) has been linked to increased corrosion potential caused by the presence of an electron acceptor in corrosion reactions (Schock 1991). Carbonic acid may result from the conversion of bicarbonate when acid is added to NF/RO feedwater as a method of controlling calcium carbonate scaling on the NF/RO membrane (i.e., membrane fouling). Decarbonation, or removal of excess carbonic acid, will help increase the finished water pH. Decarbonators are sometimes called *degasifiers*, especially in applications where the units remove hydrogen sulfide.

Decarbonation consists of an air transfer process, where, according to Henry's Law, carbonic acid (i.e., dissolved carbon dioxide) prefers to be in the air phase. Such processes as packed tower aeration (PTA), tray aeration, and more recently, hollow fiber membrane aeration, can be used for removing carbonic acid from RO permeate.

Decarbonation is used in combination with other posttreatment processes because it may be beneficial to convert some carbonic acid back to bicarbonate alkalinity. Combined use of decarbonation with pH adjustment may be more economical, because this will help control the cost of chemicals used to increase pH while still producing the desired pH, alkalinity, and CCPP.

Addition/Recovery of Alkalinity

When high concentrations of carbonic acid are not available in permeate water to convert the desired amount to bicarbonate alkalinity with pH adjustment, it may be necessary to supplement alkalinity with chemical treatment. While hydroxide addition will increase the finished water alkalinity and pH, carbonate and bicarbonate alkalinity are required to produce a CCPP within the desired range and also help provide buffering capacity that will help prevent pH variations in the distribution system. The following posttreatment methods are used to add or recover alkalinity in RO permeate water:

- Addition of caustic soda or lime to permeate containing carbonic acid

- Addition of carbonic acid followed by the addition of caustic soda or lime

- Addition of sodium carbonate or sodium bicarbonate

- Calcium carbonate–limestone contactor

Caustic soda or lime added to permeate containing carbonic acid is referred to as *alkalinity recovery*. As discussed previously, it may be necessary to combine alkalinity recovery with a decarbonation process to control chemical costs when carbonic acid concentrations are high. When NF/RO permeate water has relatively low concentrations of carbonic acid, carbonic acid can be added using a carbon dioxide gas feed system, and then converting the carbonic acid to bicarbonate alkalinity.

Perhaps a more costly method of adding carbonate-based alkalinity is the addition of sodium carbonate or sodium bicarbonate. In practice, it may be necessary to monitor dose rates to make certain that finished water sodium concentrations are kept less than the 200 mg/L standard that is proposed by the World Health Organization or the 20 mg/L drinking water concentration recommended for sodium-restricted diets.

Limestone filters/contactors have also been used for adding alkalinity (and calcium hardness) to the product water. Calcium and carbonate dissolve in the process water as the product water passes through the contactor.

Addition of Hardness

As previously discussed, calcium carbonate film deposited on pipe walls can be used as a physical barrier to prevent corrosion from occurring. There are a variety of post-treatment concepts used to add hardness back to RO permeate water. These may include:

- Blending

- Lime addition

- Limestone filters/contactors

Blending is used in membrane softening applications where chloride concentrations are low. When chloride concentrations are high, blending may be limited to control chloride concentrations. The Larson ratio should be checked in these applications. Blending may also include the addition of a hard water supply that is separate from that used for the RO feedwater. Other than blended water chloride concentrations, blending goals may include blended water CCPP, concentrations of hardness, TDS, or levels of other trace materials (i.e., NO_3, F, Na, etc.).

Slaked lime is added to permeate water to provide calcium and alkalinity (i.e., hydroxide alkalinity) as well as an adjustment of the finished water pH. When adding slaked lime to RO permeate, it is important to consider that the solubility of calcium carbonate is dependent on pH and temperature (and also ionic strength). Slaked lime may not dissolve easily and a residual turbidity may result, which is a disadvantage. Posttreatment may require the addition of an acid (e.g., H_2CO_3) to help dissolve the slaked lime to produce the desired hardness concentration and CCPP. If the permeate water is warm, slaked lime may not dissolve as quickly. Additionally, there is a risk that lime may be overfed and, due to the warm temperature, may not dissolve at all.

There are a few approaches available to foster the dissolution of slaked lime in water with temperatures higher than 25°C. One approach is to provide multiple points for carbonic acid injection and a separate lime contact chamber that creates highly turbulent conditions and provides contact times of 5 to 10 min.

Another approach used to enhance the reaction of relatively warm plant permeate with lime is by mixing the lime solution and plant permeate in the product water storage tank using large recirculation pumps. This approach is currently used at the Trinidad seawater desalination plant and is cost-effective only if the unit power cost is relatively low (i.e., $0.02 to 0.03/kW-hr).

Use of limestone (dolomite or calcite) filters/contactors in the United States has been limited to few applications, such as the St. Lucie West Water Treatment Plant in Florida. However, these filters have been used extensively in Europe and the Middle East, often in conjunction with carbonic acid addition to adjust pH, alkalinity, CCPP, to add hardness, and to produce finished water that is stable. One example, the Larnaca desalination plant in Cyprus, uses limestone filters to condition plant product water (Figure 3-22).

Figure 3-22   10.6 mgd Larnaca Seawater Desalination Plant—posttreatment system with limestone filters

Limestone filters/contactors combine two advantages: enhanced contact time and final filtration of the plant product water, allowing the controllable production of low turbidity permeate. Limestone filter cells are usually concrete structures designed at loading rates several times higher than those seen in conventional media filters. The limestone bed is typically 8 to 12 ft deep. The process can be designed with or without carbon dioxide. The limestone in the bed dissolves as the RO plant's permeate passes through the media. When the limestone bed loss is between 10 to 15 percent less than the original height, additional limestone is added. Usually, the cost of limestone is 1.2 to 2 times greater than that of lime per ton. However, the use of limestone filters requires the construction of concrete filter cells and service facilities, which adds to the overall plant construction. Ultimately, the decision for use of slaked lime addition or limestone filters has to be based on a combination of life-cycle costs (which greatly depend on the cost of lime, limestone, and facilities construction costs) as well as level of comfort-based criteria that may include operator skill level and the potential of overdosing slaked lime.

Interaction of Disinfection and Corrosion Control

It is important to consider the impact of disinfection processes on finished water pH and the resultant impact to CCPP. Chlorine gas addition decreases pH and alkalinity caused by the formation of hypochlorous acid, while sodium hypochlorite and calcium hypochlorite addition will increase pH and alkalinity.

Corrosion Inhibitors

Corrosion inhibitors may also be used to reduce the corrosivity of NF/RO treated water. Phosphate and silicate inhibitors can form protective films on pipe walls that limit corrosion or reduce metal solubility. Orthophosphates react with pipe metal ions directly to produce a passivating layer. Silicate inhibitors can form a glasslike film on pipe walls. These inhibitors are added after corrosion has already occurred. In such cases, typical practice is to add the inhibitor at approximately three times the normal concentration for several weeks to begin the protective film formation. Initial doses should be continuous, and water circulation is required to completely distribute the inhibitor to all parts of the distribution system.

Posttreatment Water Quality Modeling

Corrosion control models should be run to assess the full impact of all posttreatment chemicals on the product water corrosivity. The Rothberg, Tamburini, and Winsor Model offered by AWWA (AWWA 1996) accounts for the contribution of disinfectant, while many RO software programs do not.

Posttreatment concepts were evaluated for the model RO permeate waters presented in Table 3-4. The goals for alkalinity, CCPP, and the Larson ratio previously presented were applied in developing these concepts. Table 3-5 presents the model RO permeates before and after posttreatment. As indicated, all finished water quality goals are met.

Posttreatment consists of the following for each model permeate:

Seawater	**Brackish Water**
37 mg/L CO_2	60% removal of CO_2
37 mg/L $Ca(OH)_2$	39 mg/L $Ca(OH)_2$
1.5 mg/L NaHOCl	1.5 mg/L NaHOCl

The seawater RO permeate requires the addition of carbon dioxide, followed by lime ($Ca(OH)_2$) addition to increase the pH, add alkalinity, and convert carbonic acid to bicarbonate, which is also a component of the finished water alkalinity. Alkalinity higher than the minimum goal (i.e., 40 mg/L as $CaCO_3$) is required to reduce the Larson ratio below 5. The temperature of the seawater permeate is low enough that the lime should dissolve. Alternatively, a limestone filter could be used. Sodium hypochlorite is added as a disinfectant, which maintains biological stability in the distribution system. As discussed previously, sodium hypochlorite addition will increase the pH of the finished water. If chlorine gas is used as a disinfectant, additional lime would be required to produce the same finished water pH, alkalinity, and CCPP.

As indicated in Table 3-5, the brackish water RO permeate has approximately 34 mg/L of carbon dioxide before posttreatment. To control posttreatment chemical costs, approximately 60 percent of the carbon dioxide is removed by a decarbonation process. The remaining carbon dioxide is dissolved and converted to bicarbonate on the addition of lime. The result is the desired concentration of alkalinity, CCPP, and Larson ratio. Sodium hypochlorite is used for the reason previously discussed.

While only the CCPP was used for developing posttreatment concepts, as presented in Table 3-5, the LSI and Aggressiveness Index were also calculated. As indicated, the CCPP, LSI and Aggressiveness Index all predict slightly scaling conditions. While the LSI and Aggressiveness Index predict scaling conditions, their usefulness as a means for predicting calcium carbonate scaling should still be viewed conservatively. Readers should keep in mind the limitations of these indices, which were previously discussed and realistically only provide a qualitative indication of scaling potential. The CCPP is the preferred index for developing posttreatment concepts.

Table 3-5 Model permeate and finished water quality following posttreatment

Parameter	Unit	Seawater		Brackish Water	
		Permeate	Posttreatment	Permeate	Posttreatment
Temperature	°C	10	10	25	25
pH	S.U.	6.1	8.5	5.5	8.2
Alkalinity	mg/L as $CaCO_3$	3	50	6	55
TDS	mg/L	251	311	216	270
Calcium	mg/L	0.6	15	1.0	20.4
Carbon dioxide	mg/L	4.0	0.2	33.8	0.6
Carbonate	mg/L	0.0	1.0	0.0	0.4
Bicarbonate	mg/L	2.2	58	6.1	65
Sulfate	mg/L	3.5	3.5	4.5	4.5
Chloride	mg/L	148	148	124	124
LSI	+/−	−5.9	+0.6	−5.4	+0.6
CCPP	mg/L (as $CaCO_3$)	−17	+4.2	−73	+4.2
Aggressiveness Index		6.8	12.5	6.7	12.3
Larson ratio		118	4.5	36	3.4

Blending of Plant Permeate with Feedwater

It may be possible for membrane plants to blend some of the feedwater with permeate from the plant to increase production and increase finished water alkalinity as long as the finished water meets all required MCLs. For many NF and brackish water applications, permeate from the membrane process is relatively low in TDS and other constituents compared to potable water requirements and some bypass blending is possible. The bypass line is equipped with a flow meter and throttling valve and may be automatically controlled to maintain a target blend ratio or blended water quality.

ANCILLARY EQUIPMENT AND FACILITIES

Ancillary equipment includes a membrane cleaning system, plant instrumentation and control system, electrical system and emergency generators, laboratory equipment, HVAC equipment, and other service equipment. Ancillary facilities include the plant administration building, O&M facilities, membrane waste (spent) cleaning solution management system, the solids handling and disposal system, and the plant firefighting and utility water supply systems, and sanitary sewer system. The membrane cleaning and spent cleaning solution systems and membrane flush systems are unique to membrane plants and will be discussed in the following section.

Membrane Cleaning System

A typical NF/RO membrane cleaning-in-place (CIP) system consists of one or more CIP tanks (possibly with mixers and/or solution heater or cooling system), cleaning pump(s), cartridge filter, feed and recirculation piping, instrumentation and power supply, and control equipment (Figure 3-23). Nonchlorinated permeate is used to supply the CIP tank for cleaning solution make-up. Powdered or liquid chemicals may be fed directly into the CIP tank, separate small solutioning tank, or CIP feed recycle line used for chemical mixing.

For small membrane systems, hoses are used to connect the cleaning feed line, cleaning concentrate return, and cleaning permeate return lines of the membrane system to the CIP tank. For larger systems, *hard* piping is installed between the membrane trains and the CIP system. It is recommended that hard piping systems utilize removable piping spools or block-and-bleed valve arrangements to prevent a potential cross connection between a train being cleaned and others that are in service.

Membrane cleaning is usually done with warm solution temperatures (up to about 104°F [40°C]). For systems treating cold water (with cold permeate for solution make-up), a heater, such as a immersion heater or steam heat exchanger installed in the CIP tank, is used. For many groundwater NF/RO systems with temperatures about 77°F (25°C) or greater, a heater is often not installed or needed. In some cases where there is a possibility that the cleaning solution may exceed membrane manufacturer temperature recommendations during the cleaning (recirculation) process, solution cooling systems are used. For example, a cooling coil can be immersed in the CIP tank and supplied by a cool water source.

The cleaning solution is recycled from the CIP tank to the membrane system, then back to the CIP tank at relatively high flow rate and low pressure. For 8-in.-diameter pressure vessels, the desired CIP flow rate is at least 35 to 40 gpm per 8 in. pressure vessel. The CIP pump discharge pressure is commonly about 65 psi. The cleaning system components are sized based on the number of pressure vessels that are cleaned in each step. For multistage systems, the membranes/vessels in each stage are cleaned in a separate step to prevent forcing foulants into the subsequent stages. Therefore, in a tapered multistage RO system, the CIP system size is determined by the number of first stage pressure vessels.

Spent Cleaning Solution System

The used NF/RO membrane cleaning solutions need to be properly disposed and, depending on the composition of the spent cleaning solutions and disposal location, they may require treatment before disposal. Spent cleaning solutions are often disposed into a sanitary sewer system, or if a Class I deep injection concentrate disposal well is available, spent cleaning solutions may be disposed of with the concentrate. Treatment for pH neutralization is usually required before discharge to a sanitary sewer. Often no treatment is required for discharge to a Class I disposal well. Sometimes the treatment is done in the cleaning tank, but often a separate storage and treatment system is provided. A separate spent cleaning solutions system consists of one or two storage/treatment tanks (sometimes referred to as *scavenger tanks*), transfer/recycle pumps, acid and base addition system to the recycle line, power and control equipment, and instrumentation. Figure 3-24 shows a typical spent cleaning solution system.

Membrane Flush System

It is very common to have a means for removing the feed and concentrated water from the membrane system on shutdown to prevent osmosis during standby, to protect the membranes from mineral precipitation and scaling, microbial deposition and growth, and other potential foulants, and/or corrosion of pumps, piping and other

Figure 3-23　Typical membrane cleaning system

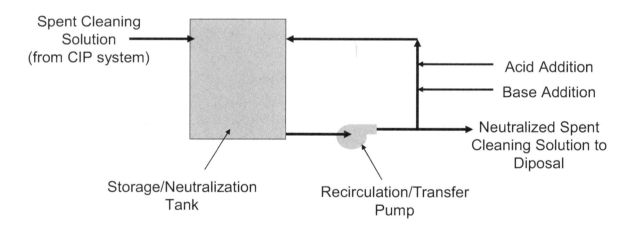

Figure 3-24　Typical spent cleaning solution system

metallic components. In many systems, this flush is automatically done on membrane system shutdown. Two common flush water sources are NF/RO permeate or simply membrane feedwater. Many low-TDS groundwater NF/RO systems use a feedwater flush by opening the concentrate control valve to minimize RO recovery and utilize the low pressure feedwater supply (often by passing it through a de-energized high pressure feed pump). This is especially common when the groundwater contains hydrogen sulfide that could precipitate detrimental colloidal sulfur in a flush water storage tank if a permeate flush is used. Some manufacturers recommend that feedwater with antiscalant not be allowed to remain in the membranes for extended periods of time, which could be possible with feedwater flush. Permeate flush is used on surface water and seawater membrane systems, on systems treating high iron or manganese content, and on systems with supersaturated source water. A permeate flush system consists of a permeate storage tank and a flush pump, along with associated power and control equipment.

INSTRUMENTATION AND CONTROL SYSTEMS

Instrumentation and control systems can be as basic as manual control with automatic shutdown features for pump and membrane protection, or as complicated as a supervisory control and data acquisition (SCADA) system. SCADA systems are often based on programmable logic controllers (PLCs) and remote telemetry units that are supervised by a host computer located in a control room near the membrane skids and high-pressure pumps. The use of personal computers or industrial grade, human–machine interfaces (HMIs) allows a compact control room installation, as shown in Figure 3-25.

Systems designed for automatic control can monitor chemical feed systems, and they have alarm and report generation capabilities. In many facilities, a personal computer is also used for membrane train performance, normalization calculations, and graph preparation that facilitate analyses and the making of decisions on when to clean the membranes (discussed in chapter 4).

Various interlocks can be provided to monitor pressure, flow, transfer pumps, scrubbers, and ancillary equipment. Other interlocks also protect the system from operating outside acceptable limits. An in-line field turbidimeter and pH analyzer can be integrated into the system to monitor pretreated membrane feedwater quality. Modern electronic sensors are often used to avoid the limitations of analog mechanical recording equipment.

Monitoring and Control Systems

SCADA system. The plant control system is typically composed of two networks; the information network and the control network. At a minimum, the information network is composed of two PC server/workstations, printers, hubs, switches, etc., located in the central control room, and the control network by PLCs, remote input/output (RIO) panels, fiber optic or serial data cable, and so forth.

Programmable logic controller. A fully automated plant includes a PLC control panel equipped with a redundant PLC and an operator interface. The PLC control panel is connected to the RIO panels via fiber optic or data cable ring. This PLC controls the entire NF/RO membrane plant, including process treatment, chemical feed and storage, and monitor and alarm conditions of all the other parameters required for reporting and compliance. This panel is connected to the SCADA workstations for remote monitoring and control. The PLC network is connected to the SCADA system via Ethernet fiber optic or data cable. Fiber optic cable minimum requirements are 4-channel multimode.

Human–machine interface. The HMI includes graphic control screens, alarm functions, trend functions, data presentation, incident recording, and the like to monitor and control the entire plant. The HMI software should be compatible with the PLC supplied and the PC server/workstations supplied. Currently, the most

Figure 3-25   Typical membrane control room

widely used HMI software is Intellution® or Wonderware®. For consistency in the graphics, the same HMI software should be used for the PLCs and at the workstations.

Local control panels. RIO (local) control panels are used for medium- and large-size plants. Their use for a small or package NF and RO membrane plants (below 5 mgd [20,000 m³/day]) is usually not cost-effective and practical. For larger NF and RO membrane plants, local control panels are provided adjacent to all key facilities, and especially to those in remote locations that are not within a walking distance from the main control panel (such as the intake pump station, product water storage tanks, etc.). All panels should be designed to comply with the appropriate National Electrical Manufacturers Assocation (NEMA) classification for the specific panel location. Figure 3-26 depicts a local control panel for a membrane process area.

Control functions. The control system should have both manual and automatic control provisions: in the manual mode locally by the operator and in the automatic mode by the PLC with operator confirmation input. At a minimum, manual/auto controls for the following facilities should be provided:

- The entire membrane plant—normal start up and shut down and emergency shutdown

- Raw water intake pump

- Pretreatment processes

- High-pressure membrane feed pumps

- Membrane units
- Energy recovery system
- CIP system
- Spent cleaning solution system
- Degasifier
- Scrubber system
- Product water transfer pumps
- Concentrate system
- Chemical feed systems
- High service pumps

Alarm and monitoring parameters. At a minimum, the following parameters should be monitored and used for controlling membrane plant operations:

- Raw water pH conductivity, turbidity, and temperature
- Raw water flow and pressure
- Train permeate and concentrate flow and hydraulic recovery
- Product transfer pump and finished water flow
- Train permeate and concentrate and plant finished water conductivity
- Degasifier effluent pH
- Finished water pH and chlorine residual
- Total plant waste concentrate flow
- Membrane control valve status
- Membrane feed, interstage, and concentrate pressures
- Product water clearwell/storage tank level
- Finished water storage tank level
- High service pump discharge pressure

Alarms should be automatically activated when these parameters reach preset low and/or high values.

Shutdown of all membrane trains. The instrumentation and control system is designed with provisions to shut down all membrane trains when the operator initiates a total plant shutdown manually or automatically under the following conditions:

- Pump "run" failure (raw water intake pumps, critical chemical feed pumps, product transfer pumps)
- Raw water pressure below a preset minimum
- Feed water pH or turbidity excursion
- Product water clearwell (or finished water storage tank if no clearwell) reaches preset high level
- Loss of power

Figure 3-26   Local control panel at a membrane process area

Shutdown of individual membrane trains. In addition to the shutdowns previously listed, the instrumentation and control system is designed with provisions to shut down individual membrane trains when the operator initiates a train shutdown manually or automatically under the following conditions:

- Membrane feed pump—low suction or high discharge pressure
- High permeate pressure
- Train recovery rate is out of range
- Train concentrate flow low
- Train permeate flow out of range
- Train permeate pressure high
- Product water clearwell (or finished water storage tank if no clearwell) reaches preset high level
- Loss of individual train power

Start/stop stations. For large- and medium-size plants, all motors servicing key equipment should have local control stations with start–stop buttons, local *running/stopped* indicator lights, local *lock-out*, and space heater local disconnect switches. The local start–stop stations have to be installed in addition to the provisions for remote control of the motor operations from the motor control center,

PLC panel, or the plant control room workstations. For plants with production capacity of less than 5 mgd or smaller package plants, local start–stop stations may not be necessary.

Uninterruptible power supply (UPS). A UPS system is recommended to be installed to provide backup power for the instrumentation monitoring and control system. One or more UPS units should be provided for the PLC panel and the workstations at the central control room. The UPS is sized to provide backup power for a minimum period of 30 min.

Instrumentation

The basic instrumentation required to monitor and control any RO system consists of control valves and devices for measuring: flow, pressure, conductivity, pH, temperature, and liquid levels.

Instrument location is determined during the design phase of the project. The installer should make sure that the instruments are adequately secured and will not be subjected to significant vibrations and undue turbulence. Instruments should be easily accessible because most instruments require frequent calibration and repairs. Guidelines published by the Instrumentation Society of America and the Hydraulic Institute should be reviewed and followed to select, locate, and install the instruments. General design guidelines for key instrumentation used at NF/RO membrane plants are presented in the following sections.

Instrumentation for flow measurement. The equipment most widely used for measurement of flow in membrane plants are magnetic flowmeters and rotameters.

Magnetic flowmeters. The magnetic flowmeters are popular flow measurement devices in large capacity membrane plants. This equipment can be used on most water streams encountered in NF/RO plants with the possible exception of some permeate streams. Low conductivity (i.e., 20 mS/cm or lower) water will not give an accurate flow reading, so these meters need to be carefully selected. Vortex shedding meters can be used for low conductivity applications.

Typically, flowmeters used at membrane plants are a pulsed DC electromagnetic induction type, which provide signals linear to the liquid flow rate. The recommended meter accuracy is plus or minus 0.5 percent of reading. All flowmeters that are used at the membrane plant have to be factory calibrated. The magnetic meters have to be grounded per manufacturer's recommendations. A NEMA 4X flow converter/transmitter matched to the flowmeter is provided for meters generating remote data signals. The output should be 4 to 20 mA into 0 to 1,000 ohms. A local indication of actual flow rate and totalization display should be provided.

The key advantages of magnetic flowmeters, as compared to other alternative types of meters, are that the flow stream is completely free from obstacles, and as a result, the head losses through the meter are minimal. In addition, magnetic flowmeters usually have a wider measuring range than most other types of flowmeters. However, when pipeline head loss is not a limiting factor, Venturi meters are used for measuring large plant intake flows. Venturi meters are lower cost flowmeters, which also could be equipped with remote data transfer.

Rotameters. These flow measurement devices are suitable only for small package plants and are acceptable low cost equipment for local indication of small volume chemical feed flows. Although rotameters can be supplied with a flow signal transmitter, this configuration is uncommon. Rotameter accuracy is sensitive to the viscosity and density of the measured liquid and to the concentration of particulates in the measured stream.

Pressure measurement devices. There are two types of pressure gauges: traditional Bourdon type pressure gauges and electronic pressure transmitters.

Pressure gauges. Typical pressure gauges are Bourdon tube actuated type, with accuracy of plus or minus 1.0 percent of span. The most commonly used are 6-in. gauge size with shatterproof glass or acrylic, $^1/_2$-in. US Standard for National Pipe Tapered Thread (NPT) connection, 316-stainless steel Bourdon tube. Each gauge is provided with a shut-off valve. Bourdon pressure gauges are used for local indication, and their main purpose is to give the operator a visual estimation of pressure rather than a high accuracy reading. Usually Bourdon pressure gauges are not used to measure differential pressure.

Electronic pressure transmitters. The electronic pressure transmitters, in contrast to the traditional Bourdon-type pressure gauges, can provide reading accuracy of 0.1 percent of span, which is very important when measuring differential pressures in critical locations in the membrane plant. These pressure transmitters can be electronically zeroed as compared to the Bourdon-type pressure gauges. The differential pressure transmitters are usually a diaphragm actuated, microprocessor-based type. They are equipped with loop powered units with a 4 to 20 mA output. Each transmitter is provided with stainless steel mounting hardware and a five-way manifold. Differential pressure transmitters are used to measure the pressure drop across the following key treatment plant facilities:

- Pretreatment filters (if pressure type pretreatment filters are used)

- Cartridge filters

- Membrane train stage feed, interstage, concentrate, and/or stage and overall train differential pressure (feed to concentrate)

Conductivity analyzers. The quality of the raw and product water is monitored by continuous reading conductivity analyzers. The conductivity sensor is an in-line type sensor unit with a local indicator and a transmitter for remote accurate continuous monitoring, indicating, and recording. Although conductivity meters are usually installed online, valved sample points for measuring conductivity/salinity using portable apparatus should also be provided at key locations, such as the raw water intake pump station, feed to the NF/RO membrane system, concentrate discharge, and the product water lines from the individual NF/RO trains. The conductivity is measured in μS/cm (microsiemens per centimeter). High conductivity readings from the analyzer located on the permeate lines from the individual NF/RO membrane trains trigger alarms locally and remotely at the central control room.

Temperature and pH analyzers. Currently, electronic pH and temperature analyzers and transmitters are industry practice. In-line temperature analyzers are recommended to be installed on the feed line to the NF/RO system, if the water temperature is expected to vary significantly (more than 5°C/10°F from the annual average temperature). A pH analyzer is installed as a minimum on the product water line.

Liquid level sensors. The type and operational parameters of the liquid level sensors are the same as those used in conventional water treatment plants. Ultrasonic-type level sensors–transmitters are used for water tanks/wells with a relatively quiescent surface, such as the product water storage and chemical feed tanks. Usually, the liquid level sensors are potted/encapsulated in corrosion-resistant housing. These sensors are provided with automatic air temperature and density compensation. A microprocessor-based transmitter/converter converts the sensor output signal to level. Level measurement accuracy of most sensors is plus or minus 1.0 percent. The output is an isolated 4 to 20 mA signal. For outdoor mounted units, NEMA 4X enclosures with sunshields are recommended to be provided. Liquid level signals for all key tanks and pump wet wells are transmitted to the PLC and the desalination plant control room workstations for continuous monitoring and alarm generation.

Electrical System

Pumps, instrumentation, and other equipment and facilities require electrical power supply. Small systems may be connected to an existing electrical supply system, but large systems require a new power supply. The switchgear on the electric utility supply is often followed by one or more transformers at a single location or dispersed throughout the plant site to step down the voltage to the desired level. The main switchboard and motor control centers provide power to major equipment, power panels, and membrane feed pumps. In many cases, emergency generators are used for auxiliary power supply. Motor control centers contain circuit breakers, starters, variable speed drives (VFDs) (if applicable), control devices, instrumentation, and other items. Because of the variable feed pressure requirements over time for many RO/NF systems, the use of VFDs for feed pumps is very common for lowering energy consumption (rather than throttling feed valves).

Distribution panels contain circuit breakers for low electrical consumption devices, such as room lights, instrumentation equipment, small motors, and other equipment. In some plants, certain equipment can also be controlled from the membrane process area via discrete local control panels.

WASTE STREAM MANAGEMENT FACILITIES

The waste products from a membrane system, such as RO/NF concentrate, must be handled and disposed of properly. The AWWA Membrane Residuals Management Subcommittee, jointly formed by the Residuals Management Research Committee, Membrane Processes Committee, and the Water Treatment Plant Residuals Management Committee, prepared and published an excellent committee report on membrane residuals in the *Journal AWWA* in December, 2004 (AWWA Membrane Residuals Management Subcommittee). Information from the committee report is presented herein as part of this section.

Residuals from NF and RO systems result from the separation process itself and the CIP process, and include two types:

1. Concentrate, which contains dissolved and particulate contaminants removed from the feedwater and may contain chemicals from pretreatment facilities

2. Spent cleaning solutions, which contain high concentrations of the cleaning chemicals, plus feedwater contaminants removed during cleaning

Concentrate is produced continuously while spent cleaning solutions are generated intermittently (every 3 to 12 months). Also, the volume of concentrate is much greater than the volume of spent chemical solution. NF and RO systems are cleaned with acid (mineral or citric) to remove inorganic foulants and alkaline solutions (caustic soda, often in combination with detergents/surfactants and sometimes chelating agents) to remove biofilms and organic foulants.

Residuals Characterization

Concentrate. Because RO/NF membrane processes produce a high purity stream by rejecting high percentages of contaminants in the feed stream, the concentrate stream is primarily a more concentrated version of the feedwater. As such, the characteristics of concentrate are directly related to the feedwater quality.

The contaminants removed during desalination and other constituents in the feedwater will be rejected by the membrane and will become part of the concentrate stream. Contaminant concentrations in the concentrate are 4 to 10 times the feedwater concentration for brackish source water, and 1.5 to 2.5 times the source water concentrations for seawater, and depend on the rejection characteristics of the membrane and the water recovery. If pretreatment is used, the feedwater to the membranes will have lower levels of certain constituents and particles. However, the pretreatment may result in a slight increase in inorganic ions, such as sulfate, chloride, and iron, if coagulants are used and possibly residual organics from polymer or sulfuric acid use. Concentrate contains low concentrations of particles, <10 mg/L TSS, because of low NF/RO feedwater concentration of particles. Concentrate quantity is a function of the amount of feedwater purified (or converted to permeate), as defined by the product water recovery. NF and brackish water RO systems commonly operate at recoveries of 80 to 90 percent and 75 to 85 percent, respectively; seawater RO systems recovery is lower, 40 to 65 percent. NF and brackish RO residuals differ somewhat because the overall NF salt rejection is lower. Therefore, for a given feed and recovery, NF concentrate is less saline than RO concentrate. Further, NF provides low rejection of monovalent ions (e.g., sodium and chloride) compared to multivalent ions (e.g., calcium and sulfate). Consequently, NF concentrate has a higher ratio of multivalent to monovalent ions than feedwater. Lastly, because RO treats higher salinity waters, the TDS levels in the RO concentrate are much higher, especially for seawater.

As previously mentioned, the concentration of contaminants is proportional to water recovery and membrane rejection, with concentration increasing as water recovery increases. Typical feed water TDS, water recovery, and residuals TDS concentrations are included in Table 3-6, where the values represent the maximum concentrations for residuals streams based on a simplifying assumption that all of the salts are rejected (100 percent salt rejection).

However, desalination membrane salt rejection is always less than complete; hence, the concentrate values in Table 3-6 are overestimated. The degree of overestimation is minor for high-rejection seawater RO membranes (99.5 to 99.8 percent sodium chloride) but more significant for NF membranes, which can have less than 50 percent monovalent ion rejection. For high-quality source waters, such as lower TDS surface and groundwater, lower salt rejection membranes are used. In these cases, contaminant levels in the concentrate stream are lower than shown in Table 3-6.

The amount of particles or TSS in desalination membrane concentrates is low, <10 mg/L, because of the extensive pretreatment required to control fouling. The acid and scale inhibitor, if added to the membrane feedwater to control mineral precipitation, will be concentrated in the desalination membrane concentrate. Scale inhibitor levels in the concentrate are typically less than 30 mg/L and consist of phosphates or organic polymers (such as polyacrylates or dendrimers).

Table 3-6   Typical NF/RO plant concentrate quality

Parameter	Surface Water	Fresh Groundwater	Brackish Groundwater	Seawater
Feed TDS, mg/L	200–400	400–500	500–10,000	30,000–40,000
Water recovery, % of feed	80–90	80–90	65–85	40–60
Concentrate quantity, % of feed	10–20	10–20	15–35	40–60
Concentrate TDS, mg/L (at example recovery)	1,330–2,660 (85%)	2,660–3,330 (85%)	2,000–40,000 (75%)	60,000–80,000 (50%)

Source: AWWA Membrane Residuals Management Subcommittee (2004).

Chemical cleaning (CIP) residuals. Cleaning solutions were developed to address specific contaminants that cause fouling and loss of performance, and CIP residuals reflect the chemical characteristics of both the spent cleaning solution and material removed from the membrane system during CIP. Reactions with foulants will tend to raise the pH of acid solutions and lower that of basic ones.

Types of solutions. Table 3-7 lists typical cleaning formulations developed to remove various types of foulants. The list reflects formulations and chemicals found to be effective by one NF/RO membrane supplier. Cleaning involves "art" and "science"; as such, each membrane supplier has developed specific solutions or formulations based on laboratory and field experience with its product. Many companies catering to the membrane industry have developed proprietary cleaners to optimize cleaning efficiency for specific fouling situations; listing such products is beyond the scope of this manual.

Solution volumes. The volume of cleaning solution and the amount of waste solution are functions of:

- Membrane process and module configuration/system characteristics

- Size/capacity of membrane train or portion of it to be cleaned (the number of membrane modules to be cleaned at the same time or given batch)

- System design conditions (flux, recovery, staging and manifolding)

- Cleaning system design (piping diameter and lengths)

- Frequency of cleaning

The *cleaning solution volumes* generated during a CIP of NF and RO membranes are about 3 gal/100 ft^2 (1.2 L/m^2) of the membrane area. This volume does not include rinse water volumes. Typical cleaning solution volume is estimated by adding the total empty vessel volume and pipe volume. For example, the eight RO vessels with six 8 in. elements per vessel, and 50 ft of 4 in. pipe, the total volume is approximately 485 gal. Assuming each 8 in. element has 340 ft^2 of membrane area, the cleaning volume is 3 gal/100 ft^2 of membrane area. The total annual volume of cleaning solution for a membrane system can be readily calculated from these unit values using the following formula:

Table 3-7   Typical NF/RO cleaning solutions

Foulant Type	Cleaning Solution(s)
Inorganic salts (e.g., $CaCO_3$, $CaSO_4$, $BaSO_4$)	0.2% HCl; 0.5% H_3PO_4; 2% citric acid
Metal oxides	2% citric acid; 1% $Na_2S_2O_4$
Inorganic colloids (silt)	0.1% NaOH/0.05% Na dodecyl benzene sulfonate/pH 12
Silica (and metal silicates)	Ammonium bifluoride; 0.1% NaOH/0.05% Na dodecyl benzene sulfonate/pH 12
Biofilms and organics	Hypochlorite, hydrogen peroxide, 0.1% NaOH/0.05% Na dodecyl benzene sulfonate/pH 12; 1% sodium tripolyphosphate/1% trisodium phosphate/1% sodium EDTA

Source: AWWA Membrane Residuals Management Subcommittee, 2004; Modified from Cleaning Procedures for FILMTEC FT30 Membranes, DOW Chemical Company.

NOTE: Oxidants, including hypochlorite and hydrogen peroxide, cannot be used with chlorine-sensitive membranes, including polyamide NF and RO flat-sheet membranes except under very specialized conditions (high pH).

$BaSO_4$ = barium sulfate; $CaCO_3$ = calcium carbonate; $CaSO_4$ = calcium sulfate; HCl = hydrochloric acid; H_3PO_4 = phosphoric acid; $Na_2S_2O_4$ = sodium hydrosulfite; NaOH = sodium hydroxide; EDTA = Ethylenediaminetetraacetic acid

$$V_{year} = V_{unit} \times A_{membrane} \times N_{CIP/year}$$

Where:

V_{year}	=	Total volume per year
V_{unit}	=	Unit volume per unit membrane area
$A_{membrane}$	=	Total membrane area in system
$N_{CIP/year}$	=	Number of membrane cleanings/year

This volume is specific for each chemical solution. Most cleanings are performed in multiple steps, so the total annual volume is the sum of the volumes used in each step. Depending on the foulants, a low-pH solution is followed by one with a high pH. The trains are also cleaned in steps. A typical approach for a two-stage system is to first clean the modules in one-half of the vessels in the first stage, then the other half of the first stage, and finally all modules in the second stage (three steps for each CIP chemical). Another approach would be to clean all of the first stage modules at one time and then clean all of the second stage modules (two steps for each CIP chemical). Spent cleaning solutions, which may be diluted with rinse water (feed or permeate), can contain detergents, surfactants, acid, caustic, or other chemicals used to remove foulants from the membrane system. The spent cleaning solution may need to be treated before disposal, as discussed later. The spent cleaning solution volume is an extremely small percentage of the treated flow (less than 0.1 percent).

Residuals Management

Successful management of NF and RO plant residuals is critical to implementing a desalination membrane system and therefore requires careful evaluation of available alternatives, regulations, capital and operating costs, and site-specific conditions. If residuals disposal is not possible or economical, then a desalination membrane process will not be used. The evaluation of alternatives should include assessment of the long-term viability of each. Regulatory changes, in particular, could adversely impact the continued operation of a desalination plant. The following sections address the considerations associated with residuals management.

Current Concentrate Disposal Methods

Based on a recent survey with 233 respondents (Mickley 2006), the most widely used concentrate disposal alternatives today are:

- Surface water discharge

- Sewer discharge

- Deep well (subsurface) injection

- Land application (rapid infiltration systems)

- Evaporation ponds

Surface water discharge is the most common method of concentrate disposal, followed by sanitary sewer discharge, and deep well injection (Figure 3-27)

A RO/NF membrane facility's capacity has a bearing on the selected disposal method as shown in Figure 3-28.

Since the first large-scale municipal RO facility in the United States was installed in 1976 in Cape Coral, Fla., using surface water discharge for residuals disposal, the locations and disposal methods for desalination facilities have expanded greatly. Approximately 95 percent of the 234 municipal membrane desalination facilities identified in a recent survey (Mickley 2006) are located in Florida, California, Texas, and Illinois (Figure 3-29).

Disposal of desalination membrane concentrate can be particularly challenging because of the large volume and high TDS concentration. These characteristics can limit the options that can be permitted and are cost-effective, particularly in regions where surface water discharge is unavailable. A decision tree for considering residuals disposal alternatives for desalination membrane processes is presented in Figure 3-30.

General regulatory overview. Several regulatory programs impact the disposal of desalination membrane residuals, including the Clean Water Act (CWA; PL 92-500 as amended), the Underground Injection Control (UIC) Program, ordinances that protect groundwater, and the Resource Recovery and Conservation Act (RCRA) for any solid waste residuals. Disposal options for desalination membrane residuals and associated regulatory and permitting agencies include:

- Disposal to surface water discharge requires a National Pollutant Discharge Elimination System (NPDES) permit.

- Sewer discharge requires a permit issued by the local sewer agency to meet its sewer ordinance and the CWA Industrial Pretreatment Program (IPP) requirements, as stipulated in the agency's NPDES permit.

Concentrate disposal by land application (percolation pond, rapid infiltration basin, landscape and crop irrigation, etc.) must comply with federal and state regulations to protect groundwater, public health, and crops/vegetation. Land application requires a permit from state agencies. Construction of evaporation ponds is subject to state requirements for pond construction.

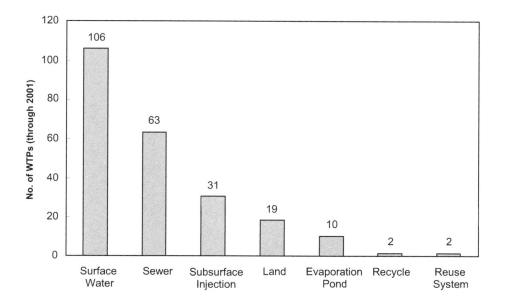

Source: Mickley 2006

Figure 3-27   Disposal methods for membrane desalination plants

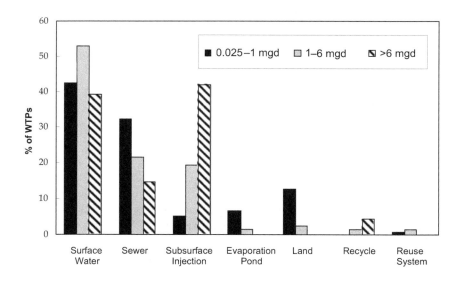

Source: Mickley 2006

Figure 3-28   Disposal methods by membrane desalination plant capacity

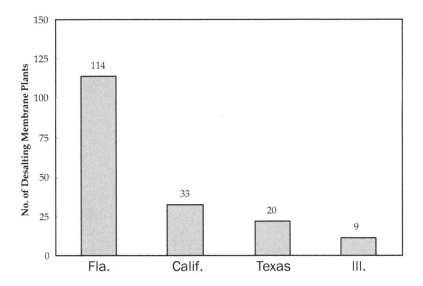

Source: Mickley 2006

Figure 3-29   A majority of the membrane desalination water plants >0.025 mgd are located in four states (data for plants installed through 2003)

- Concentrate disposal by deep well injection is regulated by the UIC program of the SDWA. The related construction, monitoring, and other permits are issued and enforced by the USEPA region or state agency that has primacy.

- RCRA regulates the disposal of solids, such as precipitated salts and sludge; if such solids contain arsenic or other toxins and do not pass the toxic characteristic leaching procedure (TCLP) test, they are considered a hazardous waste and must be handled accordingly.

The most important regulation pertaining to disposal of desalination residuals are those related to the CWA, including the NPDES program. Under the CWA, desalination membrane residuals are regulated as industrial wastes because the USEPA has not established specific regulations concerning the disposal of water treatment plant (WTP) residuals, including membrane residuals. For surface water discharge, a NPDES permit is required pursuant to the CWA; its antidegradation policy prevents the relaxation of discharge limits for contaminants specified in a NPDES permit, particularly if the receiving water is designated as sensitive or impaired. If a WTP currently has a TDS discharge limit, combining high TDS concentrate from NF/RO with the existing discharge may not be allowed.

As the CWA requires, USEPA has established minimum requirements, including specific surface water quality criteria. Any state that has USEPA-delegated authority (termed *primacy*) to administer the NPDES permit program must establish water quality standards for the protection of the designated uses of the water body at least as stringent as the federal limits. Therefore, a surface water discharge of desalination membrane residuals is regulated by a NPDES permit, which meets the CWA requirements.

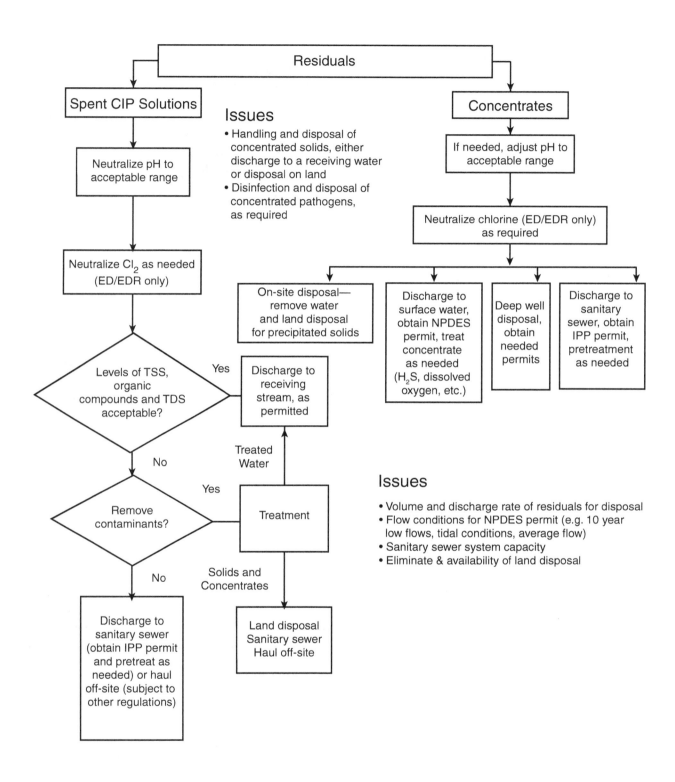

Source: AWWA Membrane Residuals Management Subcommittee, 2004.

Figure 3-30   Decision tree for disposal of desalination membrane residuals

The USEPA had not previously identified the water industry as a potential candidate for effluent guideline development. However, because of public comments and USEPA preliminary research, which indicates that there are a significant number of water treatment facilities that have nontrivial discharges, USEPA has decided to complete an effluent guideline rule-making for the water industry. Although the USEPA has not established effluent guidelines as of this writing, the USEPA has placed water treatment facilities in the industrial sector. This classification has created a negative public perception and made permitting more difficult. Better data on concentrate characteristics are needed to educate regulators and change public perception, which should simplify the permitting process in the future.

Concentrated discharge from the membrane separation process is usually the largest and most difficult to dispose of waste stream generated at the NF/RO plant. Concentrate treatment and disposal methods are briefly discussed in the following section. More detailed design and operations guidelines for concentrate disposal are provided elsewhere (Mickley 2006; Watson et al. 2003; AWWA Membrane Residuals Management Subcommittee 2005).

Surface Water Discharge

Surface water discharge involves transporting concentrate from the membrane plant to a point of discharge such as a bay, tidal lake, brackish canal, ocean, or any other surface water body. Disposal costs are low if the length of discharge pipeline is reasonable and the discharge meets NPDES permit requirements. Permit limits may include TSS, TDS, salinity, or specific contaminants, such as nutrients (nitrogen and phosphorus compounds), arsenic, or barium. Some contaminants, such as arsenic, are priority pollutants, which can increase the complexity of obtaining a permit. Rarely can a high-salinity concentrate be discharged into low-salinity receiving water if it results in the salinity at the discharge point increasing by 10 percent or more compared with the upstream receiving water. Some facilities address high salinity by diluting the concentrate with surface water or groundwater, wastewater treatment plant (WWTP) effluent, or cooling water.

A NPDES permit may include limits on whole effluent toxicity (WET), a bioassay performed according to USEPA-approved protocols to assess acute, chronic, and bioaccumulative toxicity to receiving water biota. The bioassays use approved pollutant-sensitive species. Some groundwater-fed RO systems have produced concentrates that fail WET limits tests (Mickley 2006). Most such cases in Florida were associated with high calcium levels and some were complicated by toxicity from high fluoride levels. Toxicity caused by high levels of major ions is a correctable chemical imbalance, as opposed to toxic contamination from heavy metals or pesticides. For this reason, Florida has exceptions for major ion toxicity when it is the only toxicity present in a concentrate.

Concentrates are well suited for surface water discharge because they contain increased concentrations of naturally occurring constituents (in the RO feed), which typically have no toxicity. NPDES permitting requirements vary by state and site-specific conditions. It is imperative that the local NPDES permitting agency be contacted early in the process to confirm acceptability of a proposed surface water discharge. For membrane facilities treating groundwater that is brackish or contains arsenic or radionuclides, the elevated TDS or contaminant concentrations may not meet discharge requirements for fresh surface waters within a reasonably sized mixing zone. In these cases, desalination membrane plants may be limited to areas with available brackish surface receiving streams or may need to remove the toxic contaminants prior to discharge.

Dissolved gases or lack of oxygen can also be a concern for concentrate disposal. Concentrates from the treatment of many groundwaters have very low dissolved oxygen (DO) levels. Prior to discharge, DO levels must be increased to avoid negative impacts on receiving stream biota. If the groundwater contains hydrogen sulfide, hydrogen sulfide in the concentrate must be suitably reduced before its discharge to prevent negative impacts on receiving stream biota.

At the first membrane facilities in Florida, concentrate disposal was relatively simple—all plants were near the coast, and concentrate was discharged directly into the sea or a brackish canal. However, increased regulatory pressure, public concern over any surface water discharges, and the development of inland membrane facilities may cause surface water discharge to become a less attractive and less economically feasible concentrate disposal option.

The location of the discharge and the need for concentrate treatment are determined by the state and USEPA's NPDES effluent limitations for surface water discharge. Concentrate disposal is usually affected by all regulations written to protect groundwater and surface water.

To determine if concentrate treatment will be necessary, pilot studies can be conducted or a method of theoretically determining concentrate quality can be used. Actual concentrate water will be needed to conduct bioassay tests, if they are required by the applicable discharge regulations. Toxicity concerns often determine whether specific concentrate disposal methods may be permitted. The following rules theoretically predict concentrate quality based on source water characteristics for the purposes of preliminary or feasibility studies:

- Heavy metals will be rejected in a similar ratio as calcium and magnesium. Organics are typically rejected in excess of 95 percent (except for low molecular-weight organics).

- Concentrate from brackish groundwater desalination plants will likely be anaerobic and may contain hydrogen sulfide. (Nearly all the groundwater used at membrane plants in Florida is anaerobic and contains hydrogen sulfide.)

- Concentrate pH is generally higher than the source water pH because of the greater concentration of alkalinity in the concentrate.

- For brackish water RO, the ion concentration factor based on 100 percent rejection can be calculated from the following equation:

$$CF = 1 / (1 - Y)$$

For example, assuming a recovery of 75 percent, the concentration factor is $[1/(1-0.75)] = 4.0$.

For a more precise calculation, if the salt passage (or salt rejection) is known, the concentration factor can be calculated from the following equation:

$CF = [1 - (Y \cdot SP)] / (1 - Y)$

Where:

SP = salt passage = 1 − percent salt rejection = permeate concentration (mg/L) / feed concentration (mg/L), expressed as a decimal.

For example, assuming a recovery of 75 percent and 5 percent TDS salt passage (95 percent TDS rejection), the TDS concentration factor is

$$[1 - (0.75 \times 0.05)] / [1 - (0.75)] = 3.85$$

Where:

CF = concentration factor, dimensionless

Y = recovery, expressed as a decimal

Concentrate quality can also be predicted based on a diffusion model if the operating pressure, source water quality, percent recovery, and solvent and solute mass transfer coefficients are known.

Technical description.   Concentrate may be transported via an open canal or an enclosed pipeline system. Pumping may not be required depending on the available pressure head exiting the membrane and frictional forces encountered during transport. The outfall terminates at an open-ended pipe or a perforated pipe or diffuser, as well as a surge control system. If the concentrate TDS concentration is significantly higher than the salinity of the receiving surface water body, the outfall may need to be equipped with diffusers to accelerate the dissipation of the saline discharge.

Mixing the concentrate stream with the receiving water body at the point of discharge (i.e., the mixing zone) dilutes the concentrate. If this method is acceptable for regulatory compliance, the dimensions of the mixing zone must be approved during the permitting process. Regulators often establish the distinction between acute and chronic toxicity at the point of discharge.

Transport pipeline.   The concentrate disposal site should be located as near to the membrane facility as possible. Pipeline capital costs increase with increase in total pipeline length. The volume of concentrate is also an important cost factor because larger flows require larger diameter pipes and pipeline prices increase as a function of pipe diameter. Concentrate discharge pipes should be made of corrosion- and crush-resistant pipe. Cast iron or ductile iron has historically been one of the most popular of all pipe materials; it has corrosion-resistant properties and strength that approaches steel pipe. For concentrate streams containing a high chloride concentration, however, the corrosion of iron or steel pipe will be accelerated.

Steel pipe is lighter, normally less expensive, and easier to construct than cast- or ductile-iron pipe. Another major advantage of steel is its ability to withstand higher pressures. Unprotected steel is highly susceptible to oxidation and galvanic corrosion. Pipe coatings are used on steel pipes to solve oxidation problems and cathodic protection is used to reduce galvanic corrosion.

Developments in plastics technology have made possible the manufacture of larger-diameter plastic pipe. Table 3-8 lists a few examples of plastic pipe materials and their accepted maximum diameters. PVC is a polymerized vinyl chloride derived from acetylene and anhydrous chloride. PVC piping has replaced traditional materials of construction in many piping systems. Its advantages include its corrosion resistance, chemical inertness, light weight, and resistance to galvanic attack. In certain sizes, plastic piping is also less costly than other piping materials, such as cast or ductile iron. HDPE and FRP have also been used for large diameter concentrate lines.

Table 3-8   Plastic piping materials

Plastic Material	Typical Maximum Acceptable Diameter, *in.*
Fiberglass-reinforced plastic (FRP) AWWA C950 Fiberglass Pressure Pipe 1 in.–144 in.	144
High-density polyethylene (HDPE) AWWA C906 Polyethylene pressure pipe fittings 4 in.–63 in.	63
Polyvinyl chloride (PVC)—AWWA C905 Type (Bell/Spigot) 14 in.–48 in. PVC Pipe and Fittings	48

In addition to the pipe material selected for pipeline construction, the choice of installing pipelines above- or belowground impacts the overall cost of the transport system. Belowground piping requires excavation, whereas aboveground piping systems require support structures to be constructed in carefully compacted fill. Unusual ground conditions can significantly increase the cost of pipeline system installation.

Pumping. The concentrate flow from a NF/RO system exits the system at pressures ranging from 20 to 200 psi or more. Under certain conditions, the resulting concentrate head is sufficient to overcome frictional losses within the pipe, allowing transport of the concentrate flow to the disposal site without the need for additional pumping. The need for additional pumping depends on the concentrate head exiting the membrane, the pipeline distance, and the transport head losses resulting from friction. When pumping is necessary, the energy and maintenance costs associated with operating transport pumps become important cost factors. The need for surge control should also be considered in the design. For example, in Plantation, Fla., a deep well injection system necessitated the concentrate to be transported 1,000 ft to the well. Instead of providing pumping, the design engineers used the pressure that existed as the concentrate left the membrane system for transportation to and down the injection well.

Outfall design. Outfalls terminate with a multiport diffuser or a simple open end. A multiport diffuser is designed so that the end of the transport pipe is capped and the last sections of the pipe contain lines of small ports (openings or diffuser nozzles around the circumference of the pipe). The purpose of the diffuser is to provide a greater initial dilution of the concentrate as it enters the surface water.

Most small outfalls, as well as larger ones built before 1980, have simple open ends. In recent years, multiport diffusers have become the accepted design for larger diameter outfalls. Simple open-end outfalls are recommended when the initial dilution that is achieved meets water quality standards. If standards are not met, the more expensive and more difficult to build diffusers become necessary.

Sanitary sewer discharge. This method of disposal is very popular for concentrate generated at small NF and RO plants, and membrane water reclamation plants. Discharging concentrate to the sanitary sewer is regulated by the requirements applicable for industrial discharges and the applicable discharge regulations of the utility/municipality that is responsible for wastewater collection system management. Feasibility of this disposal method is regulated by the hydraulic capacity of the wastewater collection system and by the capacity of the WWTP receiving the discharge. Typically, a WWTP's biological treatment process is affected by the high salinity when wastewater TDS concentration exceeds 3,000 mg/L. Therefore, before directing the concentrate to the sanitary sewer, the increase in the WWTP influent salinity must be assessed and considered.

Regulatory requirements.   Discharge to a sanitary sewer requires a permit from the local sewerage agency, which may impose limitations to protect sewers and treatment plant infrastructure, the treatment process, final effluent, and biosolids quality. Sanitary sewer discharge of a small volume of concentrate usually represents a low-cost disposal method with limited permitting requirements. The adequacy of sewer system and WWTP capacity and NPDES permit limits must be addressed at the project's onset. The local sewer agency may impose a one-time fee to "purchase" capacity for the concentrate discharge. In addition, operating costs may be billed based on volume and pollutants loads.

Deep well (subsurface) injection.   In deep well injection, the waste stream is injected hundreds to thousands of feet below the ground surface into an injection zone. Injection zones contain high salinity natural fluids. Injection zones are overlayed with thick, impermeable layers of rock and other materials that prevent the injected concentrate from migrating upward toward the surface. Injection zones must have a TDS level greater than 10,000 mg/L and at least one overlaying, confining layer. The concentrate waste stream is permanently stored in the injection zone.

Membrane concentrate is classified by USEPA as an industrial waste and, as such, requires additional precautions for deep well construction. More specifically, deep wells used for disposing of industrial wastes are required to have an interior tubing liner and surrounding packer. For facilities in Florida, the Florida Department of Environmental Protection also limits the velocity of flow through the well to a maximum of 10 ft/sec. This maximum velocity regulation, along with the concentrate flow rate, defines the minimum acceptable diameter of the well.

Regulatory requirements. Deep well injection systems were developed by the petroleum industry in the early part of this century to dispose of oil field brines. These brines were injected into subsurface saline aquifers. Today, municipalities and industries dispose of large volumes of wastewater in injection wells. Multiple layers of corrosion-resistant metal casing and cement are used to seal the well shafts.

Class I and class V injection wells have been used in Florida since 1963, and over 130 deep injection wells are proposed or currently operating in that state. Although most of these wells are used to dispose of treated municipal wastewater effluents, a few wells dispose of industrial wastes and membrane concentrate from RO and NF facilities. The ability of injection wells to operate under varying weather conditions is a major advantage.

Subsurface injection alternatives, such as deep well injection and boreholes, are regulated by the UIC program. Regulatory considerations include the receiving aquifer's transmissivity and TDS, the presence of a structurally isolating and confining layer between the receiving aquifer and any overlying underground source of drinking water, considered to be any water bearing formation that has less than 10,000 mg/L TDS. Subsurface injection is infeasible in areas subject to earthquakes or with geologic faults that can provide a direct hydraulic connection between the receiving aquifer and an overlying potable aquifer. The well design should allow for testing injection well integrity. Monitoring wells in proximity to the disposal well are also required to confirm that vertical movement of fluid has not occurred. The capital cost for subsurface injection is higher than surface water disposal, sewer disposal, and land application where these alternatives do not require long transmission pipelines. Disposal to subsurface injection is restricted to large volumes of concentrates where economies of scale make the disposal option more cost-effective and where soil transmissivity is good. While the UIC program does not restrict use of deep wells, geologic characteristics are not appropriate for deep well injection in many areas of the United States. A backup means of disposal must be available for use during periodic maintenance and testing of the injection well.

Technical description. A deep injection well consists primarily of a pump (if needed) and a lined well shaft protected by multiple layers of casing and grouting. The overall cost of a deep well injection system is affected by the following main factors: concentrate volume, distance from the treatment plant to the well, transport pipeline, well depth, well diameter, pumping pressure, storage, regulatory monitoring, and operation. Distance from the treatment plant and the factors affecting the transport pipeline are the same for a deep well system as for a surface water discharge system.

Injection well shaft. The type of materials selected for well shaft construction for wastewater should be compatible with the concentrate. Concentrate from RO plants requires additional corrosion protection because of its generally high TDS levels. Materials often used for the inner liner of a well shaft include fiberglass, plastic, stainless steel, and extra-thick steel pipe.

Injection wells are generally constructed by the same process used to construct extraction wells. Cable-tool and rotary drilling have been used successfully to construct deep wells. Completion of the well involves testing the casing and cement grouting to ensure they do not leak and can sustain design pressures.

Figure 3-31 is a diagram of a deep injection well shaft, complete with casings and grout, for a typical south Florida injection well.

Casing. Deep injection wells are multicased, with the innermost casing set at the top of the injection zone. Three to four casings are generally used for injection wells in Florida. The depth of each casing depends on the geological environment surrounding the well. The main purpose of multiple staged casings is to protect the upper freshwater zones from deeper, brackish zones and to reduce the possibility of fluid exchange between the different aquifers.

Grouting. The cement grouting surrounding each casing protects it from external corrosion, increases its strength, and prevents injected wastes from traveling to areas other than the designated injection zone. The type of cement and width of each cement layer surrounding a casing are regulated.

Injection zone. The location of a deep injection well is determined by the proximity of an acceptable injection zone. In order to avoid eventual plugging of the well, the water quality of the underground injection zone must be similar to the water quality of the membrane concentrate or the injection zone receiving water must be over 10,000 mg/L TDS (Conlon 1988). The injection zone should be characterized by high permeability and high transmissivity, which allow large volumes of concentrate to be injected without a large pressure buildup. The injection zone should also be located away from any abandoned wells, faults, or other hydrogeologic short circuits.

Florida has a distinctive underground environment that favors the use of deep injection wells. Five general injection zones exist within the state. The depths of these injection zones range from 700 to 8,000 ft below land surface, with the most widely used zone being a unique underground discharge zone located in southeastern Florida, referred to as the Boulder Zone. The water quality of this zone is similar to seawater. Thick, compacted layers of dolomite and limestone separate the saline water injection zone from overlying freshwater aquifers; this makes the Boulder Zone an ideal injection zone. Injection zone depths within the Boulder Zone range from 1,800 to 4,000 ft, whereas injection zone depths along Florida's west coast range from 700 to 1,600 ft. Florida's deepest injection wells are found in the Panhandle, with average depths ranging from 6,000 to 8,000 ft.

Pumping. The concentrate head is usually enough to move the concentrate to and down the injection well. If the concentrate head is insufficient, additional pumping

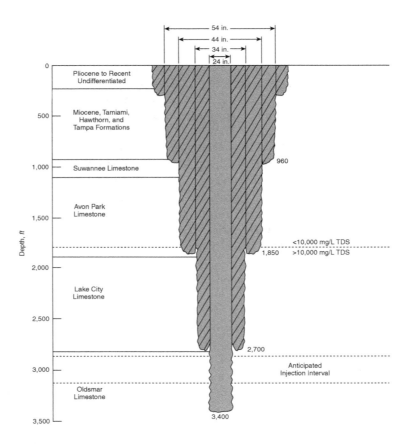

Figure 3-31   Deep injection well shaft

will be required. The material of the injection well pump should also be compatible with the physical and chemical properties of the injected concentrate. Past experiences with injection systems have indicated that many difficulties are caused by improperly selected materials, resulting in corrosion of the injection pumps.

Storage.   Temporary storage of the concentrate or an alternative method of disposal is needed to allow for maintenance and repairs of the well. Additionally, the well system may be shut down if monitoring systems and monitoring wells indicate leakage. The type of storage facility or stand-by disposal method is highly dependent on the location of the well and the conditions surrounding the well site. For example, if the injection well is located near the coast, a discharge canal or pipeline may be able to be used to temporarily discharge the concentrate flow to a saline water body.

Regulatory monitoring.   Following well system construction, detailed geophysical logs of the well site are required. Before well startup, television surveys of the well shaft and radioactive tracer surveys must be performed to validate the integrity of the well. Accidental contamination of surface and subsurface fresh waters can be avoided by continuous monitoring of concentrate flow and wellhead pressure. Readings of increasing pressure during steady operation can indicate possible clogging, whereas a sudden decrease in pressure is indicative of leaks within the casing, grout, or seal. Monthly testing of monitoring wells is also required by the

Florida Department of Environmental Protection to ensure that the well system is not leaking into underground soils or water sources.

During operation of the injection well, plugging, contamination, and wide variations in concentrate flow rates and pressures should be avoided. Plugging can be caused by various occurrences, such as bacterial growth, suspended solid precipitation, or entrained air.

Evaporation Ponds

Evaporation ponds consist of a series of lined or unlined earthen or concrete structures designed to maximize water evaporation. Solar evaporation is a viable alternative in relatively warm, dry climates with high evaporation rates, level terrain, and low land costs. Regulations require an impervious lining and monitoring wells. With few economies of scale, evaporation ponds are normally used for small volumes of concentrates. While evaporation ponds are designed to accommodate concentrate for the projected life of the desalination facility, precipitation of salts is expected and must be incorporated into the depth requirements of the pond or provisions must be made for periodic removal and disposal or beneficial use of precipitated salts. In addition, the ultimate fate of the concentrated salts and potential future regulatory implications should be considered for any evaporation pond project.

Evaporation pond operations require periodic removal of salt accumulated in the ponds. Operation of an evaporation pond system can be manually or automatically controlled. Automated operations involve time switches, float switches, tensiometers, and automatic valves. Regardless of whether a system is manually or automatically controlled, operators should observe the evaporation basins and make adjustments when necessary.

Land Application

Land application can be a beneficial reuse of concentrate when membrane plant residuals are used for spray irrigation of lawns, parks, golf courses, or cropland. Associated factors include availability and cost of land, percolation rates, irrigation needs, water-quality tolerance of target vegetation to salinity, and the ability to meet groundwater quality standards. An assessment of the compatibility with target vegetation should be conducted, including a review of the sodium adsorption ratio (SAR),[*] trace metals uptake, and other vegetative and percolation factors. Regulations governing groundwater quality and protection of drinking water aquifers should be investigated as early as possible to confirm the acceptability of this alternative. Significant concerns may arise if the concentrate contains arsenic, nitrates, or other contaminants regulated in drinking water. If allowed, the concentrate may be diluted to meet groundwater standards. When salinity levels in the residuals are high, special salt-tolerant species (halophytes) could be considered for irrigation. Land application also includes the use of percolation ponds and rapid infiltration basins, and generally is used only for small volumes of concentrates. These options are frequently limited by availability of land and/or dilution water and may also be limited by climate in locations where year-round land application is not feasible.

Rapid infiltration basins. Rapid infiltration basins (RIBs) have highly permeable soil bottoms that allow for rapid infiltration, percolation, and concentrate

---

[*]SAR meq/L = $[Na^+]/(0.5 \, ([Ca^{2+}] + [Mg^{2+}]))^{1/2}$
Where: $[Na^+]$, $[Ca^{2+}]$, $[Mg^{2+}]$ are the sodium, calcium, and magnesium ion concentrations, in meq/L.

removal. RIBs include similar structures to evaporation ponds with the main difference that most of the water is evaporating out of the pond rather than percolating into the groundwater. Treated wastewater effluent has successfully been disposed of by means of infiltration, percolation, and evaporation. Infiltration is defined as the entrance of water into the ground at the soil–water or soil–air interface. It is affected by the topography and surface conditions of the ground, the characteristics of the surface material, and the rate of precipitation. Percolation is defined as the flow of water within the soil in both the horizontal and vertical directions. It is controlled by gravity and by soil characteristics.

Rapid infiltration systems are capable of removing biodegradable organics, suspended solids, bacteria and viruses, phosphorus, nitrogen, and heavy metals. This particle removal occurs in the soil through filtration, adsorption, ion exchange, and biological action as the waste stream percolates through the soil.

Before a basin system can be constructed, extensive geological surveys are needed to determine soil permeability and background conditions. Rapid infiltration systems must also demonstrate that percolating concentrate meets water quality standards as well as primary and secondary drinking water standards. Monitoring wells are required to continually monitor groundwater quality surrounding the infiltration basin system.

Regulatory requirements. Disposal of concentrate via infiltration is controlled by a groundwater discharge permit issued under the groundwater regulations. This is an important and complex issue. Further information can be found at http://www.epa.gov/safewater/disinfection/gwr/regulation.html.

Technical description. A rapid infiltration system consists of a series of basins commonly called *rapid infiltration basins* that are constructed with highly permeable soil bottoms. The concentrate stream exits the transport pipeline, enters the basin, quickly infiltrates through the porous surface soil, and then rapidly percolates into underlying soils. Examples of suitable soils include sands, sandy loams, and other coarse-textured soils.

Uniform application of the membrane plant discharge into the basins is necessary to avoid erosion. A simple splash block at the point of discharge may be used for small basins, whereas larger basins may require a more complex arrangement, such as pipes or troughs, to dampen the impact of the flow.

Hydraulic loading rate, which depends on infiltration, permeability, and hydraulic conductivity test results, is also a critical factor in RIB system design. The design loading rate must be based on the least permeable soil layer in the soil profile and on expected worst-case weather conditions. Concentrate discharge into the RIBs should be intermittent to maintain the design loading rate and soil capacity.

Land. Rapid infiltration and evaporation systems, like spray irrigation systems, are land intensive and often require a purchase of large quantity of land. Preliminary rapid infiltration site selection is based on a land area's soil and groundwater conditions, existing land use, flood potential, and proximity to the NF/RO plant. Site topography, soil type, and soil uniformity are also important because extensive cut-and-fill requirements can dramatically increase construction costs.

The total land area required for a rapid infiltration system is determined by the amount of land needed for transmission pipe easement, infiltration basins, access roads, pumping, buffer zones, a maintenance building, and future expansion.

Pumping. Pumping requirements for a rapid infiltration system are determined by the concentrate transport distance and concentrate head. The need for booster pumps along the distribution lines depends on the distance between basins.

Operation. Labor needs for system operation vary depending on whether the system is automated or manually operated. Infiltration basin maintenance involves raking the basin's surface to break up and loosen the soil surface. Basins may be raked following each drying period if labor and equipment are available. Evaporation pond operations require periodic removal of salt accumulated in the ponds.

Operation of a percolation pond system can be manually or automatically controlled. Automated operations involve time switches, float switches, tensiometers, and automatic valves. Regardless of whether a system is manually or automatically controlled, operators should observe the RIBs and make adjustments when necessary.

Spray irrigation. Using spray irrigation for concentrate removal can result in local water savings and help conserve natural resources by allowing aquifers to recharge.

Regulatory requirements. Concentrate salinity and levels of other contaminants determine whether or not irrigation is a viable option. Many field studies and observations conducted in California were used to develop guidelines for evaluating irrigation water quality. These guidelines are based on concentrate salinity, toxicity, and soil permeability. Salt is continually added to the soil with each irrigation water application, a practice that will eventually harm vegetation. The rate of saline accumulation depends on the quantity of salt applied and the rate at which it is removed from the soil by leaching. Adequate subsurface drainage is also necessary to avoid shallow water tables, which become an additional source of salts.

In addition to the effects of total salinity on vegetative growth and soil, individual ions can cause a reduction in plant growth as well. Toxicity caused by a specific ion occurs when that ion is taken up and accumulated by the plants. The ions of most concern in wastewater effluent and desalination concentrate irrigation are sodium, chloride, and boron.

The presence of salts in the soil reduces the rate at which water moves into the soil and also reduces aeration. If the soil permeability, or infiltration rate, is greatly reduced, vegetation on the irrigation site cannot survive. Three factors affecting irrigation's long-term influence on soil permeability are the sodium content relative to calcium and magnesium, the carbonate and bicarbonate content, and the total salt concentration of the irrigation water.

If a membrane concentrate's salinity, toxicity, and soil permeability levels are determined suitable for irrigation, the concentrate's ultimate effects on nearby surface water and groundwater must also be evaluated. Factors that affect an irrigation water's impact on groundwater include soil filtering, plant uptake, soil biochemical and physiochemical reactions, and soil particle adsorption. Nearby surface waters could be affected by the runoff generated from irrigation sites. Other conditions must be met before concentrate irrigation can be considered as a practical disposal option. First, there must be a need for irrigation water within the vicinity of the membrane plant. A backup disposal or storage method must be available during periods of heavy rainfall. Monitoring wells need to be drilled before an operating permit can be obtained.

Technical description. Irrigation with concentrate involves applying the waste stream to a vegetative surface and providing a runoff control system. The concentrate stream is applied to a vegetative area by a distribution system. There are three broad categories of distribution systems: (1) sprinkler or spray systems, (2) surface systems, and (3) drip systems. Drip systems have not been the conventional means of waste stream irrigation because the drip system emitters clog easily. However, these systems have been successfully used in California without plugging problems. Surface systems use narrow-graded (less than 15 ft) and wide-graded (100 ft or greater) borders or furrows for irrigation water distribution. Sprinkler systems use spray nozzles that move across the land. These spray irrigation systems can be used on variable soils, shallow soil profiles, rolling terrain, erodable soils, and areas where high water tables exist. Disadvantages of sprinkler systems include their higher initial capital cost, higher energy costs, mechanical failures, wind drift problems, and excessive evaporation losses.

The volume of runoff generated by an irrigation process often depends on the type of irrigation system used. Spray distribution systems do not generally cause a runoff of applied water, whereas surface systems produce some runoff. Ditches or drainage canals can be dug to retain runoff, or tailwater return systems can be used instead. A tailwater return system consists of a sump or reservoir, a pump or pumps, and a return pipeline. The pumps can be any convenient size, but a minimum capacity of 25 percent of the distribution system flow capacity is recommended. Major cost parameters associated with a spray irrigation system include concentrate flow, distance to the irrigation site, transport pipeline costs, irrigation land purchase and preparation, distribution, pumping pressure, storage lagoons, subsurface drainage, and operation.

Land. Spray irrigation of concentrate is more land-intensive than other disposal methods. If an existing land area requiring irrigation, such as golf course, is not available, land areas surrounding the plant must be purchased or leased for concentrate disposal. Land costs can fluctuate with the economy and vary depending on the location and characteristics of the site. Several options exist to purchase or control land used for a concentrate disposal system. Land may be purchased outright, leased on a long-term basis, or purchased and leased back to another party, for example, to a farmer. Purchasing land allows for complete control over the land and makes future expansion of the disposal site easier.

The soil must also be able to support a vegetative surface, which in most cases is a grassy surface. The need to prepare irrigation land by clearing or grubbing adds to overall disposal site costs and should be considered in selecting potential irrigation sites. Spray irrigation systems also require land for service roads, buffer zones, storage lagoons, and equipment storage, in addition to the land area needed for the irrigation field. These additional land requirements should be taken into account in estimates of the total land requirements for the system.

Sprinkler system distribution. The predominant category of sprinkler systems, classified by their movement during application, is solid-set. Permanent solid-set sprinkler systems remain in one position during waste stream application. The major advantages of solid-set systems are low labor requirements and low maintenance costs. The main disadvantage is a high installation cost. A solid-set system consists of mainline and lateral pipes that cover the irrigation field with the sprinklers spaced along each lateral. Pumping to the distribution system is also needed to transport flow through the main pipeline to lateral pipelines and sprinkler heads.

Storage lagoons. Temporary storage facilities are necessary to retain concentrate during heavy rainfall periods or when an imbalance between concentrate supply and application occurs. The need for retention facilities is particularly important in Florida, where the average yearly rainfall approaches 52 in. in certain areas of the state.

Storage in a holding tank may be belowground in reinforced concrete structures or aboveground in reinforced concrete or steel tanks. A storage facility can simply retain concentrate until disposal is again possible, or it can be designed to further facilitate concentrate removal. Storage in a reinforced concrete structure or steel tank merely retains concentrate, whereas storing concentrate in percolation ponds or storage lagoons further reduces concentrate volume via infiltration and percolation.

Subsurface drainage. Irrigation systems can be designed to include under-drainage or subsurface drainage. Subsurface drainage is necessary to provide a root zone area conducive to good vegetative growth. The presence of a high water table indicates poor subsurface drainage and demonstrates a need for installing subsurface drains. A high water table exists when the depth of the water table is less than 10 ft. The proximity of the irrigation site to canals, rivers, and other bodies of water should be considered when the irrigation site is chosen because seepage from other water bodies can contribute to subsurface drainage problems.

Subsurface drainage systems consist of a network of buried drainage pipes with open holes or perforations that recover effluent that has percolated through the soil. A collection basin is used to recover the water collected by the underdrains. This water can be reused by the irrigation system or possibly discharged into a receiving water body. USEPA cost-estimating curves have shown that including an underdrain system can increase the spray irrigation system capital costs by as much as 25 percent.

Operation. O&M of a concentrate spray irrigation system is more labor-intensive than the other concentrate disposal methods. Labor requirements include sprinkler system repair and vegetative surface maintenance. Energy costs for pump operations also add to the system's total operational costs.

OTHER CONCENTRATE MANAGEMENT ALTERNATIVES _____

Other concentrate management and disposal alternatives such as blending with WWTP effluent or power plant cooling water may facilitate concentrate disposal and may be used in combination with disposal methods previously mentioned. Permitting requirements for blending of residuals with treated wastewater effluent are dependent on the fate of the combined stream. Blending concentrate with large-volume cooling water streams from power plants using seawater for once-through cooling will greatly reduce concentrations of the discharge and facilitate permitting. The discharge must still comply with standard surface water discharge requirements. Nevertheless, blending either with wastewater effluent or power plant cooling water provides dilution to support the implementation of a membrane desalination facility.

Zero-liquid discharge systems, such as thermal evaporators, crystallizers, and spray dryers, are available to reduce residuals to a solid product for landfill disposal. However, their capital and operating (energy) cost is typically much higher than that of the RO/NF membrane facility, making this option infeasible except for very small concentrate flows. In certain situations, the highly concentrated brine from the brine concentrator may be sent to evaporation ponds instead of precipitating the solids. This option costs less than processing concentrate to solids. Use of high-recovery RO systems in front of the thermal evaporators can reduce costs for waters of limited hardness. The selective and sequential removal of salts followed by their use may offer promise to reduce zero-liquid discharge costs (Mickley 2006).

Ongoing research is evaluating the technical and economic feasibility of using desalination membrane concentrates as a feed stock for sodium hypochlorite generation and for solar energy ponds to recover energy by heat generation. This type of research may ultimately provide additional alternatives for managing desalination residuals.

Disposal Alternatives for Spent Cleaning Solutions

The accumulation of silts or scale on the RO membranes causes fouling, which reduces membrane performance. The RO system membranes will be periodically cleaned to remove foulants and extend the membrane useful life. Typical cleaning frequency of the RO membranes is two to four times per year. Typically, one membrane train is cleaned at a time.

As discussed previously in this chapter, to clean the membranes, a chemical cleaning solution is circulated through the membrane train for a preset time. After the cleaning solution circulation is completed, the spent cleaning solution is evacuated from the train to a storage tank, and the membranes are flushed with NF/RO permeate (flush water). The flush water is used to remove all the residual cleaning solution from the RO train to prepare the train for normal operation. The flush water for membrane cleaning may be stored separately from the rest of the plant permeate in a flush tank.

The various waste discharge volumes that are generated during the membrane train cleaning process are as follows:

- **Concentrated Waste Cleaning Solution** is the actual spent membrane cleaning chemical.

- **Flush Water—Residual Cleaning Solution (First Flush)** is the first batch of clean product water used to flush the membranes after the recirculation of cleaning solution is discontinued. This first flush contains diluted residual cleaning solution.

- **Flush Water—Permeate** is the spent cleaning water used for several consecutive membrane flushes after the first flush. This flush water is of low salinity and contains only trace amounts of cleaning solution.

- **Flush Water—Concentrate Removed During Flushing** is the flush water removed from the concentrate lines of the membrane system during the flushing process. This water contains very little cleaning chemicals and is of slightly higher salinity concentration than the permeate used for flushing.

All the membrane cleaning streams previously listed are conveyed to one washwater tank, often named "spent cleaning solution tank" or "scavenger tank," for waste cleaning solution retention and treatment. This tank has to be designed to be able to retain the waste cleaning solution from the simultaneous cleaning of two membrane trains.

The scavenger tank should be equipped with mixing and pH neutralization systems. The mixing system may be an air sparger system installed at the bottom of the tanks, the purpose of which is to provide complete mixing of all four cleaning solution streams previously listed. After mixing with the flush water, the concentration of the cleaning solution chemicals will be reduced significantly. The used cleaning solution will be neutralized to a pH level compatible with the pH requirements for discharge to the wastewater collection system. At many plants, only the most concentrated first flush is discharged to the wastewater collection system. The rest of the flush water usually has only trace levels of contaminants and is often suitable for a surface water discharge.

Spent chemical cleaning solutions may be handled and disposed of either separately from the concentrate or blended with it. Prior to blending, it may be necessary to neutralize the cleaning solution's acidity or alkalinity to prevent unwanted reactions and ensure that the blended residuals are compatible with concentrate discharge regulations. Combining high pH discharges may promote precipitation of supersaturated salts in the concentrate.

The disposal methods for cleaning solutions were investigated in a survey of 70 US membrane plants, including 49 NF/RO and 27 MF/UF facilities (Kenna and Zander 2001). As shown in Table 3-9, the two most common methods for disposal of cleaning solution residuals from the NF/RO plants were sewer discharge and mixing with concentrate. A 2002 US Bureau of Reclamation survey (Mickley 2006) agreed with Kenna and Zander's results and provided statistics on treatment and disposal of cleaning wastes from 110 recently built plants (Table 3-10).

Spent cleaning solutions may be treated in the cleaning tank at the end of each cleaning step for small facilities or in separate tankage at large plants, given the latter's relatively low cost and the significant benefit of reducing membrane system downtime for the overall cleaning process. For pH adjustment, either acid (e.g., sulfuric acid) or base (e.g., sodium hydroxide) is added to the spent solutions until the desired pH is reached.

Table 3-9   Disposal methods for chemical cleaning solutions at US RO/NF plants

Disposal Method	Percent of Plants Employing Disposal Method	
	NF (7 plants)	RO (42 plants)
Sewer	43	54
Mixed with concentrate*	57	17
Deep well injection	43	—
Ocean	14	—
Evaporation pond	—	5
Other (no data)	—	24

Sources: AWWA Membrane Residuals Management Subcommittee 2004 and Kenna and Zander 2001.
*Mixed with concentrate for subsequent final discharge according to disposal option used for concentrate residual.

Table 3-10   Summary of spent cleaning solution waste disposal methods

Disposal Method	Number of Plants	Percent of Total	Treatment Methods		
			No Treatment	pH Adjustment	Settling
Sewer	67	61	53	14	
Surface water	24	22	15	9	1
Land application	8	7	7	1	
Subsurface injection	7	6	6	1	
Evaporation pond	2	2	2		
Recycle	1	1		1	
Hauling off site	1	1	1		
Totals	110	100	84	26	1

Sources: AWWA Membrane Residuals Management Subcommittee 2004 and Kenna and Zander 2001.
NOTE: One site included treatment by pH adjustment and settling.

DISPOSAL ALTERNATIVES FOR WASTE PRETREATMENT FILTER BACKWASH WATER

Spent filter backwash water is a waste stream produced by the membrane plant's pretreatment filtration system. Depending on the type of pretreatment system used (granular or membrane filters), the spent filter backwash water will vary in quantity and quality. In general, pretreatment systems using MF and UF membranes produce 1.5 to 2 times more volume of spent filter backwash water than the granular media filters. However, contrary to the MF or UF membrane pretreatment filters, the granular media filters require their feedwater to be preconditioned with coagulant (usually iron salt) prior to filtration. This adds 60 to 80 percent of additional solids load to the spent filter discharge, and therefore, its disposal results in higher solids handling costs.

The spent filter backwash water can be handled in one of the following methods.

Discharge to a Surface Water Body Along with Plant NF/RO Concentrate Without Treatment

This is one of the most widely practiced filter backwash water disposal methods currently used. This is typically the lowest cost disposal method because it does not involve any treatment prior to disposal. (Note that this is the case only in the unique situations where no NPDES permit is required or the utility's NPDES permit requirements are met through grandfathering in "conditions not consistent with current regulatory interpretations.") This method is suitable for discharge to large water bodies with good flushing—such as open oceans or large rivers.

On-site Treatment Prior to Surface Water Discharge or Recycle Upstream of the Filtration System

Often the filter backwash water has to be treated at the membrane treatment plant because its direct discharge does not meet surface water quality requirements or is not suitable for a direct disposal to deep injection wells. Typically, the most widely used granular media backwash treatment method is gravity settling in conventional or lamella plate sedimentation tanks. Spent washwater from MF or UF membrane pretreatment systems is usually settled. Sometimes the supernatant is treated with separate MF or UF systems. In other cases, the supernatant is recycled back to the incoming source water, and the blended feedwater is treated with the MF/UF system. The filter backwash sedimentation tanks are designed for a retention time of 3 to 4 hr and allow removing more than 90 percent of the backwash solids. The settled filter backwash water can be either disposed with the RO/NF concentrate or recycled at the head of the pretreatment filtration system. In many cases, it is more cost-effective to recycle and reuse the settled filter backwash water rather than to dispose it with the concentrate. However, blending and disposal with the concentrate may be more beneficial, if the concentrate water quality is inferior, and therefore, it cannot be disposed of to a surface water body without prior dilution with a stream of lesser salinity.

The solids (sludge) retained in pretreatment sedimentation basin(s) are either discharged to the sanitary sewer in a liquid form (practiced at small- to medium-size plants) or dewatered on site in a designated solids handling facility. For example, the solids separated from the settled spent filter backwash water at the Tampa Bay seawater desalination plant and the Point Lisas seawater desalination plant in

Trinidad are dewatered using belt filter presses and the dewatered sludge is disposed of to a sanitary landfill.

GENERAL TREATMENT PLANT DESIGN FUNDAMENTALS

Plant Type and Equipment Indoor/Outdoor Location

Depending on the size of the unit, RO or NF equipment may be furnished in a skid-mounted configuration (Figures 3-1 and 3-2) or prefabricated for assembly on site (Figure 3-3). Many system manufacturers offer packaged skid-mounted units in a range of capacities. A typical packaged unit consists of a cartridge filter, RO or NF feed pump, membrane modules, instruments and controls, instrument panel, motor control center, and all interconnecting piping and valves on a skid. Acid and antiscalant feed systems for pretreatment are offered on separate skids. However, for plant capacities less than 100,000 gpd, chemical feed systems may be installed on the membrane module skid.

Site conditions and aesthetic reasons determine whether the plant should be installed indoors or outdoors. Extreme weather conditions or a corrosive environment may require the plant to be installed indoors, and protection against freezing by insulation and heat tracing may be necessary. Where outdoor installation is preferred, the plant should be installed on a concrete slab and the module protected from direct sunlight.

PLANT SITE LOCATION AND LAYOUT

Location of Plant Site

The plant site is usually located near the raw water intake and/or discharge, and/or the main users of the product water. It is preferable to locate the plant site within several thousand feet from the plant intake and discharge facilities to minimize raw water and concentrate pumping and conveyance costs. On the other hand, the membrane plant site has to be located far enough from the surface water body used as a source of water and/or for concentrate disposal, therefore the finished floors of all plant buildings are placed above the elevation of the 100-yr flood level.

A significant portion of plant costs are associated with the raw water intake and waste stream discharge facilities. Therefore, locating the membrane plant in the vicinity of an existing large power plant or WWTP may be very beneficial and cost-effective. If the discharge outfalls of these facilities have adequate capacity, they could be used for disposal of the membrane plant waste streams.

As discussed previously, the co-location of a seawater desalination plant with a coastal power generation plant using seawater for once-trough cooling would minimize the costs for construction of both intake and discharge facilities, because the existing power plant intake and discharge could be shared with the desalination plant intake and discharge.

GENERAL PLANT LAYOUT CONSIDERATIONS

Key equipment layout considerations include the following:

Maintainability

Arrangement of equipment and facilities on the site should provide adequate access for maintenance. This should include removal and replacement of individual equipment items. Fork-lift access should be provided to process areas including but not limited to the RO cleaning system, chemical feed areas (in particular—chemical storage totes), cartridge filters, and dry chemical storage areas.

All installed pumps should be removable for maintenance. Pumps installed indoors (e.g., the NF/RO high pressure feed pumps) should be accessed by permanently installed facilities (such as a traveling bridge crane) or accessible by crane through removable skylights installed in the roofing system.

Hose bibbs should be provided throughout the facility for general maintenance requirements. Hose bibbs, hoses, and hose racks should be spaced to provide complete coverage of the new facilities using standard hose lengths.

Accessibility

Equipment facilities should be arranged to allow vehicle access (including emergency response vehicles) to all areas of the site as required by local codes, including parking areas and designated chemical delivery routes. This requirement is specifically in addition to any other access required for maintenance and facility expansion. Chemical bulk storage facilities should be located along the main service road to make deliveries more convenient.

Operability

All components should be arranged to ensure optimum operation of the component or system. Equipment should be installed in accordance with the recommendations of the respective manufacturers. The location of all valves and appurtenances should allow operation, adjustment, and maintenance from the normal operating floor. To the greatest extent possible, process lines should be routed adjacent to chemical storage/feed facility areas to limit runs of exposed injection piping. High points between chemical injection pumps and the injection point on the process lines should be avoided.

MEMBRANE SYSTEM LAYOUT CONSIDERATIONS _____

Adequate clearance at both ends of the membrane module must be provided for loading and unloading membranes. Clearance should be at least equal to the length of the element plus a working space of 12 to 18 in. (0.3 to 0.5 m). For example, a typical 40-in. (1-m)-long, spiral-wound membrane element would require at least a 52 in. (1.3 m) clearance.

Feedwater, concentrate and permeate headers, and their connections to the pressure vessels should be designed to facilitate easy access for pressure vessel probing. The feedwater piping should be designed to allow debris to be cleaned up before system startup. Pump-to-waste configurations, such as tee fittings with valves and piping to the ground surface, should be installed at certain strategic locations to allow the operator to run wells to waste.

Generally no restrictions should be placed in the permeate line from the module bank to the storage tank or degasifier. If isolation valves are necessary, protection should be installed so that the module cannot be brought online without these valves first being opened. Most membrane manufacturers recommend that permeate pressure never exceed the feedwater or concentrate pressure. Pressure from the permeate side can dislodge the membrane from the backing material or weaken glue lines in the case of spiral-wound membrane elements. If permeate lines contain isolation valves that can completely prevent permeate flow (deadheaded), pressure relief protection must be installed.

Membranes and pressure vessel housings should be protected from extreme conditions, such as direct sunlight, steam lines, freezing, and heater exhaust. Trenches inside and outside the building must be covered in traffic areas. In other areas where trenches need to be accessed, handrails should be constructed for worker safety.

Provision should be made for floor drains near the module banks. Product tube probing, membrane element replacement, and cleaning procedures all involve spilling large volumes of water, requiring adequate drainage facilities. In large installations, pipe trenches connected to the plant drain system serve as drains for spillage from the membrane modules.

Chemical Feed Systems

The chemical feed systems should be designed and installed to permit drawdown to as low as 1.0 in. (2.54 cm) above the suction pipe connection on the day tank. The installation should allow easy access for changing hydraulic oil when required without the need to disconnect chemical feed pumps or piping. Also, drain connections should be suitably sized and piped for safe draining of the tanks. Where possible, facilities to safely flush chemical pumps (excluding concentrated acid feed pumps) with clean water should be provided. The piping system should be free from dead-end sections, which may harbor microorganism growth.

Process Piping

General plant piping. It is recommended that all abovegrade piping is installed on supports. The abovegrade piping should be arranged so that unobstructed foot access is provided to the equipment. All process piping (excluding vertical train piping) should be located in piping trenches. No horizontal piping runs should be allowed to be supported from the pressure vessels or support rack assembly. All trenches should be covered with aluminum bar type grating, with banded openings for pipe transitions and valve operating nut access. Grating penetrations for electrical conduit are not recommended. Piping should be configured in the trenches to allow required access for maintenance, permit connection to required blind flanges for future equipment, and provide dedicated runs for future piping.

The pipe materials for all process lines should be selected, taking into account the following:

- The pipe interior should not be degraded by the transmitted fluid.

- The use of pipe lining is acceptable. However, the design engineer has to check if the lining material will protect the pipe interior from degradation and if the lining material will not be degraded by the transmitted fluid.

- The pipe exterior should be adequately protected against the exterior environment. This requirement includes but is not limited to the impacts as a result of the corrosivity of the soil, UV light, and the ambient air conditions. The use of socket-weld or flanged PVC pipe is not recommended for pipe diameters larger than 12 in. (300 mm).

The following are general guidelines that are recommended for sizing piping systems throughout the membrane plant:

- Maximum velocity in piping systems—10 ft/sec (3 m/sec). Hydraulic hammer effects should be considered during design, especially for long, large diameter plastic piping.

- Minimum diameter of chemical piping—$^1/_2$ in. (12 mm).

- Passive tank overflow/drain lines should be sized to carry the cumulative maximum flow associated with the process inlet line(s).

With the exception of control valves, valve sizes should match the diameter of connected piping. Manual operators on 10 in. (250 mm) and larger valves are recommended to be gear type. When valves are located above the trench grating, they should be furnished with handwheel type operators. Valves located beneath trench grating should be furnished with 2 in. (50 mm) square nut operators. Manual valves located more than 6.5 ft (2 m) above finished floors or grade levels should be provided with chain wheel operators with Type 316 stainless steel chain. Buried valves are recommended to be enclosed in concrete vaults or in valve boxes with cast-iron frames and covers.

All pressure piping is recommended to be rated at a minimum of 150 percent maximum operating pressure and should be fully restrained. The method of restraint should be in accordance with the pipe manufacturer's recommendation. All pressure pipes should be pressure tested to 50 psi (3.5 bars) above the design working pressure.

Pipe-coating systems and/or cathodic protection to protect buried metallic pipes from corrosion are highly recommended. Dissimilar metals should be isolated for protection against electrolysis. Piping beneath concrete slabs or structures should be encased in concrete with a minimum of 6 in. (0.15 m) cover. Buried gravity piping should be sloped uniformly without sags or crests. Minimum cover over buried pipe should be 3 ft (1 m). All process piping should be installed with $^3/_4$ in. (20 mm) vents and drains at pipe high and low points, respectively. Ball valves and hose connections should be installed to match the service.

RO process piping. All welds should be butt type with 100 percent penetration, in conformance with ASME B31.3, severe cyclic. All stainless-steel assemblies should be pickled and passivated following welding. Many systems use electropolished stainless-steel piping to produce a homogeneous, polished finish. Connections from the pressure vessel feed/concentrate ports to the pipe manifolds should be via 90-degree ell weldments with grooved pipe couplings on both ends. The use of fabricated ells is not recommended. Permeate manifold connections to the pressure vessel permeate ports should be made using Schedule 80 PVC U-bends, with a union at the connection to the vessel and a grooved pipe coupling at the connection to the manifold. Machine grooves in other PVC piping are not acceptable.

Chemical process piping. Chemical transfer and injection piping should be run on a nonmetallic framing system above grade. High points in injection lines, between the metering pumps and injection point, should be avoided. All chemical injectors should be located at the bottom or side of pipelines. All chemical lines should be run in secondary containment piping systems external to containment areas. Plexiglass enclosures should be installed at injection locations and in containment areas around metering equipment for personnel protection. All connections to chemical storage tanks (excluding vent, overflow, and top entry fill connections) are recommended to be furnished with metallic body isolation valves connected directly to the tank flange. The main chemical pump suction outlet line should be equipped with a motor-operated isolation valve (lined plug type) that will open when an injection pump starts and close when all injection pumps stop. The valve actuator should be capable of failing the valve closed on loss of power. Piping between the tank connection and valve should be metallic. All root connections to devices (e.g., calibration columns, pressure gauges, pressure switches, etc.), excluding safety relief valves, are recommended to be installed with isolation valves. Injection line backpressure regulators should be installed close to the injection point and should incorporate block and bypass valves to allow regulator maintenance.

Pump Feed Pressure Design Considerations

As fouling occurs, each membrane element will have a different pattern to increase the transmembrane pressure (TMP) with time. Therefore, the design engineer has to incorporate sufficient pressure allowances in the feedwater pump. These additional pressure allowances include pretreatment needs, fouling allowance, interstage piping losses, permeate line losses including backpressure devices, and static lift from degasifiers. Table 3-11 provides a summary of recommended pressure allowances.

Pipe type selection can be used to enhance the ability to obtain additional pump discharge pressure. Vertical turbine pumps have steep pump curves, which allow a significant discharge pressure increase to be gained by a small decrease in pump feed flow. Conversely, horizontal centrifugal pumps have flatter pump curves than vertical turbine pumps, and therefore, their use will require a significant capacity loss to compensate for an increase in the needed feed pressure. Therefore, most NF and brackish water RO plants use vertical turbine pumps to feed the membrane system. Utilizing variable frequency drives on each pump allows the ability to "overspeed" a pump, thereby delivering a higher feed pressure. For example, many pump models with a nominal design speed of 3,500 rpm can safely be operated at 3,600 to 3,800 rpm, if needed.

Because the different models of membrane elements can vary in terms of TMP, it is preferable that the membrane element model be selected in advance of the final design (i.e., the membrane elements to be preselected/prepurchased) to avoid oversizing of the membrane system feed pumps and the associated costs.

Table 3-11   Recommended pressure allowances

Item	Pressure Allowance, psi
Sand strainers and microscreens	5
Static mixers	5 (per static mixer)
Pretreatment filters	10
Cartridge filters	10
Miscellaneous pretreatment system pipes and valves	10
NF/RO membrane fouling allowance	20–25% of TMP
Permeate line losses	5–15 psi
Degasifier static lift from lowest permeate line elevation	10–15 psi

NOTE: 1 psi = 0.0703 bars

FACILITY CONSTRUCTION AND EQUIPMENT INSTALLATION ___

General Guidelines for Receiving Equipment and Materials

Because equipment arrives before installation begins, a qualified person should be responsible for receiving the equipment and storing it according to manufacturers' recommendations. On arrival, equipment should be inspected for damage and checked against the material lists supplied by the equipment manufacturer or supplier. Instruments, electronic devices, electric motors, motor control centers, and instrument panels may have to be stored in a relatively cool, dry, and secure environment. All rotating equipment should be kept accessible to allow the shafts to be moved manually at least once a week. Membrane elements should be stored in their original bags and boxes according to the manufacturer's recommendations. In extreme climates, temperature-controlled storage may be required. Preassembled piping, support frames, and other similar equipment should be properly supported to maintain their shape. This is also important for the plastic piping supplied in straight lengths. All open ends should be closed to keep dirt and debris out of the piping.

The membrane system furnished by the manufacturer may have several components shipped separately for assembly and installation on site. Each carton should include the supplier's itemized packing list of parts. Items are tagged with corresponding material list numbers. This list should be checked against the items received and retained for future reference. Any missing or damaged items should immediately be reported to the supplier for appropriate action. If possible, the problem should be noted on the delivery freight bill or other delivery data. Skid-mounted equipment should be moved by the lifting lugs. If there are no lifting lugs, a forklift may be used to pick up the equipment from under the skid. To protect the equipment and keep the warranty valid, all equipment must be stored, handled, adjusted, and maintained according to instructions provided by the manufacturer.

GENERAL GUIDELINES FOR EQUIPMENT INSTALLATION _____

The NF/RO membrane plant equipment installation has to be initiated after the following construction activities are completed:

- Civil engineering work has been completed.

- The electric utility has provided power.

- The raw-water intake facilities (surface intake system or well field and well pumps) are active and available for use.

- Arrangements have been made for the disposal of flush water, chlorinated water, and wastewater.

- Means for the disposal of concentrate have been provided.

Large and heavy equipment is set up first. Pumps, motors, control panels, transformers, storage and cleaning tanks, and any equipment that requires the use of a crane should be placed first to free up the crane as soon as possible. If the membrane unit does not arrive mounted on a skid, the next step is the erection of the RO or NF frames. After the frames have been secured, the pressure vessels should be mounted on the frames and strapped down. Feedwater, concentrate, and permeate piping should be installed and supported as soon as possible.

Once piping and support installation are completed in any area, electricians can install conduits, cable trays, local control panels, and instrument panels. Instrument tubing and sample lines should be installed after the majority of the equipment is in place. Manufacturers' recommendations should be followed to install RO or NF feed pumps, chemical-metering pumps, and instruments. Temporary pipe supports provided during the assembly of interconnecting piping should be replaced with permanent supports as soon as possible.

Intake System Construction and Equipment Installation

Surface intake systems. Small surface intake structures and pipelines are usually prefabricated and assembled before being submerged in the surface water source. A common method to construct large surface intake structures (which are usually made of concrete) is to surround the construction area with a sheetpile cofferdam system that allows the construction area to be dewatered. The installation of the intake structure is then completed in relatively dry conditions.

Depending on the prevailing current strength and direction, the intake pipeline could be laid directly on the bottom of the surface water source, or more often installed in a trench. Work would be staged on a floating platform using a crane to excavate and place material and pipeline segments. The bottom of the ocean in the vicinity of the intake pipeline would be stabilized with riprap. Riprap is typically placed at a distance of 100 to 200 ft (30 to 60 m) upstream and downstream of the intake pipeline. After the completion of the intake structure and the pipeline, the sheetpile cofferdam is removed and the system placed in service.

Subsurface intake systems. Major problems at membrane treatment plants have been caused by improper or poor subsurface intake (well) construction. In many cases, well failure causes a sudden change in water quality. The most common causes of well failure are borehole collapse, corrosion of the casing, improper or defective construction techniques, growth of organisms within the wellbore, and formation of mineral concentrations or crusts in the open-hole or screened section of the wellbore.

During well construction, selection of the drilling method and type of drilling fluid can affect the operation of a membrane treatment facility. The use of standard bentonite drilling mud in the construction of the open-hole or screened section of the well is not recommended. Residual bentonite can foul the pretreatment filters or membranes directly or, in the case of pretreatment with acid, can cause the formation of silica colloids that can foul the membranes. In permeable, lithified formations, the reverse air-drilling method can be used to drill the open hole. In the drilling of unconsolidated material to set screens, a decomposing polymer should be used. When an organic polymer fluid is used, chlorinated drilling water prevents bacterial growth problems.

Pretreatment Filtration System Construction and Equipment Installation

Gravity granular media filters. Gravity media filters are typically concrete structures. Their construction is similar to that of other plant structures of this type. Two very important issues associated with the construction of gravity filters are: (1) proper hydrostatic testing and inspection for microcracks; (2) installation of protective coating of the filter walls and bottom; and (3) installation of protective covers on the filter cells to minimize biological growth on the filter media, troughs, and other auxiliary equipment.

Thorough hydrostatic testing and inspection for microcracks on the concrete walls and bottom of the filters are of critical importance because the raw water (sea or brackish water) is very corrosive and if it reaches the structural rebar, can cause accelerated loss of structural integrity and ultimately could result in the collapse of the filter structure within a relatively short period of time (3 to 5 yr) after facility commissioning.

Pressure granular media filters. The following steps describe the initial installation procedure for media pressure filters:

1. Set the units in place, ensuring they are properly leveled.

2. Connect all face piping, if not factory assembled, and align according to drawings furnished by the manufacturer or system supplier.

3. Anchor all units to the foundation to ensure stability during operation.

4. If internal filter components (filter support, backwash troughs, air and/or water scour, etc.) are not installed, install them at this time, carefully following manufacturer's instructions and drawings. Make sure all internal filter components are properly supported.

5. Load filter media by following the manufacturer's instructions and as outlined in this step. Filter media are shipped in bags or marked containers that can weigh 50 to 150 lb depending on the type of media used. Erect a temporary scaffold next to the vessel porthole, and use a forklift or crane to lift the bags to a platform where they can conveniently be opened and the media lowered into the tanks. A factory-trained representative should be consulted for any questions that may arise. Media should be stored unopened in a dry place until just before they are loaded in the tank. A dust mask should be worn during media loading.

   a. Remove the cover on the upper tank porthole by loosening the bolts that secure the cover.

   b. Inspect internal components visually to ensure that no damage occurred during shipping. Verify the equipment with drawings furnished by the manufacturer.

   c. Gently lower (do not pour) the filter media and level.

   d. Carefully add water as the media are installed to level each layer and eliminate air pockets.

   e. Remove and account for all materials and tools used in loading before closing the tank with the porthole cover.

   f. Verify that the gaskets are well seated and properly aligned so that the porthole cover is secure.

6. Connect service piping to the unit, supporting and securing all piping to prevent excessive vibrations and strains.

7. Connect drain piping to the unit.

Membrane pretreatment filters. Pressure membrane pretreatment system installation is similar to that of the installation of NF/RO membrane facilities and is described in detail in the following sections. Immersed membrane filter modules are installed in concrete structures similar to those of the gravity granular media filters. As indicated previously, the concrete structures of the membrane pretreatment systems have to be hydrostatically tested and inspected very thoroughly for cracks. The walls and bottom of the membrane filter cells have to be lined with a protective coating to withstand the corrosive seawater or brackish water environment. Filter cells have to be covered with a protective coating to minimize biological growth on their surface.

If the filters are installed in a building, all metal surfaces of the building walls and all equipment exposed to high chlorine emissions must be covered with a protective coating or manufactured of materials that can withstand the high chlorine concentrations in the air, caused by the intermittent CEB cleaning of the filter membranes, sometimes required to be completed once to two times per day for cost-effective operation of the membrane pretreatment system. Because chlorine dosages of 25 to 50 mg/L may be needed for the CEB cleaning of the membranes, the chlorine emissions during the period of cleaning may be significant and may cause measurable corrosion on the building interior, structures, and equipment, if the membrane system is installed in a building. The building HVAC system has to be designed to be able to handle the elevated levels of chlorine in the air and to be equipped with an air scrubber system. As an option for vacuum-type MF and UF systems, the fumes from chlorination of the membranes can be effectively controlled by covering the tanks and evacuating the space under the cover.

NF/RO Membrane System Installation

General guidelines.   RO and NF units may arrive largely preassembled or may require some field assembly. The following installation guidelines provide an idea of the range of preassembly available.

Skid-mounted units.   Skid-mounted units are delivered preassembled. Typically, a concrete slab is provided to support the skid. The skid is placed on top of this slab and anchored to it where the manufacturer has provided bolt holes. The only field piping connections required are for the feedwater, concentrate, and permeate. The only electrical connection needing installation should be the power supply to the skid-mounted panel containing the motor starter and control circuitry.

Field-erected units.   Because of their physical dimensions, larger RO and NF units are field erected. The system manufacturer furnishes a prefabricated steel or fiberglass structure for assembly on the jobsite in order to support the pressure vessels. Either type of structure requires a concrete pad with anchor bolts provided as indicated by the manufacturer-supplied plot plan. The erector determines whether or not grouping of the support frame is required. The first step in the assembly is placement of the vertical frame sections. Laser technology may be employed to arrive at a properly aligned assembly. If grouping is required, a minimum allowance of 1 in. should be made. If the frame rests directly on top of the concrete, a sealing compound should be applied between the concrete and the frame to keep water out.

The next step involves installing sway supports and straps to tie the different sections together. All fasteners used in the assembly should be stainless steel, with flat washers under the bolts and the nuts. Any repairs to steel coatings or FRP should be made at this point because access to the frame is nearly impossible once the pressure vessels are in place.

Pressure Vessel Installation

Pressure vessels should be installed according to the manufacturer's instructions. To ease installation, the process can start with the farthest vertical row first. If necessary, the vessels should be turned so that any identification code is visible. The saddles and straps provided by the vessel manufacturer should be used to secure the vessels to the frame. Installation continues with the next vertical row until all vessels have been installed. After all vessels have been installed, the feed, concentrate, and permeate headers should be placed in their respective positions. Connections between these headers and the pressure vessels are established with J-bends or hoses according to the design.

The manufacturer's instructions for installing pressure vessels must be carefully studied and followed for product-specific information. The following guidelines provide general information:

1. Position each vessel on its mounting frame so that it is centered between heads. Drain holes must always face downward and be free of obstruction.

2. The mounting design must allow for vessel expansion, both axially and radially. Mount the vessel using the manufacturer's supplied or recommended straps and saddles. Do not use a U-bolt to hold down the vessel. Straps should be tightened to hold the vessel while still allowing for vessel expansion. Use flexible piping connections at both ends to permit decoupling of the header from the vessel. Typical connections are J-bends or flexible hoses. Grooved-end coupling connections are preferred for J-bends.

3. Feed, concentrate, and permeate headers should be supported independently. Follow the manufacturer's recommendations for the maximum allowable weight of branch piping.

4. Do not support piping or other components on the pressure vessels without first consulting the vessel manufacturer. Vessel ports must not be used to support any piping or other components.

5. End closures, also known as end cap assemblies, furnished by the different vessel manufacturers may differ in design. Follow the vessel manufacturer's instructions for building the end closures. It is recommended that the installer use only the closure assembly tools supplied by the vessel manufacturer. During assembly and disassembly of the end closures, examine all parts for any damage that could affect structural strength or sealing properties. Inspect all components for any condition that may have promoted corrosion.

6. Be careful not to scratch the inside wall of the pressure vessel, especially in the O-ring sealing area inside the retaining ring groove near each end.

7. Before using a forklift to handle the vessel, pad the forks to lessen the chance of damaging the shell.

Membrane Element Installation

The membrane elements are installed only after the pretreatment is fully functional; instruments have been calibrated and correctly ranged; the control system has been checked out (typically with orifice plug functional testing); all of the piping from the cartridge filters through, and including, the pressure vessels have been well cleaned; and the system has been hydrotested and has met disinfection requirements. It is important to follow the membrane manufacturer's guidelines to install elements. A qualified representative from the membrane manufacturer's facility should be present during the installation of elements and system startup. Special precautions should be taken in case the membrane elements have no tolerance for oxidants such as chlorine. Before elements that require an oxidant-free environment are loaded, the system should be flushed with nonchlorinated water. It may be necessary to flush the system with sodium bisulfite solution.

Element loading. This section addresses general loading procedures for spiral-wound membrane elements. The manufacturer's information should always be consulted for detailed instructions. Safety equipment should be worn during the handling of new elements to protect handlers from the biocide solution and occasional fiberglass strands. Membrane elements are shipped in sealed polyethylene bags containing a pH-adjusted biocide solution, a 0.5 to 1 percent solution of sodium metabisulfite or 0.2 percent solution of glutaraldehyde. For freeze protection, manufacturers may add glycerin to the biocide solution.

Appropriate safety equipment should be worn for all operations discussed in this section. Figure 3-32 shows two workers manually loading an element into a pressure vessel. Figure 3-33 illustrates a machine-assisted loading of a membrane element. Elements in each pressure vessel should be loaded as follows:

1. Remove the elements from their plastic bags and stand vertically with the flow arrow pointing down.

2. Install the brine seals on each element on the upstream end, making certain the open groove of the brine seal is toward the upstream (feed) end of the element. Check that each element has a brine seal on the end opposite the direction of the arrow.

3. Lubricate the brine seals and interconnector O-rings with a glycerin and water solution or the lubricant recommended by the membrane manufacturer, if different. When installing O-rings, do not roll them into position.

4. Open and remove the pressure vessel end caps according to the pressure vessel manufacturer's instructions.

5. Inspect the interior of the pressure vessel for any surface damage. The interior of the pressure vessel should be perfectly smooth, without nicks or protrusions. Spray clean water through the open pressure vessel to remove any dust or other foreign matter. If additional cleaning is required, contact the vessel manufacturer for the recommended procedure. Lubricate the inside of the entrance of the pressure vessel with glycerin.

6. Carefully pick up the first element and slide it into the pressure vessel, making sure that the brine seal is properly seated in the groove on the feedwater end of the element. The elements should be loaded in the same direction as the feedwater flow. Allow the element to protrude from the pressure vessel by approximately 8 to 10 in (20 to 25 cm). Then install the first interconnector with O-rings into the first element with a pushing and twisting motion until it is fully seated.

7. For safety and efficiency, two people should load the elements. The lead person places one hand firmly on the side of the first element to properly position it and guides the next element into position. With a slight twisting motion, one end of the interconnector is gently inserted into the permeate tube of the element. If external interconnectors are used, the interconnector will fit over the permeate tube of the element. Slowly push the element into the pressure vessel, leaving 6 to 8 in. protruding from the pressure vessel.

8. Repeat the preceding steps until the required number of elements have been coupled and inserted.

9. Although most manufacturers use similar interconnectors for elements, end adapters could vary depending on the vessel manufacturer. Follow the vessel manufacturer's assembly instructions to make the final connection between the element and the end cap of the pressure vessel.

10. Follow the preceding instructions for the end cap assembly.

11. Repeat the preceding steps for the remaining pressure vessels.

Element unloading.   It is recommended that at least two individuals unload membrane elements from the pressure vessels. The general procedure outlined here, as well as all instructions provided by the system manufacturer, should be followed. After the system has been shut down, it is important to make sure the pressure from the system is completely released. All pressure gauges should read zero pressure before any pressure vessel is opened.

1. Disconnect the hard plumbing at each end of the pressure vessel. Mark all removed parts for reassembly at the same location.

2. Remove end cap assemblies according to the vessel manufacturer's instructions.

3. Push the elements from the pressure vessel in the same direction in which feedwater flows. Push the elements out one element at a time. Support each element as it is being pushed from the vessel until the element is free of the pressure vessel.

Figure 3-32   Manual membrane element loading

Figure 3-33   Machine-assisted membrane element loading

TREATMENT COSTS

Costs for both construction and operation of membrane processes are dependent on site-specific factors. Plants of the same capacity and process type can therefore have very different construction costs. Site-specific factors affecting construction costs include the following:

- Plant size or capacity

- Site improvements

- Blending of source water with permeate

- Plant components included in the cost

- Concentration of TDS and other constituents of the source water, requiring removal

- Concentrate disposal

- Intake type for source water

- Pre- and posttreatment requirements

- Indirect costs

- Other costs

Reference Design

To determine how costs are affected by these site-specific factors, a reference design for typical brackish water, low pressure RO membrane system treating groundwater, and seawater from well supplies are included in this section. Cost changes can be determined based on the reference design. Figures 3-34 and 3-35 provide process flow diagrams for the reference designs. Table 3-12 lists design parameters, and Table 3-13 gives the capital or construction cost information. In this chapter's discussion, all costs presented are in 2004 dollars represented by an Engineering News Record (ENR) construction cost index (CCI) value of 7109.

A review of this information reveals that the following site-specific factors have been included in the reference design:

- Plant size is 10.0 mgd

- No blending of source water occurs

- Major components include

    — Wellfield

    — Pretreatment (chemical addition and cartridge filters) and posttreatment (chemical addition and, for the groundwater system, degasification system)

    — RO trains with feed pumps and ER device for the seawater example

    — Product storage and high-service pumping

- Concentrate disposal is to a nearby surface body of water

The following paragraphs address differences in capital costs for changes in these site-specific factors.

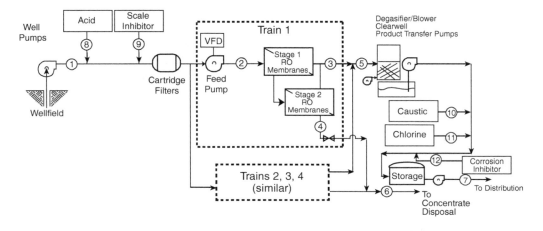

Process Stream	① Raw Water	② Train Feed Water	③ Train Permeate	④ Train Concentrate	⑤ Total Permeate	⑥ Total Concentrate	⑦ Finished Water	⑧ Acid (H_2SO_4)	⑨ Scale Inhibitor	⑩ Caustic	⑪ Chlorine	⑫ Corrosion Inhibitor
Flow, mgd	12.5	3.125	2.5	0.625	10.0	2.5	10.0					
Pressure, psi	50	215	15	165	15	30	80					
TDS, mg/L	2,000	1,995	70	9,695	70	9,695	85					
Dose, mg/L (100% concentration)								20	4	10	2	1

Figure 3-34   Brackish groundwater reference design

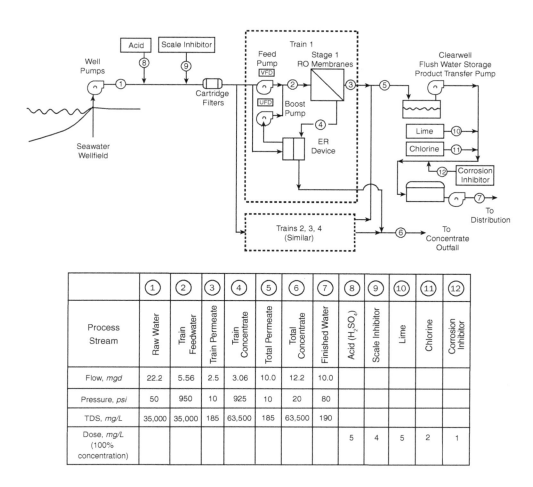

Process Stream	① Raw Water	② Train Feedwater	③ Train Permeate	④ Train Concentrate	⑤ Total Permeate	⑥ Total Concentrate	⑦ Finished Water	⑧ Acid (H₂SO₄)	⑨ Scale Inhibitor	⑩ Lime	⑪ Chlorine	⑫ Corrosion Inhibitor
Flow, *mgd*	22.2	5.56	2.5	3.06	10.0	12.2	10.0					
Pressure, *psi*	50	950	10	925	10	20	80					
TDS, *mg/L*	35,000	35,000	185	63,500	185	63,500	190					
Dose, *mg/L* (100% concentration)								5	4	5	2	1

Figure 3-35   Seawater reference design

Table 3-12   Reference design parameters

Parameter	Value or Type	
Water supply source	Groundwater	Seawater
Raw water TDS, *mg/L*	2,000	35,000
Permeate TDS, *mg/L*	70	185
Permeate quantity per train, *mgd*	2.5	2.5
Finished water quantity, *mgd*	10.0	10.0
Finished water TDS, *mg/L*	90	190
Number of trains	4	4
Pressure vessel staging (total per train)	44:21 (65)	97
Number of membranes (total per train)	455	679

Table continued next page.

Table 3-12 Reference design parameters *(continued)*

Parameter	Value or Type	
Number of raw water pumps	4	4
Electrical requirement (with energy recovery and all pumps), *kW*	1,800	5,700
Process recovery, %	80	45
Product water flux, *gpd/ft²*	15	10
Concentrate disposal	To surface water body	To surface water body

Table 3-13 Construction cost for the reference designs

	Costs in $1,000	
	10 mgd Brackish Groundwater RO Plant	10 MGD Sea Water RO Plant
Installed membrane equipment	$7,625	$25,980
Additional process items	2,300	3,125
Buildings	1,440	2,045
Site development	300	300
Wells	750	1,350
Electric utilities and switchgear	1,455	4,300
Finished water storage	520	520
High service pumping	625	625
Waste concentrate disposal	500	800
Raw water piping	100	180
Finished water piping	50	50
Emergency generator	475	840
Miscellaneous items	805	2,005
Contingency	2,990	7,435
Total construction cost	$19,935	$49,555
Total construction cost, *$/gpd*	$1.99	$4.96

NOTE: All costs in 2004 dollars, ENR CCI = 7109.

Plant Capacity

The required plant capacity, in conjunction with the recovery factor, determines the required feedwater capacity and establishes the cost of the membrane process, source water supply, and pretreatment and posttreatment systems. The capacity determines the number of membranes required, and the recovery factor defines the size of the auxiliary equipment. Once this cost has been established for a particular recovery rate, the cost for a plant of different capacity may be estimated from the following expression:

$$C_B = C_A \ (S_B/S_A)^n$$

Where:

C_B = cost of the new size plant, in US dollars
C_A = cost of known plant, in US dollars
S_B = capacity of new plant, in gpd
S_A = capacity of known plant, in gpd
n = scaling factor

For a brackish water process, a scaling factor of 0.80 may be used to determine costs of different sized plants. As an example, assume a 10-mgd plant capacity has a total construction cost of $19,935,000. Based on the equation shown previously, the construction cost of a 20-mgd plant would be estimated at $34,709,000. Note that the unit cost has been increased from $1.99/gpd for the 10-mgd plant to $1.74/gpd for the 20-mgd plant. This decrease in unit costs with increasing plant capacity is referred to as *economy of scale*.

Economy of scale can be seen in Figure 3-36, where the unit costs for process equipment alone are plotted for plant capacities between 1 and 20 mgd. This information indicates that the unit cost for a 20-mgd plant size is roughly two-thirds the unit cost of a 1.0-mgd plant size.

Indirect Costs

Once the installed construction costs have been determined, the indirect costs should be estimated, including:

- Project contingency
- Engineering design, legal, and administrative costs
- Working capital—interest during construction

Construction cost plus indirect costs equal the total capital cost.

O&M Costs

O&M costs include:

- Labor
- Chemicals
- Power
- Cartridge filters
- Membrane replacements
- Other materials

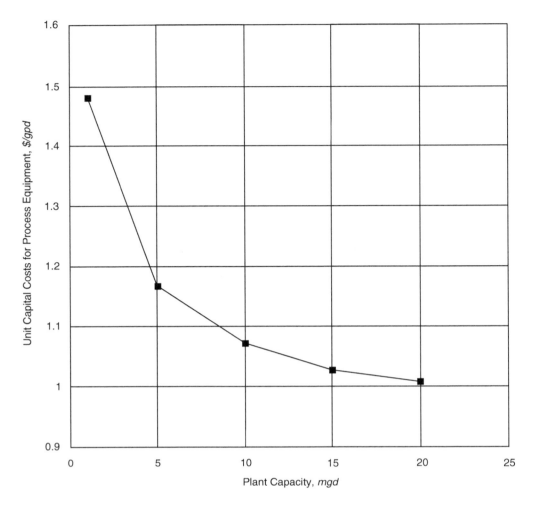

Figure 3-36 Economy of scale for RO plant process equipment

Table 3-14 presents typical O&M costs for the reference 10 mgd brackish water and seawater RO plants. A breakdown of the O&M costs for the reference designs is shown in Figure 3-37.

Total Product Water Costs

Total treated water costs include amortized capital costs (fixed charges) plus annual O&M costs. Assuming amortization at 7 percent over a 20-yr period, the total treated water costs for the reference designs are presented in Table 3-15.

The reference designs previously presented assumed a relatively low fixed cost for concentrate disposal. Description of alternative methods for concentrate disposal is provided earlier in this chapter. According to the results of a recent study completed by the USBR (Mickley 2006), the concentrate disposal methods most widely used in the US are presented in Figures 3-27 and 3-28.

Table 3–14   O&M costs for the reference designs

	Annual Costs in $1,000/Year	
	10 mgd Brackish Groundwater RO Plant	10 mgd Seawater RO Plant
Labor	$685	$685
Chemicals	465	485
Power	1,255	3,985
Cartridge filters	30	55
Membrane replacements	165	340
Other materials	145	145
Total O&M costs	$2,745	$5,695
Total $/1,000 gal*	$0.75	$1.56

NOTE: All costs in 2004 dollars. Power at $0.08/kwh.
*Assumes production of 10 mgd, 365 d/yr.

Brackish Groundwater RO Reference Plant

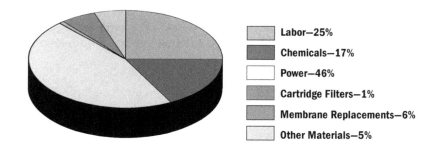

Labor—25%
Chemicals—17%
Power—46%
Cartridge Filters—1%
Membrane Replacements—6%
Other Materials—5%

Seawater RO Reference Plant

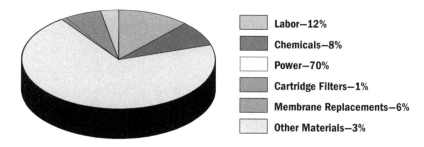

Labor—12%
Chemicals—8%
Power—70%
Cartridge Filters—1%
Membrane Replacements—6%
Other Materials—3%

Figure 3-37   O&M cost breakdown for reference plants (assumes relative costs in 2004)

Table 3–15   Total treated water costs for the reference designs

Annual Costs in $1,000/Year	10 mgd Brackish Groundwater RO Plant	10 mgd Seawater RO Plant
Amortized capital (fixed charges)	$1,880	$4,680
O&M	2,745	$5,695
Total	$4,625	$10,375
Total $/1,000 gal*	$1.27	$2.84

NOTE: All costs in 2004 dollars. ENR CCI = 7109.

*Assumes production of 10 mgd, 365 d/yr.

Concentrate Disposal Costs

Since the development of desalting membranes in the 1960s, desalting membrane treatment plant costs have declined, driven primarily by reduced costs for both membrane modules and systems and improvements in membrane and system performance. With the possible exception of enhanced evaporation systems for use with ponds, costs associated with conventional disposal options have not decreased. As a consequence, the capital and operating costs associated with residuals management will continue to increase as a percentage of overall plant costs. This is particularly true for large capacity plants with limited low-cost disposal options for high residuals flows. High residuals management costs will therefore limit future decreases in membrane plant capital and operating costs (Mickley 2006). Moreover, future residual management costs are likely to increase due to growing difficulty in finding economical and environmentally sound means of disposal. A number of site-specific factors may limit the range of concentrate management options at a given site, including:

- Suitability of geological/hydrological conditions for deep well disposal
- Concentration of dissolved solids and toxic ions in the concentrate
- Low seasonal flows in local surface waters
- Adequate capacity of the local sewers and WWTP for the concentrate volume
- Limitations in the local sewer ordinance
- Availability and cost of land
- Availability of dilution water for land applications
- Climate suitability for year-round land application
- Availability of land for evaporation ponds or other disposal methods
- Local value of water
- Demand (amount and seasonal variations) for irrigation water

Some cost generalizations can be made in cases where all disposal options are available, permitting is possible, and distances from the desalting membrane plant to the alternative management options are similar. Figure 3-38 presents the relative costs for concentrate management options as a function of concentrate flow based on the above cost considerations. Table 3-16 provides costs for some of the concentrate management options as a function of flow rate. These costs are based on available

Costs, in $1,000[†]											
Spray Irrigation[‡]				Evaporation Pond[§]				Subsurface Injection[**]		Brine Concentrator[‡]	
Acres at 2 ft/yr	$ at 2 ft/yr	Acres at 20 ft/yr	$ at 20 ft/yr	Acres at 0.5 gpm/ acre	$ at 0.5 gpm/ acre	Acres at 2.0 gpm/ acre	$ at 2.0 gpm/ acre	$ at 2,500 ft	$ at 10,000 ft	$, capital	$/y ene
6	200	0.6	40	14	1,600	4	400	1,750	5,700	1,300	
60	1,000	6	200	140	16,000	35	4,000	1,750	5,700	2,000	1,2
600	6,000	60	1,200	1,400	160,000	350	40,000	2,500	8,100	8,750	3,8
—	—	120	2,400	—	—	—	—	2,800	8,500	14,900	6,8
—	—	300	6,000	—	—	—	—	3,600	10,000	38,500	17,2

e: AWWA Membrane Residuals Management Subcommittee 2004.

All costs in 2004 dollars.

ive costs are presented; site-specific costs may vary greatly.

exclude cost of conveying concentrate to site; costs based on Mickley 2006.

exclude: means of blending/dilution, pretreating to meet water quality requirements, monitoring wells.

exclude solids disposal and seepage monitoring.

s exclude pretreatment and standby disposal system.

ed on power cost at $0.10/kW· h. Costs exclude solids disposal and disposal of possible small brine stream.

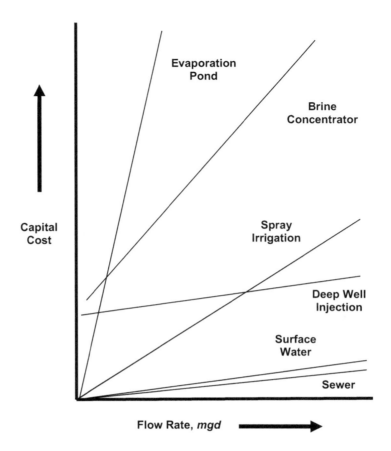

Figure 3-38   Relative capital cost of concentrate management options

information updated to 2004 dollars and only represent relative costs in the absence of any site-specific information. Figure 3-38 and Table 3-16 are based on information available from published sources (Mickley 2006; Watson et. al 2003).

Sanitary sewer and surface water discharges are the two most cost-effective methods of concentrate disposal, which explains their popularity. Subsurface injection, evaporation ponds, and spray irrigation could be competitive alternatives if local conditions are conducive. Typically, the zero-liquid discharge systems, such as brine concentrators, have the highest capital and operating costs. Under specific circumstances (such as cold climate, low evaporation and soil uptake rates, high land costs, and low power costs) the zero-liquid discharge systems could be cost competitive with evaporation pond and spray irrigation alternatives. A more detailed breakdown of the capital and operating costs for the concentrate disposal methods is provided in Mickley (2006) and Watson and colleagues (2003). The key cost factors for each disposal method are discussed in the following sections.

Surface water discharge costs. Costs for surface water discharge are influenced by many site-specific factors and are difficult to generalize. The key cost factors are those of concentrate conveyance to the outfall, outfall construction and operation, concentrate treatment to meet NPDES permit limits, and environmental monitoring of the discharge.

The concentrate conveyance costs are closely related to the concentrate volume and the distance to the discharge outfall. The outfall capital costs depend on outfall diameter, length, piping material, and diffuser system configuration. This cost could be eliminated if an existing outfall can be used. Outfall discharge operating costs are closely related to the need to aerate the concentrate before disposal or to treat to control WET. Environmental monitoring costs may be significant, especially if the discharge is near an impaired or sensitive water body, or area of limited natural flushing.

Sanitary sewer discharge costs.   Sanitary sewer discharge conditions are very site specific. The key cost elements for this disposal method are the cost of conveyance (pump station and pipeline), and fees for connecting to the sanitary sewer and treatment/disposal of the concentrate at the WWTP. Sewer connection and treatment fees can vary significantly from none to several orders of magnitude larger than the conveyance costs. Sewer connection fees are related to the available capacity of the sewer facilities and the effect of the concentrate discharge on the WWTP's operating costs. Discharge to sewer is used more often with small- and medium-sized plants, because small concentrate volumes affect WWTP systems less.

Subsurface injection costs.   The key factors that influence subsurface injection costs are well depth and the diameter of well tubing and casting rings; well diameter seems to have a limited influence on the costs. Several other key cost factors are the need for concentrate pretreatment prior to disposal; pump size and pressure that vary depending on the geologic conditions and depth of the injection zone; monitoring well system size and configuration; and site preparation, mobilization, and demobilization. Disposal via deep well injection is expensive, but it has economies of scale for large-capacity desalting plants.

Evaporation pond costs.   The key cost variables for evaporation ponds are evaporation rate (climate), concentrate volume, land and earthwork costs, the liner costs, and salinity of the concentrate, which determines the useful life of the ponds. The main cost variable is the evaporative area, because evaporation rates are lower than soil uptake rates; disposal of the same volume of concentrate using evaporation ponds requires more land than disposal by spray irrigation. Capital costs for evaporation ponds have lower economies of scale and typically are only acceptable for small plants. The largest municipal plant discharging to evaporation ponds has a capacity of 1.5 mgd; the others have capacities of less than 0.4 mgd.

Land application costs.   Usually, land application or spray irrigation is cost-effective only if the concentrate can be blended with fresh water to reduce salinity to a level acceptable for irrigation. Its feasibility also depends on the type of crops/vegetation and on the soil uptake rates. The key costs for this disposal method are the costs of land, the storage and distribution system, and the irrigation system installation, which in turn are driven by the concentrate volume and salinity. In addition, because irrigation is a seasonal operation, a second disposal method must be available. Similar to evaporation ponds, spray irrigation is feasible for very small systems.

Zero-liquid discharge costs. Achieving zero-liquid discharge with brine concentrators or other methods is usually the least cost-effective, because it requires costly mechanical equipment for evaporation, crystallization, and concentration (dewatering) of the salts in the concentrate. Further, the operation of this equipment is energy intensive and has high O&M costs. Although this method has found practical application in industrial water reuse facilities, it has not yet been used for disposal of concentrate from a RO or NF plant (Mickley 2006).

REFERENCES

Adham, S.A. 2003. *Development of an MF/UF Knowledge Base*. Proceedings. AWWA Annual Conference. June 15–19, Anaheim, Calif.

AWWA. 1996. Rothberg, Tamburini and Winsor Model for Corrosion Control and Process Chemistry, Denver, Colo.

AWWA Membrane Process Committee. 2005. Manual of Water Supply Practices, M53—*Microfiltration and Ultrafiltration Membranes in Drinking Water.*

AWWA Membrane Residuals Management Subcommittee.[*] 2004. Committee report: Current Perspectives on residuals management for desalting membranes, *Jour. AWWA,* 96(12): 73–87.

AWWA Water Desalting Committee. 2004. *Water Desalting Planning Guide for Water Utilities.* John Wiley & Sons, Inc., Hoboken, N.J.: 122–123.

City of Huntington Beach. 2002. *Draft Environmental Impact Report, Poseidon Seawater Desalination Project,* September.

Conlon, W.J. 1988. Disposal of Concentrate from Membrane Process Plants. AWWA Seminar on Membrane Processes. Denver, Colo.: American Water Works Association.

Gille, D. 2003. Seawater Intakes for Desalination Plants. *Desalination,* 156: 249–256.

Hunt, H.C. 1996. Filtered Seawater Supplies—Naturally. Desalination and Water Reuse, August/September, 6(2): 32–37.

Irwin, K.J., Thompson, J.D. 2003. Trinidad SWRO—Orinoco Fluctuations Fail to Make Filters Falter. *Desalination and Water Reuse,* November/December 13(3): 12–16.

Kartinen, E., Jr., and C. Martin. 2003. *Solving Morro Bay's Seawater Reverse Osmosis Plant's Iron Problem.* 2003 AWWA Membrane Technology Conference Proceedings, Atlanta, Ga.

Kenna, E.N., and A.K. Zander. 2001. Survey of Membrane Concentrate Reuse and Disposal.

Larson, T. 1970. Corrosion by Domestic Waters, Illinois State Water Survey, Bulletin 56. Urbana, Ill.

Mickley, M.C. 2006. Membrane Concentrate Disposal: Practices and Regulation. Desalination and Water Purification Research Program Report No. 123, US Bureau of Reclamation.

Missimer, T.M. 1994. *Water Supply Development for Membrane Water Treatment Facilities.* Lewis Publishers/CRC Press: Boca Raton, Fla.

Missimer, T.M. 1999. Raw Water Quality—The Critical Design Factor for Brackish Water Reverse Osmosis Treatment Facilities. *Desalination and Water Reuse,* 9(1) (May/June): 41–47.

Rovel, J.M. 2002. *Current and Future Trends in SWRO (Pretreatment),* 2002 IDE Conference Proceedings, Bahrain.

Schock. M.R. 1991. *Internal Corrosion and Deposition Control in Water Quality and Treatment.* New York: McGraw Hill.

Schwartz, J. 2000. *Beach Well Intakes for Small Seawater Reverse Osmosis Plants,* The Middle East Desalination Research Center, Muscat, Sultanate of Oman, August.

Thompson D., D. Prah, W. Surratt, and G. Dernlan. 2001. *Sweat the Small Stuff—Correcting Membrane Design Flaws Before They Can Happen.* American Water Works Association. Membrane Conference Proceedings.

US Bureau of Reclamation et al. 2004. Industry Consortium Analysis of Large Reverse Osmosis/Nanofiltration Element Diameters. Desalination and Water Purification Research and Development Report No. 114.

USEPA. 2003. *Membrane Filtration Guidance Manual,* Office of Ground Water and Drinking Water. Standards and Risk Management Division, Technical Support Center.

Voutchkov, N. 2004a. Seawater Desalination Costs Cut Through Power Plant Co-location, *Filtration + Separation,* (September 2004).

Voutchkov, N. 2004b. Thorough Study is Key to Large Beach Well Intakes, *The*

---

*AWWA Membrane Residuals Management Subcommittee: Paul Malmrose (Chair), Jim Lozier, Michael Mickley, Robert Reiss, Jerry Russell, James Schaefer, Sandeep Sethi, Jennifer Manuszak, Robert Bergman, and Khalil Z. Atasi

International Desalination and Water Reuse Quarterly, (May/June 2004).

Water Treatment Plant Design, 4th ed. AWWA and ASCE. McGraw-Hill. 2005.

Watson, I.C. et al., 2003. Desalting Handbook for Planners, 3rd ed. Desalination and Water Purification Research Program Report No. 72, US Bureau of Reclamation.

Wright, R.R., and T.M. Missimer. 1997. *Alternative Intake Systems for Seawa-ter Membrane Water Treatment Plants*. Proceedings of International Desalination Association, Madrid, 3: 407–422.

Zahnow. R. 2002. UV Disinfection In Conjunction With Large-Scale Membrane Systems. *Ultrapure Water*, (October): 42–46.

This page intentionally blank.

Chapter **4**

Operations and Maintenance

Scott Freeman

INTRODUCTION

RO and NF plants require specialized O&M procedures. Information is presented on troubleshooting guidelines, proactive tasks to avoid problems, data collection, process monitoring, calculation methods, biological and other types of fouling, scaling, chemical cleaning, mechanical integrity, conductivity profiling and probing, instrument calibration, and safety.

This chapter focuses on O&M procedures specifically related to RO/NF membranes; therefore, procedures for other types of water treatment processes are not discussed in detail. General concepts and guidelines for the O&M of RO/NF systems are presented; however, this text cannot replace the instructions from the manufacturers of specific equipment. The specific instructions and warranty have to take precedence to ensure that the operating conditions are compatible with the equipment. In addition, RO/NF is a rapidly changing field, so some of the information in this chapter may not be applicable in all cases.

Quick Reference Guides

Quick reference guides on RO/NF troubleshooting to correct problems and suggested proactive tasks to avoid problems are presented in Tables 4-1 and 4-2, respectively.

Table 4-1   RO/NF troubleshooting ideas to correct problems

Condition	Ideas to Consider
Increase in salt passage	Verify accuracy of the instrument readings Conduct conductivity profile(s) to find problem vessel(s). Compare to historical data for that train and others. Conduct probe of problem vessels and/or replace seals and/or elements. Check posttreatment chemical addition, if that operation is upstream of the measurement location. Consider CIP.
Increase in permeate conductivity or concentration	Check feed concentration and salt passage value. If indicated, follow the instructions for "Increase in salt passage."
Increase in feed–concentrate pressure drop	Verify accuracy of the instrument readings and related calculations. Check if feed or concentrate flow rate is higher than baseline condition. If recovery is reduced and permeate flow rate held constant, then feed and concentrate flow rates will be increased, and so will the pressure drop. Confirm that the pretreatment and other process steps upstream are functioning properly. Shut down train and open lead element side of some pressure vessels for visual inspection. Construction debris or other materials may have gotten past the cartridge filter and plugged the entrance to the first elements, resulting in higher pressure drop. Consider CIP. High pressure drop indicates a possibility of a "fluffy" precipitate, such as calcium carbonate, such that an acid CIP may be sufficient to eliminate the problem. Subsequently, adjust operating conditions, such as feed rates of pretreatment acid or antiscalant and/or lowering recovery, to prevent recurrence.
Increase in permeate flow rate	Verify accuracy of the instrument readings. Check control system. Perhaps permeate flow set point has been changed. Check temperature and consider the impact of temperature on operations. Higher temperature yields an increase in permeate flow if other conditions held constant (i.e., feed pressure, feed quality, and recovery). Check other operating parameters. For example, lower feed TDS will naturally result in higher permeate flow rate, if the feed pressure and other conditions are held constant. Check permeate water quality (e.g., conductivity). A seal or O-ring leak may allow significant flow to pass to the permeate.
Decrease in permeate flow rate	Verify accuracy of the instrument readings. Check control system to determine whether permeate flow set point has been changed. Check temperature and consider the impact of temperature on operations. Lower temperature yields a decrease in permeate flow if other conditions held constant (i.e., feed pressure, feed quality, and recovery). Check other operating parameters. For example, higher feed TDS will naturally result in lower permeate flow rate, if the feed pressure and other conditions are held constant. Verify accuracy of calculations. If calculations have been done by computer program or control system, collect independent data and perform hand calculation to verify. Consider CIP.

Table continued next page.

Table 4-1   RO/NF troubleshooting ideas to correct problems *(continued)*

Condition	Ideas to consider
Decrease in normalized permeate flow rate (or increase in normalized driving pressure)	Verify accuracy of the instrument readings. Verify accuracy of calculations. If calculations have been done by computer program or control system, collect independent data and perform hand calculation to verify. Check other operating parameters. For example, higher feed TDS will naturally result in lower permeate flow rate, if the feed pressure and other conditions are held constant. Consider CIP.
Increase in pressure required to maintain set permeate flow rate	Please refer to previous item, regarding decrease in normalized permeate flow rate (or increase in normalized driving pressure).
Interval between CIPs too short	Verify accuracy of the instrument readings. Verify accuracy of calculations of parameters that indicated a need for CIP, such as pressure drop or normalized permeate flux. Calculation methods are presented elsewhere in this chapter. If calculations have been done by computer program or control system, collect independent data and perform hand calculation to verify. It is possible that unnecessary CIPs have been conducted. Consider effectiveness of CIP. If added effectiveness is needed, consider source of make-up water (e.g., use low TDS permeate), increased temperature, more extreme pH, higher concentrations and/or stronger cleaning agents, longer soak time, higher velocity agitation. Contact membrane manufacturer to discuss CIP regime and potential recommended modifications. In very difficult cases, revising operating conditions may be advisable, such as lowering flux or recovery.
CIP does not return unit to clean baseline	Verify instrument readings. Verify accuracy of calculations. If calculations have been done by computer program or control system, collect independent data and perform hand calculation to verify. It is possible that unnecessary CIPs have been conducted. Consider effectiveness of CIP. If added effectiveness is needed, consider source of make-up water (e.g., use low TDS permeate), increased temperature, more extreme pH, higher concentrations and/or stronger cleaning agents, longer soak time, higher velocity agitation. Contact membrane manufacturer to discuss cleaning conditions and recommendations for improvement. In very difficult cases, revising operating conditions may be advisable, such as lowering flux or recovery.
Increase in feedwater SDI, turbidity, or other parameter (i.e., decrease in feedwater quality)	Verify instrument readings. Revise and reoptimize pretreatment conditions. Consider if unwanted materials are being accidentally introduced in pretreatment, such as by chemical addition, cartridge filtration, and/or corrosion by-products. Pressure test raw water line for potential leak.

Table 4-2   RO/NF suggested proactive tasks to avoid problems

Condition	Ideas to Consider
General	1. Understand the design goals and limitations of your equipment. 2. Conduct a good routine maintenance program. 3. Repair leaks as they occur. 4. Keep instruments calibrated. 5. Maintain historical data for reference. 6. Maintain records on each RO/NF unit to facilitate unit-to-unit comparison and comparison of current to past performance. 7. Maintain records on CIP successes and failures. 8. Conduct conductivity profile of each train (measuring conductivity of permeate from each vessel and common feed and concentrate for each stage) at regular intervals and 24 hr after each CIP. 9. Periodically meet with other operators to compare experience. The AWWA Membrane Technology Conference includes workshops and the American Membrane Technology Association sponsors forums for operators. 10. Form and attend meetings of operator's groups in your local area.

Seasonal temperature change	1. Understand impact of temperature on operations and normalization calculations, including:
	  • Higher temperature requires lower feed pressure to maintain the same permeate flow rate.
	  • Lower temperature requires higher feed pressure to maintain the same permeate flow rate.
	2. Temperature also has an impact on salt passage, but much less pronounced than the effect on permeate flow rate. As temperature increases, permeate concentration may slightly increase, if the permeate flow rate is held constant (i.e., if the pressure is lowered to yield the same permeate flow rate).

Seasonal feedwater quality change	1. Improved pretreatment operations may be needed. For example, granular media filters may require more frequent backwashing and/or longer filter-to-waste step. 2. Consider lowering RO/NF flux and/or recovery. 3. Increased frequency of cartridge filter replacement may be needed. 4. Increased frequency of CIP may be needed. 5. If possible, increase concentrate velocity.
Before starting a period with higher finished water demand	1. Calibrate major instruments. 2. Check calibration on chemical feed equipment, such as acid and antiscalant pumps. 3. Check stock and order important consumable materials, such as cartridge filters, acid, antiscalant, and CIP chemicals. 4. Consider CIP of all RO/NF units before high demand period starts. 5. Conduct conductivity profiles. 6. Repair/replace questionable RO/NF membrane elements and seals. 7. Service overall plant, especially pretreatment equipment that could affect RO/NF operations (such as feedwater SDI, turbidity, TOC, UV-254, and/or SUVA).

PROCESS MONITORING

System monitoring is essential to prevent fouling/scaling and to identify problems early when they may more easily be reversed. Proper system monitoring and maintenance cannot be overemphasized, because it will maximize membrane life and available plant capacity, while minimizing system downtime and operating costs. Figure 4-1 shows an operator collecting samples from an RO unit.

Maintaining treatment plant capacity is one of the major challenges in operating an RO/NF system. In general, it is easier to maintain finished water quality than to maintain plant capacity, because RO/NF systems are susceptible to the collection or formation of material that adds resistance to flow through the membrane. The primary mechanisms are as follows:

- Plugging is caused by debris blocking or partially blocking the flow channels on the leading element(s). Frequently this is caused by construction materials not properly flushed from a new system before loading the RO/NF elements.

- Scaling is caused by precipitation of inorganic material in the element. Frequently this is caused by operating at excessive recovery or by failure of antiscalant feed systems.

- Fouling is caused by organic material deposited on or absorbed by the membrane.

- Biofouling, a special type of fouling, is caused by biological growth in the membrane system.

Table 4-3 lists typical monitoring parameters, tests, frequency of testing, and limiting conditions. Figure 4-2 provides an example of a typical operating log.

Courtesy of Black & Veatch

Figure 4-1 Operator collecting samples from RO unit at Dare County Utilities, Kill Devil Hills, N.C.

Table 4-3 Monitoring of RO and NF systems

Parameter	Measurement	Frequency	Limits (typical)
Pretreatment monitoring:			
Feedwater particulates	Turbidity	Continuous	<1 to 0.1 ntu
	SDI	1–3/day or continuous	<3–5 SDI units
	Particle count	Some projects apply continuously	Project specific
Dissolved material	Saturation of scaling salts	Project specific, typically 4–12/yr	Depends on antiscalant Typical limits: $CaCO_3$: LSI <2 $BaSO_4$ <60 × K_{sp} CaF <100 × K_{sp} $CaSO_4$ <2 × K_{sp} $SrSO_4$ <8 × K_{sp} SiO_2 ~150–180 mg/L
Membrane unit monitoring:			
Flow	Permeate, concentrate (feed by difference)	Continuous	Project specific
	Percent recovery	Continuous	Project specific
	Normalized permeate flow or analogous parameter	Daily data points, graphed weekly	Project specific
Pressure	Feed, concentrate, permeate, interstage	Continuous	Project specific
Pressure drop	Feed-concentrate, each stage	Continuous	Project specific
Conductivity	Feed and permeate	Continuous	Project specific
Concentration	TDS of feed, permeate, and finished water	Periodically to check relationship to conductivity and/or for permits	
Rejection	Calculation based on conductivity and concentration measurements	Continuous	Project specific
pH	Feed and finished water	Continuous	Project specific
Temperature	Feed	Continuous	Project specific
Biological monitoring:			
HPC or other indicator	Feed and concentrate	Varies, possibly 2–4/yr	Project specific
Chlorine residual*	Feed	Continuous, if applicable	0 mg/L for PA 0.5–1 mg/L for CA
Chlorine	Finished water	Continuous	Project specific
Instrument calibration:			
Various	Flow, pressure, conductivity, etc.	1–2/yr	Varies
System balance check	Flows and conductivities	Weekly	Within 5–10%

*CA (cellulosic) membrane requires chlorine residual. PA (polyamide) membrane is degraded by chlorine residual. Sometimes an ORP or bisulfite residual monitor is applied.

Pretreatment

Pretreatment of source water before it reaches the membrane system protects the unit from dissolved and suspended particles that can foul, scale, and physically or chemically damage the membrane elements. The fouling potential of suspended substances is indicated by measurements of turbidity and silt density. Fouling potential of organic material may be indicated by measurements of DOC and specific ultraviolet absorbance (SUVA). This is an active topic of applied research and researchers are developing these and what may become more precise indicators of organic fouling. Currently, there are no definitive rules, but as a guideline, concentration of DOC greater than 3 mg/L may indicate increased risk of fouling. SUVA is the ratio between UV absorption and the DOC concentration. SUVA of 2 L/mg-m indicates a higher percentage of the DOC is composed of fulvic and humic acids, which may also indicate an increased risk of fouling. The potential for biofouling can be indicated by measurement of the microbial concentrations of the organisms of concern. The scaling potential of dissolved substances is indicated by measurements of conductivity and the concentrations of specific ions, coupled with related calculations of saturation levels of sparingly soluble compounds.

Turbidity

RO and NF manufacturers generally require source water to have a turbidity value of less than 1 ntu, although a lower turbidity is preferred. Continuous, on-stream turbidity measurement of RO/NF feedwater is practiced at most facilities. Alarm and shutdown conditions are frequently activated if the feed turbidity exceeds setpoint values. This instrumentation needs to be regularly calibrated.

Silt density index. The SDI* is an indicator of the fouling potential due to particles in water. Because fouling and plugging are major potential problems in RO/ NF systems, this is an important measurement. Most RO experts consider SDI to be an imperfect indicator, and various researchers have tried to develop better methods to predict particulate fouling potential; however, in general the industry currently accepts SDI as the main method. Perhaps a better method will eventually be accepted, but until then, pretreatment systems should be designed, maintained, and operated to provide the lowest practical SDI. During system upsets, the SDI should be measured frequently to ensure low-SDI water. If possible, the membrane unit should not be operated with a feedwater SDI higher than 5; and a value less than 3 is preferred. In any case, the manufacturer's recommendation concerning SDI levels should be followed.

Clarifiers, filters (granular media or MF/UF membranes), and cartridge filters are the most common process steps used to remove particulate matter from water. Filter backwashes, coagulant and polyelectrolyte dosages, and cartridge filter replacements should be carefully monitored and adjusted to give the lowest practical SDI value. It should be noted that polyelectolytes are only rarely used in RO/NF pretreatment because of concern that overdosing or carryover may irreversibly foul the membranes. Generally, cartridge filters are not specifically designed to lower turbidity or SDI in RO/NF feedwater but are used instead to provide an extra level of protection for the RO/NF, essentially acting as a guard filter for larger, more *catastrophic* damaging particles/debris. The primary means of particle control is accomplished by process steps upstream.

---

*ASTM D 4189-95, Standard Test Method for Silt Density Index (SDI) of Water.

RWS WATER FLOOR LOG IN SHEET

NAME _____
DATE _____
TIME _____

ELECTRIC ROOM

AFD # 1
% Power _____
Hours _____

AFD # 2
% Power _____
Hours _____

EMONS
HPP # 1 _____
HPP # 2 _____

PRE-TREATMENT INSTRUMENTS

Feed Conductivity _____
Feed Pressure _____
Feed Turbidity _____
Bypass Flow _____
Feed pH _____

FINISH WATER

Free Cl_2 _____
Fluoride _____

DIST. WATER

Free Cl_2 _____
Fluoride _____

TRAIN # 1

Inlet of Cartridge Filter _____
Outlet of Cartridge Filter _____
Delta P _____
HPP Suction Pressure _____
Flow Percentage _____
Discharge Valve Position _____
Concentrate Flow _____
Concentrate Pressure % _____
Feed Pressure _____
Interstage Pressure _____
Delta P _____
Concentrate Pressure _____
Delta P _____

TRAIN # 2

Inlet of Cartridge Filter _____
Outlet of Cartridge Filter _____
Delta P _____
HPP Suction Pressure _____
Flow Percentage _____
Discharge Valve Position _____
Concentrate Flow _____
Concentrate Pressure % _____
Feed Pressure _____
Interstage Pressure _____
Delta P _____
Concentrate Pressure _____
Delta P _____

POST INSTRUMENT STAND

Permeate Conductivity RO # 1 _____
Permeate Conductivity RO # 2 _____
Pre-Chemical Conductivity _____
Distributed Cl_2 _____

Permeate Flow RO # 1 _____
Permeate Flow RO # 2 _____
Finish Water Cond. _____
Finish Water pH _____

HIGH SERVICE PUMPS

Pump # 1 Suction Pressure _____
Pump # 1 Discharge Press. _____

Pump # 2 Suction Pressure _____
Pump # 2 Discharge Press. _____

Pump # 3 Suction Pressure _____
Pump # 3 Discharge Press. _____

CHEMICAL ROOMS

Scale Inhibitor Level _____ Stroke _____ Speed % _____ Drawdown _____ (Dose ____.____ mg/l)
H_2SO_4 Level _____ Stroke _____ Speed % _____ Drawdown _____ (Dose ____.____ mg/l)
NaOH Level _____ Stroke _____ Speed % _____ Drawdown _____ (Dose ____.____ mg/l)
Corrosion Inhib. Level _____ Stroke _____ Speed % _____ Drawdown _____ (Dose ____.____ mg/l)
Fluoride Level _____ Stroke _____ Speed % _____ Drawdown _____ (Dose ____.____ mg/l)
Chlorinator Setting in Pounds per Day _____ →→→→→→→→→→→→ (Dose ____.____ mg/l)

CHLORINE FEED ROOM

1 Chlorinator Pounds per Day _____
Pacer Setting: Auto   Man

2 Chlorinator Pounds per Day _____
Pacer Setting: Auto   Man

CHLORINE BULK STORAGE

Scale # 1 Reading _____
Scale # 2 Reading _____

GROUND STORAGE TANK LEVEL: _____

BULK STORAGE CHEMICALS: Diesel Level _____ Acid Level _____ Caustic Level _____

LAND OF BEGINNINGS

Courtesy of Dare County, N.C.

Figure 4-2 Example of an operating log

Figure continued next page.

DARE COUNTY RWS DESALINATION WATER TREATMENT FACILITY DAILY MACHINERY AND CHEMICAL STATUS

FOR: 8.00 AM   To   8 00 AM   NAME____   DATE:_____   TIME:_____

COMPUTER CONSOLE - PRETREATMENT STATUS

INLET FLOW (Gallons)   _____   WEATHER DATA:
TURBIDITY (NTU)   _____
FEED CONDUCTIVITY (UMHOS)   _____   TEMPERATURES:
pH   _____   RAIN GAUGE _____ "   HIGH _____ DEG. F.
SCALE INHIBITOR FLOW (CC / MIN)   _____   PRESENT_____ DEG. F.
                                                                          LOW _____ DEG. F.

COMPUTER CONSOLE - TRAIN STATUS

	TRAIN #1	TRAIN #2
PUMP SPEED CONTROL (%)	_____	_____
PUMP SPEED (%)	_____	_____
FEED PRESSURE (PSI)	_____	_____
DIFFERENTIAL PRESSURE (PSI)	_____	_____
PERMEATE FLOW (Gallons)	_____	_____
CONCENTRATE FLOW (Gallons)	_____	_____
PERMEATE RECOVERY (%)	_____	_____
PERMEATE COND. (UMHOS)	_____	_____
CONC. VALVE POSITION (%)	_____	_____

COMPUTER CONSOLE - POSTTREATMENT STATUS

RO BLEND FLOW (Gallons)   _____
BLEND VALVE POSITION (%)   _____
TOTAL BLENDED FLOW (Gallons)   _____
FINISHED PRODUCT pH   _____
FINISH PRODUCT CONDUCTIVITY (UMHOS)   _____
CONDUCTIVITY SET POINT (UMHOS)   _____
TOTAL CONCENTRATE FLOW (Gallons)   _____

COMPUTER CONSOLE - CHEMICAL METERING PUMP STATUS

	CHEMICAL PUMP #1 ON/OFF	%	CHEMICAL PUMP #2 ON/OFF	%
SCALE INHIBITOR	____		____	
SULFURIC ACID	____		____	
SODIUM HYDROXIDE	____		____	
CORROSION INHIBITOR	____		____	
FLUORIDE ACID	____		____	

SCADA CONSOLE - OPERATING WELLS AND FINISHED PRODUCT STORAGE

GROUND WELLS RUNNING: #1 _____   #2 _____

FINISHED PRODUCT:

1.0 MG STORAGE LEVEL _____ FT.   .2 MG ELEV STORAGE LEVEL _____ Feet
FREE CHLORINE RESIDUAL _____ Mg/L   FREE CHLORINE RESIDUAL _____ Mg/L
FLUORIDE RESIDUAL _____ Mg/L   FLUORIDE RESIDUAL _____ Mg/L

Courtesy of Dare County, N.C.

Figure 4-2   Example of an operating log *(continued)*

Conductivity. A conductivity meter measures the charged, dissolved substances (generally inorganic salts) in the water, not the uncharged substances, such as organics or silica. Measuring the conductivity of feedwater is necessary to track changes in the dissolved substance levels of feedwater or pretreated feedwater and to perform the monitoring calculations discussed later. Because of its relative ease of measurement, conductivity is often used as a surrogate measure of TDS. For a particular water, a constant relationship between conductivity and TDS can be established. Depending on the particular water, the ratio of TDS to conductivity is in the 0.5 to 0.75 range. Generally, the TDS:conductivity ratio tends to be greater at higher TDS values. In the absence of site-specific data, the TDS can be estimated in mg/L by multiplying the conductivity in μS/cm or μmhos/cm by 0.6.

Saturation level. The concentration at which any scaling compound in the RO/NF concentrate reaches saturation must be determined because a value in excess of the compound's saturation point leads to inorganic scaling. The saturation level of each dissolved constituent depends on several factors, including concentration, pH, temperature, and ionic strength (a measure of the combined dissolved substances and their charges).

An *antiscalant* (also known as a *scale inhibitor*) can raise the concentration at which compounds precipitate or scale. An optimal dosage of antiscalant will inhibit scaling, but overdosing can result in organic fouling of the membrane and increased operating costs due to the expense of the antiscalant chemical itself. When an antiscalant is used, the RO/NF system should be flushed promptly on shutdown to prevent post-shutdown precipitation. This is because an antiscalant does not prevent precipitation from occurring; it only delays the chemical reactions that result in precipitation and scaling.

The most common scaling compounds, sometimes called *sparingly soluble salts*, are calcium sulfate, calcium carbonate, barium sulfate, strontium sulfate, and calcium fluoride. Silica is not a salt, but it can also precipitate, limiting RO operations. Generally, operators monitor the concentration of these and other major ions, such as sodium and chloride, in the feedwater. While hand calculations can be applied to determine the limiting scalants for a given system and the maximum recovery without causing scaling, these calculations are relatively complex. Thus, it is common to use computer models provided by the RO/NF membrane manufacturer or the antiscalant supplier.

Acid is frequently added to the feedwater to help control calcium carbonate scaling. In most cases, sulfuric acid (H_2SO_4) is used, but some plants use hydrochloric acid (HCl) to avoid adding more sulfate to the water, because the limiting scalant may be sulfate-based. However, switching from sulfuric to hydrochloric acid at a existing facility may be difficult if the design did not account for that option, because hydrochloric acid requires the use of more corrosion-resistant materials of construction, which are also more expensive. Proprietary antiscalants (such as polyphosphonates or polyacrylates) are added to the RO/NF feedwater, generally upstream of the cartridge filter or static mixer, to inhibit scaling by calcium carbonate and the other sparingly soluble salts in the RO/NF system.

In some cases, the operator must lower the recovery to prevent scaling. At lower recovery, the concentration in the concentrate is reduced; therefore, there is less risk of scaling. However, this method of scale control produces a greater volume of concentrate wastewater that must be disposed.

Because of the variability of surface waters, feedwater from such sources should be tested as frequently as is practical for the first year or two of operation until the seasonal variability is well characterized. For groundwater, testing less frequently may be sufficient.

Membrane System

Several membrane system parameters, including flows, pressures, and temperature, must be monitored to ensure the system is working properly.

Flow.   Monitoring flow rates is essential for a well-operated RO/NF system. If flow readings are incorrect, the system may be damaged by accidentally operating at excessive recovery or flux, which can result in excessive fouling/scaling. Flowmeters should be calibrated or verified annually according to the manufacturer's specifications. At some plants, a periodic check can be made by applying a mass balance. The total flow rate of water supplied to the plant should equal the flow rate of water leaving the plant, including finished water and concentrate. Properly calibrated flowmeters should result in a less than one percent difference in flow measurements.

The reference system shown in Figure 4-3 is the basis for the sample calculations and related discussion in this chapter. Although individual RO/NF system parameters may vary from this reference system, the example in the figure will help to illustrate the general concepts.

Example 1.   If measured Q_f = 100 gpm, the measured Q_p = 75 gpm, and measured Q_c = 20 gpm, then:

$$Qf = Qp + Qc \qquad \text{(Eq 4-1)}$$

Where:

Q_f = feed flow, gpm

Q_p = permeate flow, gpm

Q_c = concentrate flow, gpm

100 gpm = 75 gpm + 20 gpm

100 gpm = 95 gpm (The values do not match; therefore, flowmeter calibration is needed.)

The recovery is the ratio of the permeate flow rate to the feed flow rate, as shown in the following equation. Frequently, recovery is expressed as a percent.

$$R = \frac{Q_p}{Q_f} \qquad \text{(Eq 4-2)}$$

Where:

R = recovery

The term *concentration factor (CF)* is frequently used to describe the ratio of the concentrations in the concentrate to the feed. If one assumes a very low concentration in the permeate, then the following equation can be used to approximate the *CF*.

$$CF = \frac{Q_f}{Q_c} \qquad \text{(Eq 4-3)}$$

Where:

CF = concentration factor, dimensionless

Example 2.   For flow values of Q_f = 100 gpm and Q_c = 25 gpm, the concentration factor is found as follows:

$$CF = \frac{100\,\text{gpm}}{25\,\text{gpm}} = 4 \qquad \text{(Eq 4-4)}$$

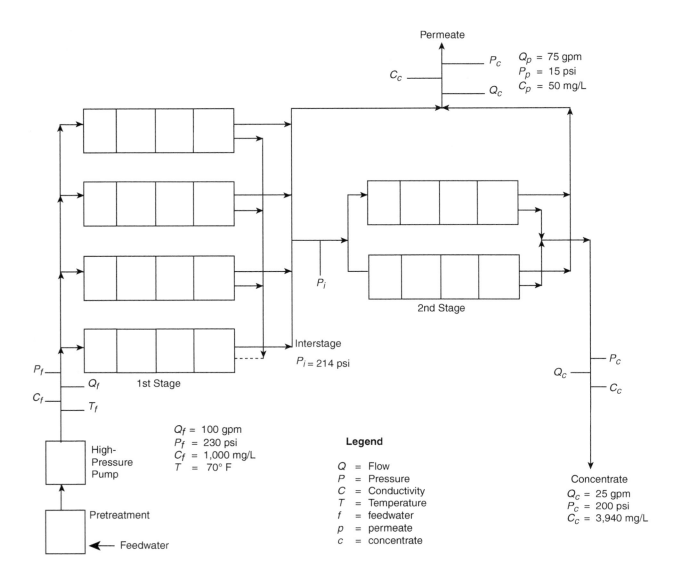

Permeate

Q_p = 75 gpm
P_p = 15 psi
C_p = 50 mg/L

Q_f = 100 gpm
P_f = 230 psi
C_f = 1,000 mg/L
T = 70° F

Interstage
P_i = 214 psi

Legend

Q = Flow
P = Pressure
C = Conductivity
T = Temperature
f = feedwater
p = permeate
c = concentrate

Concentrate
Q_c = 25 gpm
P_c = 200 psi
C_c = 3,940 mg/L

Figure 4-3 RO or NF process flow diagram, including reference values used in sample calculations

This calculation indicates that the concentration factor is 4. Because most of the dissolved substances and all of the suspended substances that were in 100 gpm of feedwater are now in 25 gpm of concentrate, they are about four times more concentrated in the concentrate stream than in the feed. If a decision is made to increase or decrease recovery, the concentration factor will change.

Example 3. If the feedwater flow is 100 gpm and the permeate flow is increased from 75 gpm to 80 gpm (i.e., an increase in recovery from 75 percent to 80 percent), the concentrate flow will correspondingly decrease from 25 gpm to 20 gpm. The new concentration factor will be about 5.

In this example, increasing the permeate production 5 gpm causes salts to be concentrated by a factor of five instead of four. Note that the design value in Figure

4-3 (Q_p= 75 gpm) has been exceeded. Because increasing the concentration factor can lead to scaling problems, the impact should be carefully considered based on accurate data and related calculations before making significant changes to operations.

Pressure. Two pressures are critical to monitor: feedwater pressure (P_f) and pressure drop or differential pressure (ΔP) across each membrane stage. The pressure drop from feed to concentrate is a measure of the flow resistance through the membrane system. After start-up (generally after two days of operation), the pressure drop across each stage of the system should be measured to determine the resistance to flow in the new system while the membrane elements are clean. An increase in the pressure drop (given the same feedwater temperature and flow rates) indicates an increased resistance to flow caused by fouling, scaling, or plugging of the flow channel. The pressure drop is simply the feed pressure minus the concentrate pressure:

$$\Delta P_{fc} = P_f - P_c \qquad \text{(Eq 4-5)}$$

Where:

ΔP_{fc} = differential pressure drop from feed to concentrate, psid
P_f = feed pressure, psig
P_c = concentrate pressure, psig

Example 4. For the reference system in Figure 4-3, the pressure drop across all stages is:

$$\Delta P_{fc} = P_f - P_c \qquad \text{(Eq 4-6)}$$

= 230 psig – 200 psig
= 30 psid

The pressure drop across the first stage is:

$$\Delta P_1 \quad = 230 \text{ psig} - 214 \text{ psig}$$
$$= 16 \text{ psid} \qquad \text{(Eq 4-7)}$$

The pressure drop across the second stage is:

$$\Delta P_2 = 214 \text{ psig} - 200 \text{ psig}$$
$$= 14 \text{ psid} \qquad \text{(Eq 4-8)}$$

In addition to the pressure drop across the membranes, the feedwater pressure is also an important parameter. If the feedwater pressure has to be increased over time to yield the same permeate flow rate, assuming all other operating conditions remain constant (e.g., temperature, concentration, and recovery), it is an indication that fouling or scaling have occurred. In such cases, the membrane elements may need to be chemically cleaned.

Temperature. Temperature is a very important parameter as water viscosity can significantly impact the driving pressures required to transport water through the membrane. Therefore, the operating data have to be normalized for temperature to fully understand how well the system is performing. As the temperature of water decreases, its viscosity increases. Therefore, at lower temperatures, an RO/NF system requires more pressure to produce the same permeate flow rate, assuming other operating conditions remain constant. Related calculations are summarized later in this chapter.

Membrane Performance

When membrane performance is observed to be worse than the baseline results, it is likely that scaling, fouling, chemical degradation, or some other membrane damage has occurred. Three types of performance parameters should be continually monitored: percent salt passage (SP) or salt rejection (SR), normalized permeate flow or normalized driving pressure, and pressure drop. Most membrane manufacturers supply software programs for monitoring membrane performance and their use is highly recommended. The equations in this section are simplified versions of the more detailed and precise equations used in such proprietary software programs. However, it is beneficial if the operators also conduct simple hand calculations to periodically check the automated data and control systems and ensure their understanding of operations.

Percent salt rejection.   Each membrane has the ability to reject a certain percentage of salts found in feedwater. Most RO membranes can reject 95 to 99.5 percent of feedwater salts. Many NF membranes reject more than 75 percent of feedwater TDS, while others are intended to reject only 10 percent. Each system operator needs to understand the details and design basis of the site-specific equipment to accurately assess the operating performance. The percentage of SR is calculated as follows:

$$SR = \left(\frac{C_f - C_p}{C_f}\right) \times 100 \qquad \text{(Eq 4-9)}$$

Where:

$SR =$ salt rejection, percent
$C_f =$ feed concentration, mg/L
$C_p =$ permeate concentration, mg/L

Example 5.   For the reference system in Figure 4-3, the feed salt concentration is 1,000 mg/L and the permeate salt concentration is 50 mg/L. Thus, the SR is 95 percent.

$$SR = \left(\frac{1,000 \text{ mg/L} - 50 \text{ mg/L}}{1,000 \text{ mg/L}}\right) = 95\% \qquad \text{(Eq 4-10)}$$

Percent salt passage. SP is a more sensitive variable and, therefore, is a very useful tool to help the operator monitor membrane performance. The percent SP is equal to 100 minus the SR. It is important to note that a decrease in salt rejection from 98 to 96 percent could seem like a small difference; however, this would result in roughly a doubling of the salt passage from 2 to 4 percent. This would also result in doubling the permeate TDS concentration. An increase in SP may indicate that there are O-ring leaks (possibly due to damaged O-rings), a scaling or fouling layer may have formed on the membrane causing a localized high concentration right at the membrane surface, or that the membrane may have become damaged (e.g., via hydrolysis; chemical degradation; tears, cuts, or holes; or glue line leaks that could be caused by excessive feed–concentrate pressure drop). Based on typical operating experiences, the most likely cause is damaged O-rings, so damaged O-rings/seals should be considered early in the troubleshooting evaluation.

SP is calculated as follows:

$$SP = \left(\frac{Cp}{Cf}\right) \times 100 \qquad \text{(Eq 4-11)}$$

$$= \left(\frac{50 \text{ mg/L}}{1,000 \text{ mg/L}}\right) \times 100 = 5\%$$

Where:

SP = salt passage, percent

Normalized permeate flow. When an RO/NF system is new, a certain permeate flow rate will be produced given the start-up temperature, feedwater pressure, pressure drop, recovery, and feedwater salt concentration. Subsequently, if less permeate is produced at the same operating conditions, scaling, fouling, or plugging have probably occurred. If the normalized permeate flow rate (NPF) is significantly lower, chemical cleaning is advised. Many manufacturers define a significant decline as 10 or 15 percent, when compared to the 24- or 48-hr baseline value. While manufacturer-supplied computer models are applied to conduct these calculations, NPF can be approximated by the following equation:

$$NPF = Q_p \times \text{TCF}_{77} \times \left(\frac{NDP_{\text{initial}}}{NDP_{\text{today}}}\right)(\text{MC}) \qquad \text{(Eq 4-12)}$$

Where:

NPF = normalized permeate flow, gpm

Q_p = permeate flow measured at ambient temperature, gpm

TCF_{77} = temperature correction factor (TCF) to normalize to operation at 77°F (25°C)

NDP_{initial} = net driving pressure during initial operation (i.e., typically based on readings taken during the first 24 to 48 hr of operation), psig

NDP_{today} = net driving pressure when Q_p was measured, psig

MC = membrane compaction factor or aging factor; for most modern membrane manufacturers consider MC = 1

Note that TCF values are provided by the membrane manufacturer in the form of tables or equations.

NPF or an analogous variable must be monitored as it tracks the status of the membrane system and determines when the system needs to be chemically cleaned. Alternative variables that might be applied by RO/NF specialists or monitoring programs include normalized permeability, which is sometimes called *normalized specific flux*. This is the permeate flux divided by the NDP and normalized to a reference temperature and the initial baseline NDP. It is essentially the NPF divided by the active membrane area. Typical units of measurement are gfd/psig in the United States or Lmh/bar(g) in other countries.

Net driving pressure. NDP is the pressure available to force water through the membrane; it is equal to the average pressure on the feed–concentrate side of the membrane minus the permeate backpressure and minus the differential osmotic pressure across the membrane. Osmotic pressure is a function of the concentration and mixture of ions in the water. A rule of thumb is that for every 100 mg/L of TDS, there is about 1 psi of osmotic pressure. This method of approximation is more accurate with brackish water than with seawater desalination plants. Therefore, multiplying the TDS concentration by 0.01 provides an estimate of the osmotic pressure. The average NAP may be expressed as:

$$NDP = P_{fc\ avg} - P_p - P_{osm} \qquad \text{(Eq 4-13)}$$

Where:

NDP =   average NDP, psig
$P_{fc\ avg}$ =   average feed–concentrate pressure, psig

    $= \dfrac{P_f + P_c}{2}$

P_f =   feed pressure, psig
P_c =   concentrate pressure, psig
P_p =   permeate pressure, psig
P_{osm} =   osmotic pressure, psig

    $\sim$ approximately $= \dfrac{C_f + C_c}{2} \times (0.01)$

C_f =   feed concentration of TDS, mg/L
C_c =   concentrate concentration of TDS, mg/L

Note that the osmotic pressure of the permeate stream is often ignored in simplified hand calculations, because it is relatively low in comparison to the average value on the feed–concentrate side of the membrane.

Example 6.   For the reference setup in Figure 4-3, NDP may be determined as follows:

$$P_{fc\ avg} = \frac{P_f + P_c}{2} = \frac{230\ \text{psig} + 200\ \text{psig}}{2} = 215\ \text{psig} \qquad \text{(Eq 4-14)}$$

$$P_{osm} \sim \left(\frac{C_f + C_c}{2}\right) \times 0.01$$

$$= \frac{1{,}000\ \text{mg/L} + 3{,}940\ \text{mg/L}}{2} \times 0.01$$

$$= 24.7\ \text{psig}$$

$$NDP = P_{fc\ avg} - P_p - P_{osm}$$

$$= 215\ \text{psig} - 15\ \text{psig} - 24.7\ \text{psig}$$

$$= 175\ \text{psig}$$

Table 4-4   Typical TCF$_{77}$ values

Temperature		TCF$_{77}$
°F	°C	
100	37.8	0.69
95	35.0	0.74
90	32.2	0.81
85	29.4	0.88
80	26.7	0.95
75	23.9	1.03
70	21.1	1.12
65	18.3	1.22
60	15.6	1.32
55	12.8	1.44
50	10.0	1.56
45	7.2	1.69
40	4.4	1.84
35	1.7	1.99

NOTE: Some manufacturers use a different equation or table for TCF values, but these values will provide a reasonable approximation in the absence of specific data. Some manufacturers and researchers use a TCF that is the inverse, in which case the equations need to be modified accordingly.

Temperature correction factors.   Membrane manufacturers supply TCFs to allow normalization at a reference temperature, generally to 77°F (25°C). Note that some manufacturers use a TCF that is the inverse of the type presented in this example (i.e., equal to 1/TCF discussed here). The TCF$_{77}$ in Eq 4-15 is a ratio of permeate flow at 77°F (25°C) divided by the permeate flow that would be produced at the ambient temperature, T, assuming an ideal, nonfouling feedwater. If the membrane manufacturer has not provided TCF values, the values in Table 4-4 or the related general equation can be applied.

Example 7.   For the reference system, compare NPF for the initial operating conditions to results three months later. Base the initial NPF on Q_p = 75 gpm, *NDP* = 175 psig, and temperature = 70°F. For the NPF after three months, assume Q_p = 75 gpm, *NDP* = 206 psig, and temperature = 60°F. Assume MC = 1.0.

(Eq 4-15)

$$NPF_{initial} = Q_p \times TCF_{77} \times \left(\frac{NDP_{initial}}{NDP_{today}}\right)$$

$$TCF_{77} \sim \frac{1}{1.03^{(T-25)}}$$

$$(TCF_{77})_{initial} = \frac{1}{1.03^{(21.1-25)}} = \frac{1}{0.89} = 1.12$$

$$NPF_{initial} = 75 \text{ gpm} \times 1.12 \times \left(\frac{175 \text{ psig}}{206 \text{ psig}}\right) = 84 \text{ gpm}$$

$$(TCF_{77})_{3 \text{ month}} = \frac{1}{1.03^{(15.6-25)}} = \frac{1}{0.76} = 1.32$$

$$NPF_{3 \text{ month}} = 75 \text{ gpm} \times 1.32 \times \left(\frac{175 \text{ psig}}{206 \text{ psig}}\right) = 84 \text{ gpm}$$

Conclusion: NPF was the same after three months, even though the *NDP* was higher. The increased operating pressure was needed because the water temperature was lower.

An NPF calculation should be determined daily and graphed daily or weekly. Each subsequent NPF measurement should be compared to the NPF at start-up. When the NPF drops 10 to 15 percent relative to initial start-up values (or as advised by the manufacturer), the system should be chemically cleaned.

Pressure drop. The pressure will decrease as the water flows through each membrane element and associated piping. The pressure drop value varies with flow rate (increased flow results in an increased pressure drop) and inversely with temperature (increased temperature results in a decreased pressure drop). An increase in the pressure drop at the same operating conditions (temperature, flow rate, and recovery) indicates a greater resistance to flow than demonstrated by new, clean membrane elements. This indicates fouling by particulate matter, scaling by dissolved substances that have precipitated, or plugging by deposition of debris. An increase in the feed–concentrate pressure drop across any stage or array in excess of the values set by the membrane manufacturer indicates a need for chemical cleaning. Many manufacturers recommend cleaning if the pressure drop across a stage increases by 10 to 15 percent over the baseline values. Depending on the application, some facilities base the decision to clean on a greater increase in pressure drop, such as 25 percent. An element may be damaged if the pressure drop across a 40-in.-long element exceeds 10 psid. Thus, the pressure drop is an important parameter to monitor.

BIOLOGICAL MONITORING

Fouling of noncellulosic (e.g., polyamide thin film) RO/NF membrane systems by bacteria is possible because the currently available noncellulosic membranes do not tolerate oxidizing disinfectants, such as chlorine. Bacterial growth is minimized by operating the system at design flow rates and by maintaining proper pretreatment conditions. The shear force imparted by the feedwater flow of an operating system helps to limit bacterial growth. When a system is shut down, however, bacterial formation may increase. Within 24 to 48 hr of nonoperation, bacteria can multiply and produce extracellular substances (such as polysaccharides) that can adhere to the membrane itself.

If a RO/NF unit must be shut down, it should be flushed with permeate or feedwater to limit bacterial growth. Manufacturers typically recommend daily flushing during a shutdown or storage of the membranes in a special solution, such as glycerin–sodium bisulfite solution. Informally, these are called *pickling* solutions.

It should be noted that RO/NF membranes must be kept moist after the initial wetting. If allowed to dry out, the membrane elements may become permanently damaged. If biological growth occurs during a shutdown, the system may need to be chemically cleaned before commencing operations.

Bacteria are quantified by several methods, including the standard plate count, field cassette, direct count (via electron microscopy and epifluorescence), and most commonly, HPC. A significant increase in bacteria exiting RO/NF pressure vessels indicates excessive growth in the system, requiring chemical cleaning.

Bacterial layers cause significant increases in resistance to flow. When biofouling occurs, the pressure drop across the system will rise and NPF will be decreased. The need for chemical cleaning may be determined by monitoring pressure drop, NPF, and bacterial counts.

CHEMICAL CLEANING

If an RO/NF system becomes fouled or scaled, the deposited material must be removed by chemical cleaning with a CIP system. Ideally, a well-operated membrane unit would never require cleaning. In this ideal system, the pretreatment would always remove fouling material and the membranes would be operated at sufficiently low flux and recovery to avoid problems. However, in real systems, this is not generally the case due to cost considerations or other factors. Therefore, it is often most cost-effective to provide cleaning chemicals for periodic cleaning. In comparison, more conservative pretreatment and/or RO/NF membrane system designs must be balanced so that cleanings are conducted at an acceptable frequency.

An operator needs to select the CIP mode based on evaluation of the operating data. The main parameters that may indicate a need to clean are declines in NPF or SR and/or increases in NDP, feed–concentrate pressure drop, or SP. Chemical cleaning is intended to accomplish the following:

- Dissolve and remove inorganic scales
- Dislodge and remove particulate material
- Break down and remove microbial material

Note that general guidelines, including discussion of typical cleaning agents, are presented in this section. However, any cleaning practice should be verified with the membrane manufacturer. Some of the cleaning methods discussed here could irreversibly damage some membrane systems.

Figure 4-4 illustrates a typical cleaning system for an RO/NF unit. Chemicals used for cleaning must be compatible with the membranes and the construction materials. The mix tank should be sized for sufficient detention time. Typically, a cover, exhaust fan, heater, mixer or recirculation loop, temperature indicator, and pH indicator are provided. Some CIP systems include a cartridge or bag filter to capture solids and particulates released during cleaning, because the cleaning solution is recirculated. Cleaning can be facilitated by a soak period alternated with a high recirculation rate and minimal permeation rates to remove loosened material. Elevated temperature and pH extremes are applied, but within the limits of the

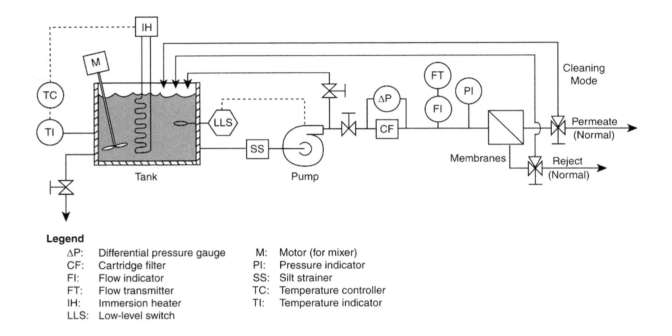

Legend

ΔP:	Differential pressure gauge	M:	Motor (for mixer)
CF:	Cartridge filter	PI:	Pressure indicator
FI:	Flow indicator	SS:	Silt strainer
FT:	Flow transmitter	TC:	Temperature controller
IH:	Immersion heater	TI:	Temperature indicator
LLS:	Low-level switch		

Figure 4-4 Cleaning system flow diagram

given membrane. For example, some will allow cleaning at up to 113°F (45°C) and a pH of 12; however, other membranes only allow cleaning at up to 104°F (40°C) and a pH of 10.5. The limits of each specific system should be verified, noting that some membranes may be damaged if exposed to both the maximum temperature and extreme pH at the same time.

Membrane manufacturers recommend certain cleaners, and membrane chemical cleaning vendors sell proprietary chemical cleaners. Only those chemicals that have been approved in writing by the membrane manufacturer should be used, otherwise the membranes may be damaged and the warranty may be voided. Table 4-5 summarizes typical cleaning chemicals for different types of problems.

The procedures for chemically cleaning RO/NF membrane systems are primarily variations on the following procedure:

1. Mix and heat the cleaning solution to desired parameters. It is best to make up cleaning solutions from the cleanest available water, which is generally permeate water. If the membranes are sensitive to oxidants, it should be verified that there is no chlorine present in the make-up water.

2. Circulate the cleaning solution through the RO/NF membranes for 30 to 60 min, discharging the first 10 percent to waste.

Table 4-5   Chemical cleaning approaches for different problems

Problem	Typical pH	Typical Cleaning Agents
Inorganic scale	Low: • With most acids pH 2 or 1, depending on membrane • With citric acid, about pH 3	• Citric acid • Hydrochloric acid • Phosphoric acid • Sulfamic acid NOTE: Not sulfuric acid
Silt and particulate matter	High: pH 10.5 to 12, depending on membrane	Caustic (NaOH) with • Sodium dodecylsulfate
Organic fouling and biofouling	High: pH 10.5 to 12, depending on membrane	Caustic (NaOH) with • Sodium dodecylsulfate or • Sodium ethlylene diamine tetraacetic acid (EDTA) or • Sodium triphosphate and/or trisodium phosphate
Iron complexed with organic material	pH 4 to 4.5	Ammoniated citric acid, typically ~ 3–4% citric, by wt, adjusted to pH with ammonia
Silica	N/A*	Ammonium bifluoride NOTE: Silica is inert and can be impossible to clean. The typical cleaning agent (ammonium bifluoride) is difficult to handle, and so it may be more cost effective to replace the elements if none of the standard cleaning agents listed above are successful and if silica scale is the problem.

NOTE: No chemical or cleaning method should be used unless approved in writing by the membrane and system manufacturer. The wrong cleaning method can cause irreversible damage.
*N/A = Not applicable.

3. Allow the system to soak for 1 to 12 hr.

4. After soaking, pump cleaning solution through the system at high velocity (at least 40 gpm per 8-in. vessel in parallel) for about 30 to 60 min.

5. Flush out by discharging the permeate and concentrate to waste.

6. The system should be rinsed with permeate after each cleaning step.

7. Return the system to service.

Each stage is generally cleaned separately. Performing multiple cleanings with the same cleaner or alternating among different cleaners is sometimes necessary to thoroughly clean the system. The system is clean when the pressure drop and the NPF have returned to the projected values.

Failure to clean at an early stage may lead to irreversible fouling or scaling. Cleaning is more likely to be effective if conducted sooner rather than later. It should be noted that cleaning is not an exact science, and that some trial-and-error may be necessary. Keeping good records of cleaning successes and failures is strongly advised, as is comparing notes with operators of other systems. The effectiveness of a cleaning cannot be assessed until after returning the unit to service and monitoring system performance. If the performance is still not adequate, the unit must be cleaned again. If a repeated cleaning is still ineffective, it may be advisable to alter the cleaning strategy.

MECHANICAL INTEGRITY

The performance of any RO/NF membrane system is determined by monitoring the quality and quantity of permeate produced by each train in the system. When one or more factors are outside projected values, the problem should be investigated and corrective action taken as soon as possible. If the problem is left unchecked, permeate water quality may deteriorate, and the loss in performance may become irreversible. Probing is a method of checking the mechanical integrity of the membrane.

When analysis of the system indicates high SP, a two-step investigation is recommended to locate the source of the problem—a conductivity profile to find the problem vessel and probing of that vessel to isolate the location of the problem.

Conductivity Profile

To perform a conductivity profile, an operator measures the permeate conductivity from each vessel as well as the conductivity of the feed and concentrate from each stage. An initial profile should be collected from every train in the plant after the first 24 to 48 hr of operations as part of the start-up activities to establish a baseline record. To facilitate record keeping, each vessel's reading should be recorded on a diagram or table that is arranged and labeled in the same manner as the rack assembly. A sample is shown in Figure 4-5. To help the operator monitor membrane performance, profiles should also be conducted periodically, and the data should be compared to past results, including the baseline performance. A typical frequency for profiling is every six months, but the needs of individual plants may vary. The conductivity or SP of all the vessels in the same stage should be about the same, while the conductivity in subsequent stages will be higher, because the concentration of the feedwater to those stages is higher. If one of the vessels within a given stage exhibits a higher conductivity than the others, that indicates a problem.

Probing the Vessels

If a problem with mechanical integrity is suspected, the vessels that have higher conductivity or SP may have to be probed. Alternatively, an operator may choose to replace all of the seals within a problem vessel and then recheck the conductivity before probing. Probing is a technique used to determine the relative performance of each element within a pressure vessel and to locate any element or O-ring leaks that are the source of the problem. Conductivity measurements are taken by probing the product water tube at different locations with a plastic or metal tube. To accomplish this, a plastic or metal tube that fits into the permeate line and that is approximately 5 to 6 ft longer than the pressure vessel should be chosen. Before probing begins, the distances from the permeate plug to each O-ring (i.e., at the ends of each element) and to the center of each element should be measured. The tubing should be marked so that when the probe is inserted to each mark, the operator knows where the probe is located within the vessel, as shown in Figure 4-6.

Date _____ Operator _____

Train __**A**_____

Stage 1		Stage 2	
Vessel Number	Permeate Conductivity, uS/cm	Vessel Number	Permeate Conductivity, uS/cm
A1-1		A2-1	
A1-2		A2-2	
A1-3		A3-3	
A1-4		A2-4	
A1-5		A2-5	
A1-6		A2-6	
A1-7			

Stage 3	
Vessel Number	Permeate Conductivity, uS/cm

Stage 1	
A1-8	
A1-9	
A1-10	
A1-11	
A1-12	

Stage 3	
A3-1	
A3-2	
A3-3	

NOTES:

Additional data: Conductivity, uS/cm

Combined Stage 1
Permeate

Combined Stage 2
Permeate

Combined Stage 3
Permeate

Total Permeate

1st Stage Concentrate

2nd Stage Concentrate

Final Concentrate

Feed

Courtesy of Black & Veatch

Figure 4-5   Sample conductivity profile data sheet

The permeate plug should be removed from the end cap (at the opposite end from the permeate manifold), and the tubing should be inserted through the length of the product water tube, as shown in Figure 4-7. Some plants are equipped with special valves to facilitate probing. To ensure that the permeate water from neighboring pressure vessels does not flow into the vessel being probed, a seal of some type may be required around the tubing. A rag wrapped around the probe tubing and held against the opening in the permeate port works well as a seal, provided the permeate backpressure is not too high. An improved method to minimize leaks around the probe tube applies tube fittings that are "snug", and just loose enough to allow movement through the permeate core without leaking.

To begin the probing process, the probe tubing should be pushed through to the opposite end of the pressure vessel with short oscillating motions as required to pass over the interconnectors. The end point of the probe should be moved to the first sample point. A portion of the combined permeate from this area of the pressure vessel will pass into the tubing, allowing the operator to collect a sample and measure its conductivity. This location should be held until the conductivity remains constant. This usually takes a minute or so. The conductivity reading should be recorded at the appropriate position, as shown in Figure 4-8. The tubing should then be pulled out to the next mark. Once the conductivity reading has stabilized, the second reading should be recorded. The procedure should be repeated until the vessel probe is complete.

Interpreting Probe Data

As feedwater flows through a pressure vessel from one element to the next element, it becomes more concentrated. This means that permeate water from the upstream (feedwater side) element will have a lower conductivity reading than the downstream (concentrate side) element. A six-element pressure vessel will operate at about 50 percent recovery, and the concentrate exiting the vessel will have approximately twice the conductivity of the feedwater entering the vessel. The permeate conductivity from the element farthest downstream in the pressure vessel can be expected to be approximately twice that from the element farthest upstream. As the probe position is moved from the upstream element to the downstream element, the conductivity readings should increase uniformly.

An abrupt increase in conductivity likely indicates a leak or poorly performing element. Feedwater is sealed from the permeate stream by O-rings. If an O-ring becomes out of round or unseats, some feedwater can flow into the permeate. Occasionally membrane elements are defective, become torn, or are chemically degraded, in which case feedwater or concentrate can also leak into the permeate stream. Sometimes high feed–concentrate pressure drop causes damages such as glue line leaks within an element or, in more extreme cases, telescoping.

Interpretation of the probe data collected by this technique is sometimes difficult because of the effects of dilution and the inherent variability of rejection characteristics between individual elements. However, the procedure can be very useful in detecting O-ring leaks and problems with the elements.

INSTRUMENTATION CALIBRATION _____

The performance of membrane systems is determined by monitoring pressure drop, NPF, percent SP, and other parameters. These measurements are performed with online and bench-top instruments that must be routinely calibrated. This should include verifying the accuracy of automated equipment and data recording, such as

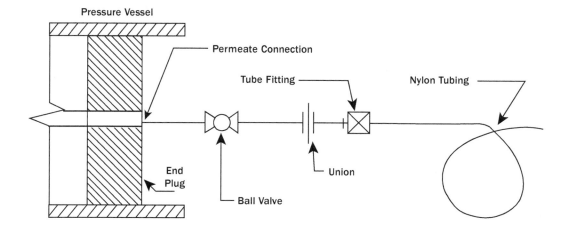

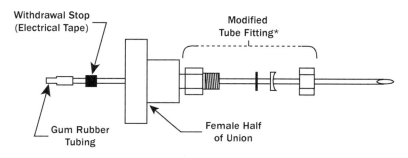

*Tube fitting modified by extending the ¼-in. bore through the body and discarding the gripper ring.

Figure 4-6   Permeate probing apparatus for a spiral-wound membrane

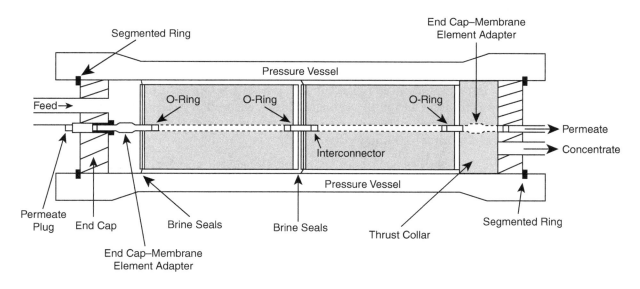

Figure 4-7   Probing a spiral-wound membrane

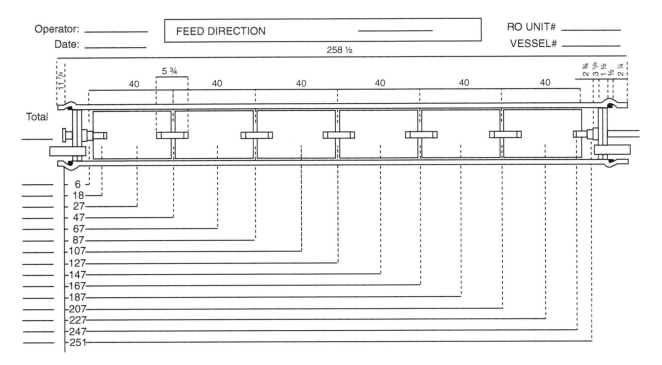

Figure 4-8 Sample pressure vessel probing sheet

valve positioning indicators, chemical feed delivery rates, and calculated data, as well as traditional instruments. Calibration should initially be conducted on the schedule recommended by each instrument manufacturer, although in some cases experience may demonstrate that some instruments require calibration more frequently than recommended.

The importance of calibration cannot be over emphasized. RO/NF systems are generally highly automated, but the automated operations are only as good as the accuracy of the instruments. Consequently, many problems can be avoided by implementing a regular calibration program.

SAFETY

Safety is a fundamental responsibility for all personnel in a WTP. Industry goals include zero accidents and total compliance with all regulatory statutes. To achieve these goals, water treatment personnel involved in membrane processes need the following training and knowledge:

- A hazard review of all operating steps with appropriate follow-up audits,

- Operating instructions, including design criteria and prints, posted where they are easily accessible to all personnel,

- Training for operations, maintenance, and supervisory staff on an ongoing basis,

- Appropriate tools and clothing,

- A thorough understanding of and compliance with Occupational Safety and Health Administration (OSHA), USEPA, and other relevant regulations, and

- A facility evacuation plan, with adequate fire protection and fire-fighting equipment.

The following sections address major safety considerations for an RO/NF plant. The information presented is not a complete listing but is intended to assist in efforts to start up and operate a WTP safely.

General Safety Precautions

General safety precautions for RO/NF plants are no different from those for conventional treatment plants. All operators should know and follow operating instructions, OSHA requirements, and environmental regulations. Proper protective equipment (e.g., gloves, safety glasses, safety shoes, hearing protection, protective clothing, and face shields) should be worn as appropriate.

Good housekeeping standards should be maintained. Floors should be clean and dry with excess material stored on shelves and away from operating equipment. Oily rags and waste paper should be properly discarded.

Fire exits should never be locked or blocked. Safety equipment, fire extinguishers, and hoses should be available and always in good working order. An evacuation plan should be prepared and personnel should practice it. The fire-fighting team must be adequately trained and their expertise routinely updated. All operating equipment safety interlocks and pressure relief devices should be checked. All rotating equipment should be shielded.

Materials heavier than the safe-weight standard established by the employer should not be lifted by hand. All work should be within individual ergonomic limitations. Eyewash stations and safety showers should be maintained and tested. Floor markings should clearly define safety areas as well as slipping and tripping hazards. Plant management should institute routine training programs to ensure that all personnel are thoroughly familiar with the operations, maintenance, environmental, and safety requirements for the facility.

Membrane Pressure Vessel Safety

Because RO/NF plants are pressure driven, the following safety standards relating to all pressure-driven water treatment processes need to be emphasized:

- Do not over-pressurize equipment, operate at too high a temperature, or modify a pressure vessel without the expressed written approval of the manufacturer. Label equipment with the appropriate operational limitations.

- Follow in detail the manufacturer's written instructions for O&M of the pressure vessel. Do not assume that one manufacturer's instructions are necessarily applicable to all such devices.

- All pressure vessels must be suitably anchored and restrained. Where possible, avoid standing in front of pressurized equipment.

- Use maximum care in handling, installing, dismantling, and maintaining pressure vessels. It is very important to be sure devices are depressurized before conducting maintenance work.

- Install proper relief and shutdown protection devices. Regularly inspect these devices and vessels for equipment integrity.

- Minimize equipment and piping vibrations, and avoid water hammer.

Handling Chemicals

A number of chemicals are handled in a RO/NF plant, and these must all be used safely to avoid injury.

Material safety data sheets (MSDS) for each chemical in the plant should be properly displayed and made available to employees.

The manufacturer's instructions for chemical use should be followed at all times, and all containers and piping should be labeled. Unauthorized chemicals should never be used. Chemical certification from the equipment and membrane suppliers should be obtained if there are any concerns about material compatibility. Equipment in contact with chemicals must be properly vented, decontaminated, and flushed, as necessary. All chemical use should be conducted conforming to safety and environmental regulations.

It is important to follow safe and environmentally sound procedures for chemical disposal, as well. Chemical suppliers should always be consulted for particular disposal recommendations. Suitable protective equipment should be worn when handling chemicals, particularly for acids and caustics. Emergency and containment procedures for fires, spills, and hazardous off-gases should be determined and practiced.

Treatment personnel may consider dedicating specific equipment for individual chemicals. Chemicals should not be mixed unless the chemistry is thoroughly known. Storage areas must be adequately vented safely away from the membrane plant.

Pumps, Piping, and Instrumentation

Equipment and associated instrumentation in an RO/NF plant include such items as filters, pumps, tanks, computers, compressors, valves, pipes, and racks. All must be given special consideration for safe and proper functioning. The following are guidelines to achieve these goals:

- Always follow the manufacturer's recommendations for O&M. Written instructions should be readily available for all to use.

- Label all equipment and piping.

- Never exceed the specified pressure and temperature limits.

- Routinely inspect equipment for defects, corrosion, and other signs of abnormal wear.

- Anchor and restrain all equipment, and guard rotating parts.

- Never violate electrical safety and lockout practices, interlocks, or pressure relief devices. Inspect all instrumentation and electrical connections at least annually, particularly for grounding.

- Know the design criteria, functions, and limitations of all processing steps, equipment, and instrumentation.

- Provide adequate space around equipment for routine maintenance and, if necessary, for its removal.

- Minimize equipment and piping vibrations.

- Piping must be resistant to corrosion and properly designed for actual system pressures.

Appendix **A**

SI Equivalent Units Conversion Tables

	To Convert		
	Customary Units	to SI Units	Multiply by
Water Treatment			
Plant capacity	gpd	m^3/d	3.785×10^{-3}
		or ML/d	3.785×10^{-6}
Plant capacity	mgd	m^3/d	3.785×10^3
		or ML/d	3.785
Source water flow	gpm	m^3/sec	6.308×10^{-5}
		or L/sec	6.308×10^{-2}
Source water flow	ft^3/min	m^3/sec	4.720×10^{-4}
		or L/sec	4.720×10^{-1}
Source water temperature	°F	°C	(°F − 32) × 5/9
Chemical dosage	ppm	mg/L	1
Chemical feed rate	lb/d	kg/d	4.536×10^{-1}
Chemical feed rate	gal/h	L/h	3.785
		or ML/sec	1.051
Gas feeder supply pressure	psi	kPa	6.9848
Gas feeder differential pressure	in. H_2O	kPa	2.488×10^{-1}
Gas feeder vacuum pressure	in. Hg	kPa	3.377
Displacement velocity	ft/sec	m/sec	3.048×10^{-1}
Power	hp	Watt	746
Settling rate	ft/h	m/h	3.048×10^{-1}
Weir overflow rate	gal/ft/d	L/m/sec	3.449×10^{-3}
Filter head loss	ft	kPa	2.989
		or m	3.048×10^{-1}
Filtration rate	gpm/ft^2	m/h	2.444
		or $m^3/m^2/h$	2.444
Filter backwash rate	gpm/ft^2	$L/m^2/sec$	6.789×10^{-1}

Continued on next page.

	Customary Units		to SI Units	Multiply by
			To Convert	

Water Distribution

	Customary Units		to SI Units	Multiply by
Area	mi^2		km^2	2.590
		or	m^2	2.590×10^6
Area	acre		ha	4.047×10^{-1}
Head loss	ft		kPa	2.989
		or	m	3.048×10^{-1}
Hydrant spacing	ft		m	3.048×10^{-1}
Hydraulic gradient	ft/1,000 ft		mm/m	1
		or	m/km	1
Level gauging	ft		m	3.048×10^{-1}
Pipe cross section	in.^{2}		mm^2	6.452×10^2
Pipe diameter	in.		mm	2.540×10
Pipe flow velocity	ft/sec		m/sec	3.048×10^{-1}
Pipe length	ft		m	3.048×10^{-1}
Pressure	psi		kPa	6.895
Pump capacity	gpm		m^3/sec	6.308×10^{-5}
		or	L/sec	6.308×10^{-2}
Pump capacity	ft^3/min		m^3/sec	4.720×10^{-4}
		or	L/sec	4.720×10^{-1}
Residual chlorine	ppm		mg/L	1
Storage elevation	ft		m	3.048×10^{-1}
Storage volume	gal		m^3	3.785×10^{-3}
		or	ML	3.785×10^{-6}
Storage volume	ft^3		m^3	2.832×10^{-2}
		or	ML	2.832×10^{-5}
Water consumption	gal		m^3	3.785×10^{-3}
		or	L	3.785
		or	ML	3.785×10^{-6}
Water consumption	ft^3		m^3	2.832×10^{-2}
		or	ML	2.832×10^{-5}
Metering	gph		m^3/h	3.785×10^{-3}
Metering	ft^3/h		m^3/h	2.832×10^{-2}

General Units for Water and Solute Mass Transfer Coefficients

General equation for water flux: $F_w = K_w P$

Where:

F_w = water flux
K_w = water mass transfer coefficient
P = pressure

Customary Units	SI Units
F_w : 1 gpd/ft^2 = 0.1337 ft/d	= 0.0407 m/d
K_w : 1 gpd/ft^2/psi = 0.0578/day^{-1}	= 0.0578/day^{-1}

General equation for solute flux: $F_s = K_s C$

Where:

F_s = solute flux
K_s = mass transfer coefficient
C = solute concentration

Customary Units	SI Units
F_s : 1 lb/ft^2/d = 0.016 ft/d	= 4.893 kg/m^2/d
K_s : 1 lb − mg/ft^2/d/L = 16.031 ft/d	= 4,886 m/d

Appendix **B**

Equations

The full derivation of these equations is beyond the scope of this manual. Various manufacturers and design engineering firms use computer programs based on these and similar equations to define reverse osmosis (RO) and nanofiltration (NF) system quality and quantity. Chapter 2 of this manual provides an overview of the design considerations arising from the use of equations presented in that chapter and in this appendix.

Converting to Site-Specific Conditions

Equations B-1 and B-2 are of great practical importance in the design and construction of RO devices and plants because they may be used to convert from a manufacturer's standard conditions (SC) to site-specific operating conditions (OC).

RO product flow can be derived as shown in Eq B-1 (which is a minor variation of Eq 1-4):

$$Q_p = K_w A(\Delta P - \Delta \pi) \qquad \text{(Eq B-1)}$$

Where:

$$
\begin{aligned}
A &= \text{membrane surface area} \\
Q_p &= \text{permeate flow} \\
K_w &= \text{mass transfer coefficient (defined by membrane supplier)} \\
\Delta P &= \text{transmembrane pressure differential or gradient} \\
\Delta \pi &= \text{osmotic pressure differential or gradient of the aqueous solution} \\
&\quad \text{across the membrane}
\end{aligned}
$$

This equation shows that flow through the membrane is directly proportional to the applied pressure differential across the membrane minus the osmotic pressure differential.

The SP Q_s through the membrane is similarly derived. Salt flow is given by Eq B-2 (which is similar to Eq 1-5):

$$Q_s = K_s A \Delta C \qquad \text{(B-2)}$$

Where:

Q_s =   site-specific salt flow
K_s =   solute flow constant defined by membrane supplier
ΔC =   concentration differential across the membrane

This equation states that salt flow is proportional only to the concentration differential across the membrane. Thus, increasing the operating pressure will not affect salt flow; it will, however, based on Eq B-1, increase the water flow. Thus, it improves product quality because of the dilution resulting from the higher product flow.

Mathematically, if the operating conditions equation is divided by the standard conditions equation, two things occur. First, the C constants are canceled, making their actual value immaterial. Second, the division permits the mathematical development of a correction factor (the ratio of the OC to the SC). Based on this technique, as well as introducing a membrane aging factor (to account for fouling, compaction, and plastic creep), Eq B-3 and Eq B-4 may be developed. Equation B-3 represents flow normalization procedures; Eq B-4 shows salt passage normalization procedures.

$$Q_p = (PCF)(TCF)(MFRC/FF)Q_i \qquad \text{(Eq B-3)}$$

$$S_p = (SPCF)(SP_i) \qquad \text{(Eq B-4)}$$

Where:

Q_p =   product water flow at operating conditions
TCF   =   temperature correction factor (generally about 3 percent per degree Celsius)
MFRC   =   membrane flux retention coefficient (generally about 0.65 to 0.85 over 3 to 5 yr)
FF   =   fouling factor (generally about 0.8 to 0.9 over 3 yr)
Q_i =   initial product water flow at standard conditions
S_p =   SP of RO or NF device at operating conditions
SPCF   =   SP correction factor (generally 0.5 to 1.5 of initial)
SP_i =   SP of RO or NF device at standard conditions
PCF   =   pressure correction factor (not easily generalized because of osmotic pressure and bundle pressure drop effects) but can be estimated as follows:

Once the flow of an individual RO or NF device has been determined at OC, it is possible to calculate how many of these modules are required for a project:

$$\text{number of modules or elements needed} = \frac{\text{project capacity}}{Q_p} \qquad \text{(Eq B-5)}$$

$$\text{number of pressure vessels} = \frac{\text{project capacity}}{Q_p e} \qquad \text{(Eq B-6)}$$

Where:

e =   number of modules or elements in a pressure vessel

Limiting Salt Calculation

This section provides equations for determining limiting salts and acid additions, and examples for their use.

$$A_nB_m = nA^{+p} + mB^{-q} \qquad \text{(Eq B-7)}$$

$$K_{sp} = [A^{+p}]^n[B^{-q}]^m \qquad \text{(Eq B-8)}$$

Where:

A_nB_m	=	salt under consideration
A^{+p}	=	cation of formed salt, moles/L or M
B^{-q}	=	anion of formed salt
K_{sp}	=	solubility product
p	=	charge of cation
q	=	charge of anion

Determination of Recovery from the Solubility Product

$$K_{sp} = \left[(A^{+p})^n\left(\frac{1 - \text{SP}_A}{1 - R}\right)\right]\left[(B^{-q})^m\left(\frac{1 - \text{SP}_B}{1 - R}\right)\right] \qquad \text{(B-9)}$$

Where:

A^{+m}	=	feedwater concentration of cation under consideration
B^{-n}	=	feedwater concentration of anion under consideration
R	=	permeate recovery rate (expressed as decimal)
SP_A	=	passage of cation A through membrane (decimal)
SP_B	=	passage of anion B through membrane (decimal)

NOTE: SP_A and SP_B are available from membrane suppliers.

For most diffusion controlled membrane process (RO and NF) applications, SP_A and SP_B can be considered to be negligible, and the previous equation simplifies to:

$$K_{sp} = \left[\frac{A^{+p}}{(1 - R)}\right]^n\left[\frac{B^{-q}}{(1 - R)}\right]^m \qquad \text{(B-10)}$$

Example Calculations (using data from Table B-1)

Limiting salt—$CaCO_3$

$CaCO_3 \rightarrow Ca^{+2} + CO_3^{-2}$
$K_{sp} = [Ca^{+2}]\ [CO_3^{-2}] = 10^{-8.3}$
$Ca^{+2} = 8$ mg/L $= 0.0002$ moles/L $= 2 \times 10^{-4}$ M
$CO_3^{-2} = 3$ mg/L $= 0.00005$ moles/L $= 5 \times 10^{-5}$ M

thus:

$$10^{-8.3} = \left[\frac{(2 \times 10^{-4}\ \text{moles})}{X}\right]\left[\frac{(5 \times 10^{-5}\ \text{moles})}{X}\right]$$

$$X \quad = \quad 1.41$$

or

$$R \quad = \quad 1 - 1.41$$
$$R \quad = \quad -0.41$$

Table B-1 Assumed initial water quality for hypothetical system

Parameter	Concentration mg/L
Cations	
Barium	0.04
Calcium	8
Iron	0.5
Magnesium	2
Manganese	0.02
Potassium	8
Sodium	695
Strontium	2
Anions	
Bicarbonate	631
Carbonate	3
Chloride	730
Fluoride	1.1
Orthophosphate	0.7
Sulfate	79
Other	
pH	8.0*
Silicate	24

*Dimensionless value (not milligrams per liter)

This indicates that the solubility of $CaCO_3$ is already exceeded and $CaCO_3$ will precipitate in the feedwater.

Limiting salt—$SrSO_4$

$$SrSO_4 \rightarrow Sr^{+2} + SO_4^{-2}$$

$$K_{sp} = [Sr^{+2}][SO_4^{-2}] = 10^{-6.2}$$

$$Sr^{+2} = 2\ mg/L = 0.00002\ moles/L = 2 \times 10^{-5}\ moles$$

$$SO_4^{-2} = 79\ mg/L = 0.0008\ moles/L = 8 \times 10^{-4}\ moles$$

thus:

$$10^{-6.2} = \left[\frac{(2 \times 10^{-5}\ moles)}{X}\right]\left[\frac{(8 \times 10^{-4}\ moles)}{X}\right]$$

$$X = 0.16$$

or

$$R = +1 - 0.16$$
$$R = +0.84$$

This indicates that a water recovery rate of 84 percent is possible before the solubility limit of $SrSO_4$ is exceeded in the feedwater.

Acid Addition to Control Calcium Carbonate Scaling

Example:

$$\begin{aligned} Ca^{+2} &= 8 \text{ mg/L} \\ HCO_3^- &= 631 \text{ mg/L} \\ pH &= 8.0 \end{aligned}$$

Target product water recovery rate = 75%

Find the sulfuric acid (93 percent solution) dose necessary to prevent calcium carbonate scaling.

1.   Determine required feedwater pH

$$\text{For } CaCO_3 \rightarrow Ca^{+2} + CO_3^{-2} \qquad \text{(Eq B-11)}$$

$$K_{sp} = [Ca^{+2}] [CO_3^{-2}] = 10^{-8.3}$$

Where:

$$\begin{aligned} Ca^{+2} &= 8 \text{ mg/L} = 0.0002 \text{ moles/L} = 2 \times 10^{-4} \text{ moles} \\ CO_3^{-2} &= \text{Unknown, must calculate from } HCO_3^- \text{ concentration} \\ HCO_3^- &= 631 \text{ mg/L} = 0.010 \text{ moles/L} = 1 \times 10^{-2} \text{ moles} \end{aligned}$$

Given $HCO_3^- \rightarrow H^+ + CO_3^{-2}$

$$K_2 = \frac{[H^+]\left[CO_3^{-2}\right]}{\left[HCO_3^-\right]} = 10^{-10.3} \qquad \text{(Eq B-12)}$$

or

$$\text{(Eq B-13)}$$

$$CO_3^{-2} = \frac{[K_2][HCO_3^-]}{[H^+]}$$

$$CO_3^{-2} = \frac{[10^{-10.3}][0.010 \text{ moles/L}]}{[H^+]}$$

Substitute the expression for CO_3^{-2} (Eq B-13) into Eq B-7.

$$K_{sp} = \left[\frac{Ca^{+2}}{X}\right]\left[\frac{CO_3^{-2}}{X}\right]$$

$$K_{sp} = \left[\frac{2 \times 10^{-4} \text{ moles/L}}{0.25}\right]\left[\frac{(10^{-10.3})(1 \times 10^{-2} \text{ moles/L})}{(0.25H)}\right] = 10^{-8.3}$$

$$H^+ = 3.2 \times 10^{-7} \text{ moles}$$

$$pH = 6.5$$

2.   Determine sulfuric acid (93% solution) dose to achieve pH of 6.5.

$$K_1 = \frac{[H^+][HCO_3^-]}{[H_2CO_3]} = 10^{-6.3} = \frac{[10^{-6.5}]\left(\left[\dfrac{631 \text{ mg/L}}{61{,}000 \text{ mg/mole}}\right] - x\right)}{[0 + X]}$$

Where:

$X = [H^+]$ required to react with $[HCO_3^-]$

$X10^{-6.3} = 3.27 ¥ 10^{-9} - 10^{-6.5}X$

$X = 0.004 \text{ moles/L } H^+ = [0.004 \text{ moles/L}]\left[\dfrac{2EQ}{\text{mole}}\right]\left[\dfrac{49{,}000 \text{ mg}}{EQ}\right]\left[\dfrac{1}{0.93}\right] = 421$

$X = 211 \text{ mg/L of } 93\% \text{ } H_2SO_4$

Determination of Membrane System Configuration

This section uses an example to demonstrate how a membrane system configuration can be determined. The following assumptions were made for this example:

- Spiral-wound membranes (calculation methods presented are similar for hollow fine-fiber membranes except for the element surface area)

- Membrane element flux = 15 gpd/ft^2

- 4-2-1 array (first stage: four pressure vessels; second stage: two; third stage: one)

- Seven elements per pressure vessel (PV)

- Element surface area of 350 ft^2

- Recovery of 75 percent

The following calculations need to be made:

1.   Water one membrane element can produce:

$$Q_p = F_w A = \left(15\frac{\text{gpd}}{\text{ft}^2}\right)\left(350\frac{\text{ft}^2}{\text{element}}\right) = 5{,}250\frac{\text{gpd}}{\text{element}} \qquad \text{(Eq B-14)}$$

2.   Number of elements on one $4 - 2 - 1$ array:

$$\left(\frac{\text{PV}}{\text{array}}\right)\left(7\frac{\text{elements}}{\text{PV}}\right) = 49\frac{\text{elements}}{\text{array}} \qquad \text{(Eq B-15)}$$

3. Gallons per day produced per array:

$$\left(5,250\frac{gpd}{element}\right)\left(49\frac{elements}{array}\right) = 257,250\ \frac{gpd}{array} \tag{Eq B-16}$$

4. Arrays needed to supply 1 mgd (10^6 gpd):

$$(10^6 gpd)\left(\frac{1\ array}{257,250\ gpd}\right) = 3.9\ array\ (4\ arrays\ would\ be\ used) \tag{Eq B-17}$$

5. Total number of elements needed:

$$(4\ arrays)\left(49\frac{elements}{array}\right) = 196\ elements \tag{Eq B-18}$$

6. Feedwater flow in and permeate flow out of one array:

$$total\ feedwater\ flow\ rate = \frac{total\ permeate\ flow\ rate}{recovery} = \frac{1mgd}{0.75} - 1.33\ mgd \tag{Eq B-19}$$

$$flow\ in\ per\ array = \frac{1.33\ mgd}{4} = 0.33\ mgd = 231\ gpm \tag{Eq B-20}$$

$$flow\ out\ per\ array = \frac{1\ mgd}{4} = 0.25\ mgd = 174\ gpm$$

NOTE: All arrays could be assembled into one train.

Check of Configuration of Elements

Recommended recovery per element: $3\% < R_{element} < 20\%$

1. Flow into stage 1 per PV per day:

$$\left(332,500\ \frac{gal}{array\ day}\right)\left(7\frac{array}{4\ PV}\right) = 83,125\frac{gal}{4\ PV\ day}\ for\ stage\ 1 \tag{Eq B-20}$$

2. Permeate flow per element per day assuming a flux of 15 g/ft^2/d:

$$\left(350\frac{ft^2}{element}\right)\left(15\frac{gal}{ft^2/day}\right) = 5,250\ \frac{gal}{element\text{-}day} \tag{Eq B-21}$$

3. Recovery in first and last element of a PV in stage 1:

$$R_{E11} = \frac{Q_p}{Q_f} = \frac{5,250\ gal}{83,125\ gal} = 0.06\ or\ 6\% \tag{Eq B-22}$$

$$R_{E17} = \frac{Q_p}{Q_f} = \frac{5,250\ gal}{83,125\ gal - [(7-1\ elements)\ \yen\ (5,250)]\ gal} = 0.09\ or\ 9\%$$

4. Recovery in first and last element of a PV in stage 2:

Flow into a PV in stage 2 = 2[83,125 gal − 7(5,250)] = 92,750 gal

$$R_{E11} = \frac{Q_p}{Q_f} = \frac{5{,}250 \text{ gal}}{(92{,}750 \text{ gal})} = 0.06 \text{ or } 6\%$$

$$R_{E17} = \frac{Q_p}{Q_f} = \frac{5{,}250 \text{ gal}}{92{,}750 \text{ gal} - (6 \text{ ¥ } 5{,}250) \text{ gal}} = 0.09 \text{ or } 9\%$$

(Eq B-23)

5. Recovery in first and last element of a PV in stage 3:

Flow into a PV in stage 3 = 2[92,750 gal − 7(5,250)] = 112,000 gal

$$R_{E11} = \frac{Q_p}{Q_f} = \frac{5{,}250 \text{ gal}}{112{,}000 \text{ gal}} = 0.05 \text{ or } 5\%$$

$$R_{E17} = \frac{Q_p}{Q_f} = \frac{5{,}250 \text{ gal}}{112{,}000 \text{ gal} - (6 \text{ ¥ } 5{,}250) \text{ gal}} = 0.07 \text{ or } 7\%$$

(Eq B-24)

Posttreatment Equations

Alkalinity (all species in moles per liter):

$$\text{Alkalinity} \rightleftarrows 2(CO_3^{2-}) + (HCO_3^-) + (OH^-) - (H^+)$$

(Eq B-25)

Calcium carbonate precipitation:

$$CaCO_3(s) \rightleftarrows Ca^{2+} + CO_3^{2-}$$

(Eq B-26)

Solubilization of carbon dioxide gas:

$$CO_{2(g)} \rightleftarrows CO_{2(aq)}$$

(Eq B-27)

$$pK_H = 1.5$$

$$CO_{2(aq)} + H_2O \rightleftarrows H_2CO_3$$

$$pK_m = 2.8$$

Where:

$$pK_H = -\log K_1$$
$$pK_m = \text{equilibrium constant}$$

Ionization of aqueous carbonic acid:

$$H_2CO_3^- \rightleftarrows H^+ + HCO_3^{2-}$$

(Eq B-28)

$$pK_1 = 6.3$$

Ionization of bicarbonate:

$$H_2CO_3^- \rightleftarrows H^+ + HCO_3^{2-}$$

(Eq B-29)

$$pK_2 = 10.3$$

Caustic stabilization:

$$HCO_3^- + H^+ + HCO_3 \qquad \text{(Eq B-30)}$$

$$H_2CO_3 \rightarrow CO_{2(g)} + H_2O \qquad \text{(Eq B-31)}$$

Alkalinity recovery:

$$CO_{2(2)} + OH^- \rightarrow HCO_2^- \qquad \text{(Eq B-32)}$$

Elemental sulfur turbidity production (inefficient hydrogen sulfide stripping):

$$2H_2S + O_2 = 2H_2O + 2S_{(s)} \qquad \text{(Eq B-33)}$$

Hydrogen sulfide reactions with water:

$$H_2S + H_2O = H_3O^+ + HS^- \qquad \text{(Eq B-34)}$$

$$pK_1 = 7.0$$

Where:

pK_1 = ionization constant 1

and

$$HS^- + H_2O = H_3O^+ + S^{2-} \qquad \text{(Eq B-35)}$$

$$pK_2 = 14.0 \qquad \text{(Eq B-36)}$$

Where:

pK_2 = ionization constant 2

Hypochlorous acid formation:

$$Cl_2 + H_2O = HOCl + H^+ + Cl^- \qquad \text{(Eq B-37)}$$

$$K_{a,1} = \frac{[H^+][Cl^-][HOCl]}{[Cl_2]} = 4 ¥ 20^{-4} \text{ (at 77° F)}$$

Where:

$K_{a,1}$ = equilibrium constant for acid ionization

Hypochlorous acid dissociation:

$$HOCl = H^+ + OCl^- \qquad \text{(Eq B-38)}$$

$$K_{a,2} = \frac{[OCl][H^+]}{[HOCl]} = 2.7 ¥ 10^{-a} \text{ (at 68° F)}$$

Where:

$K_{a,2}$ =   equilibrium constant for acid ionization

Chlorine reactions with hydrogen sulfide:

$$H_2S + HOCl = HCl + H_2O + S_{(s)} \text{ for pH} > 3.8 \qquad \text{(Eq B-39)}$$

$$H_2S + 4HOCl = 4HCl + H_2SO_4 + S_{(s)} \text{ for pH} > 3.8 \qquad \text{(Eq B-40)}$$

pH of saturation:

$$pH_s = -\log\frac{K_2}{K_{sp}}[Ca^{2+}][Alk] \qquad \text{(Eq B-41)}$$

Where:

K_2 = H_2CO_3 second ionization constant
K_{sp} = $CaCO_3$ solubility product constant
Ca^{2+} =   calcium ion concentration, in moles/L
Alk =   alkalinity, in moles/L

Lime stabilization:

$$CO_2 + Ca(OH)_2 = CaCO_3 + H_2O \qquad \text{(Eq B-42)}$$

Calcium carbonate stabilization:

$$CO_2 + CaCO_3 + H_2O = Ca^{2+} + 2HCO_3^- \qquad \text{(Eq B-43)}$$

Caustic stabilization:

$$CO_2 + 2NaOH = 2Na^+ + CO_3^{2-} + H_2O \qquad \text{(Eq B-44)}$$

Soda ash stabilization:

$$Na_2CO_3 = 2Na^+ + CO_3^{2-} \qquad \text{(Eq B-45)}$$

Appendix **C**

Silt Density Index Procedure

The equipment required to perform the test to determine the silt density index (SDI) includes the SDI apparatus (shown schematically in Figure C-1), a 500-mL graduated cylinder, and a stopwatch. The procedure is as follows:

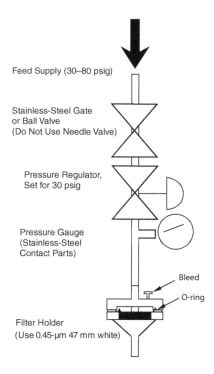

Feed Supply (30–80 psig)

Stainless-Steel Gate or Ball Valve (Do Not Use Needle Valve)

Pressure Regulator, Set for 30 psig

Pressure Gauge (Stainless-Steel Contact Parts)

Bleed

O-ring

Filter Holder (Use 0.45-μm 47 mm white)

Figure C-1   SDI apparatus

205

1. Using the apparatus shown schematically in Figure C-1, set the pressure regulator to 30 psig.

2. Flush the sample line to be sure it is free from accumulated debris that would interfere with filtration before installing the 0.45-μm membrane filter disk. Allow the water to run long enough to establish a constant temperature.

3. Open the filter holder and insert the membrane filter. Avoid handling the membrane filter with fingers. It should be handled only with dull tweezers around the edges to avoid punctures and contamination.

4. Reposition the O-ring and close the top half of the filter holder, but do not tighten the wing nuts.

5. Open the ball valve just enough to allow trapped air to bleed from the apparatus and water line. Close the ball valve and tighten the filter holder.

6. Open the ball valve, and with a stopwatch immediately begin to measure the time required to collect 500 mL of filtrate. Record this time (t_i). Allow water to continue to flow through the filter under constant pressure (30 psig).

7. After 15 min of total elapsed time, measure and record the time (t_f) required to collect another 500 mL of filtrate.

8. The SDI is calculated from the following equation:

$$\text{SDI} = \frac{100\left[1 - \left(\dfrac{t_i}{t_f}\right)\right]}{t_t} \qquad \text{(Eq C-1)}$$

Where:

t_i = time to collect the initial 500 mL of filtrate

t_f = time to collect 500 mL of filtrate after the filter has been online for a period of time, usually 15 min

t_t = total test time, usually 15 min

Appendix **D**

Langelier Saturation Index and Stiff and Davis Scaling Index

The Langelier saturation index (LSI), as modified by Larson and Buswell (1944), is defined as follows:

$$LSI = pH - pCa - pAlk - C \qquad \text{(Eq D-1)}$$

Where:

pCa	=	negative logarithm of the calcium molarity
pAlk	=	negative logarithm of the alkalinity in equivalents per liter
C	=	constant to account for the change in calcium carbonate solubility with temperature and ionic strength (Figure D-1)

Consider water that has the following attributes:

- pH of concentrate stream (by measurement), 8.5

- Calcium ion concentration, 150 mg/L

- Total alkalinity as calcium carbonate, 300 mg/L

- Total dissolved solids, 2,000 mg/L

The individual terms in Eq D-1 are

$$pCa = -\log\left(\frac{50 \text{ mg/L as CaCO}_3}{40,000 \text{ mg/mole}}\right) = 2.42$$

$$pAlk = -\log\left(\frac{300 \text{ mg/L as CaCO}_3}{40{,}000 \text{ mg/equiv.}}\right) = 2.22$$

Where:

$$
\begin{aligned}
C &= 2.34, \text{ from Figure D-1}\\
LSI &= 8.5 - 2.42 - 2.22 - 2.34 = +1.52
\end{aligned}
$$

The Stiff and Davis Scaling Index (SDSI) (Stiff and Davis 1952) is defined as follows:

$$SDSI = pH - pCa - pAlk - K \qquad (\text{Eq D-2})$$

Where:

pCa = negative logarithm of the calcium molarity, as in LSI

$pAlk$ = negative logarithm of the alkalinity in equivalents per liter, as in LSI

K = different empirical constant from LSI to account for temperature and ionic strength (Figure D-2)

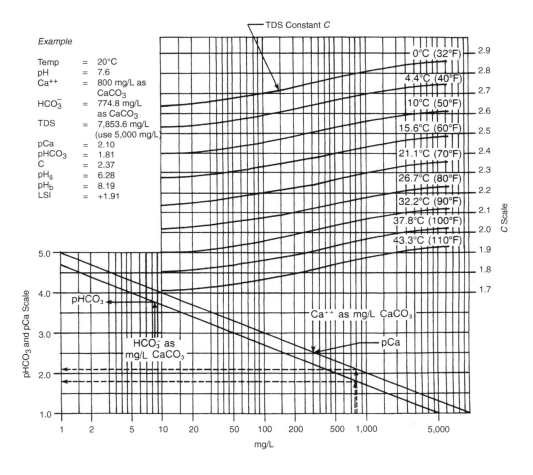

Figure D-1   Nomograph for calculating the Langelier saturation index

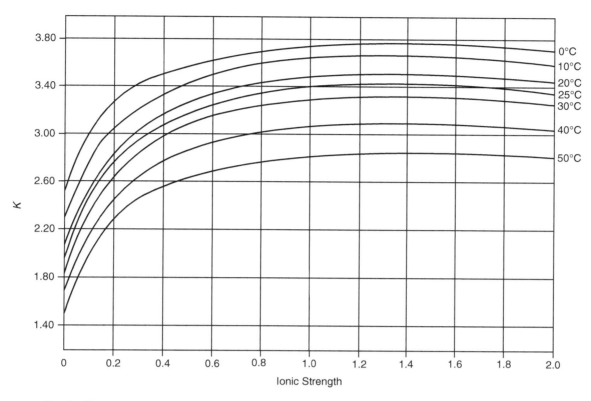

Figure D-2   Stiff and Davis K versus ionic strength and temperature

REFERENCES

Larson, T.E., and A.M. Buswell. 1944. Calcium Carbonate Saturation Index and Alkalinity Interpretations. *Jour. AWWA,* 34:1667.

Stiff, H.A., and L.E. Davis. 1952. *A Method for Predicting the Tendency of Oil Field Waters to Deposit Calcium Carbonate.* Petroleum Transactions, AIME.

This page intentionally blank.

Appendix **E**

Glossary and Acronyms

ambient temperature: The temperature of the surroundings.

anion: The ion in an electrolytic solution that migrates to the anode. It carries a negative charge.

anode: The positive electrode of an electrodialysis cell.

antiscalant: A chemical that inhibits scale formation.

antitelescoping device: A plastic cover, resembling a wheel with spokes, attached to the ends of a spiral-wound cartridge to prevent movement of the cartridge leaves in the feed flow direction.

AOC: Assimilable organic carbon.

applied pressure: The feedwater hydraulic pressure. For pressure-driven membrane systems, the feedwater pressure minus permeate pressure.

array: A group of pressure vessels installed in parallel and in series with common feedwater, product, and concentrate lines.

autopsy: The dissection of a membrane element to investigate causes for unsatisfactory performance.

AWWA: American Water Works Association.

bactericide: An agent capable of destroying bacteria.

bacteriostat: A substance that inhibits bacterial growth and metabolism.

bank: A grouping of membrane modules or pressure vessels in a common control unit or stage.

BAT: Best available technology.

biofouling: Membrane fouling that is attributable to the deposition and growth of microorganisms on the membrane surface and/or the adsorptive fouling of secretions from microorganisms.

blinding: In depth and surface filtration, a buildup of particulates on or within the filter, preventing fluid flow through the filter at normal pressures.

boundary layer: A very thin, low-velocity layer forming on the feedwater surface of a membrane.

brackish water: In general, water having a total dissolved solids concentration ranging from about 1,000 to 10,000 mg/L.

211

brine: The concentrate stream associated with a desalination process.

brine seal: A rubber lip seal on the outside of a spiral-wound membrane element that prevents feed bypass between the cartridge and the inside pressure vessel wall.

bundle: A collection of parallel filaments or fibers.

B-value (salt diffusion coefficient): The mass of salt transferred per unit area of membrane per unit of concentration difference across the membrane.

BWRO: Abbreviation of brackish water desalination using RO.

cartridge: For spiral-wound RO and NF, a membrane element.

cathode: The negative electrode of an electrodialysis cell.

cation: A positively charged ion in solution that migrates to the cathode.

cellulose acetate: A polymer used to make some types of semipermeable membranes.

channeling: A condition of unequal flow distribution in a membrane bundle or filter bed.

chelating agent: A sequestering agent that, in aqueous solution, renders a metallic ion inactive through the formation of an inner ring structure with the ion.

CIP: Clean-in-place.

compaction: Compression of RO membranes due to long-term exposure to pressure, which may result in a decreased water permeability or specific flux.

composite membrane: A membrane with a very thin rejecting layer on a porous support made of differing materials.

concentrate: The membrane output stream that contains water which has not passed through the membrane barrier, and concentrated feedwater constituents that are rejected by the membrane (also known as *reject*, *retentate*, *brine*, or the *residual stream*).

concentration factor (CF): Ratio of solute concentration in the concentrate stream to solute concentration in the feed stream.

concentration polarization: The phenomenon of increased solute (salt) concentration relative to the bulk solution that occurs in a thin boundary layer at the membrane surface on the feed side.

contaminant: Any undesirable foreign substance.

control block: A group of vessels having a common piping and control system.

crossflow: A type of filtration with the feedwater flowing tangential to the surface of the filter medium or membrane.

DBP: Disinfection by-product.

decarbonation: The process of removing carbon dioxide in the form of CO_2 gas from water.

degasification: The process of removing dissolved gases from water.

demineralization: The process of removing minerals from water, usually through anion and cation exchange resins, RO, electrodialysis, or distillation.

desalination: *same as desalting.*

desalting: A process that removes salts from feedwater.

differential pressure: The difference in pressure between two points in a system (for RO and NF, typically the pressure drop from the feed to concentrate).

DOC: Dissolved organic carbon.

double-pass system: A RO or NF system in which the permeate is further processed by a subsequent RO or NF unit.

drawback: The reverse flow of permeate from the permeate side across the membrane to the feedwater or concentrate side as a result of osmosis.

ED: Electrodialysis.

EDR: Electrodialysis reversal.

electrodialysis: Dialysis conducted with the aid of an electromotive force applied to electrodes adjacent to both sides of the membrane.

electrodialysis reversal (EDR): A type of electrodialysis where the polarity of the electrodes change (reverse) periodically to lower the concentration of scaling materials at a membrane surface.

element: *See membrane element.*

feed and bleed: An operating mode in which a portion of the concentrate stream is repressurized and continuously recycled to the feed and another portion is disposed.

feed channel spacer: Netting layer between membrane leaves that acts as a spacer material and increases the turbulence of the feed–concentrate stream.

feed distributor: The plastic mesh cylinder found at the core of the fiber bundle in a hollow fine-fiber membrane element that distributes the feed evenly.

feedwater: Influent water flowing into the membrane process.

fiber bundle: Materials consisting of a hollow fine-fiber polymer membrane, epoxy tube, sheet, nub, and feed distributor.

filtrate: The portion of the feedwater that has passed through a filter.

flat sheet membrane: A membrane manufactured in a flat form. Commonly used in spiral-wound membrane elements.

flux: The rate of water flow across a unit surface area, (Q_p/A), expressed in gallons per day per square foot (gpd/ft^2 or gfd) or liters per hour per square meter (L/hr-m^2 or Lmh).

fouling: The gradual accumulation of contaminants on a membrane surface or within a porous membrane structure that inhibits the passage of water, thus decreasing permeability.

FRP: Fiberglass-reinforced plastic.

GAC: Granular activated carbon.

gfd: Gallons per square foot per day.

gpd: Gallons per day.

HAA: Haloacetic acid.

HSD: Homogenous solution diffusion.

hydrophilic: The water attracting property of membrane material.

hydrophobic: The water rejecting property of membrane material.

hyperfiltration: An older term that is sometimes used interchangeably with "reverse osmosis."

interconnector: Device that connects the permeate water tubes of spiral-wound membrane elements which are installed in series in a pressure vessel.

IOC: Inorganic compound.

ion: An electrified portion of matter of atomic or molecular dimensions.

ionic strength: A measure of the overall electrolytic potential of a solution.

Langelier saturation index: A calculated value based on total dissolved solids, calcium concentration, total alkalinity, pH, and solution temperature, indicating the tendency of a water solution to precipitate or dissolve calcium carbonate.

leaf: A combination of a flat sheet membrane, a product channel spacer, and another flat sheet membrane, layered and glued together on three sides.

LSI: Langelier saturation index.

mass transfer coefficient: A coefficient quantifying material passage through a membrane.

MCL: Maximum contaminant level.

membrane: A thin layer of material capable of separating materials as a function of their chemical or physical properties when a driving force is applied.

membrane configuration: The arrangement of individual elements (cartridges) in a membrane treatment process.

membrane element: The smallest component of a membrane unit without a pressure housing. A common term for spiral-wound RO and NF membranes with concentrate and permeate spacers, central permeate tube, outer wrapping material, and antitelescoping devices at each end.

membrane softening: The use of membranes for removing hardness ions (e.g., calcium and magnesium) from water.

membrane system: A complete membrane treatment unit.

MF: Microfiltration.

module: The smallest component of a membrane unit where the membranes are housed in a device with a permeate outlet. For spiral-wound NF or RO, a module is a pressure vessel containing one or more membrane elements.

Molecular weight cut-off: A nominal value describing the approximate size, in Daltons, of an organic molecule that will be rejected by a membrane.

MWCO: Molecular weight cut-off.

nanofiltration: A crossflow membrane separation process that removes particles in the 300 to 1,000 molecular weight range, selected salts, and organics. NF membranes capable of high rejection of calcium and magnesium are commonly used for membrane softening.

Net driving pressure (NDP): The hydraulic pressure differential across the membrane minus the osmotic pressure differential across the membrane that is available to force water through the membrane. Equal to the average hydraulic pressure on the feed–concentrate side minus the permeate pressure and subtracting the average feed–concentrate osmotic pressure minus the permeate osmotic pressure.

NF: Nanofiltration.

NOM: Natural organic matter.

O&M: Operations and maintenance.

OEM: Original equipment manufacturer.

operating pressure: The pressure at which feedwater enters a device.

osmosis: The naturally occurring transport of water through a membrane from a solution of low salt content to a solution of high salt content in order to equalize salt concentrations.

osmotic pressure: A measurement of the potential energy difference between solutions on either side of a semipermeable membrane due to osmosis.

permeability: Membrane flux normalized for temperature and pressure, expressed as gallons per square foot per day per pound per square inch (gfd/psi) or liters per square meter per hour per bar (Lmh/bar); also called *specific flux*.

permeate: The portion of the feed stream that passes through an RO or NF membrane.

permeate channel spacer: *See* product channel spacer.

permeate staging: *See* double-pass system.

PCE: perchloroethylene.

plate-and-frame: A membrane configuration in which the membrane layers are mounted in flat sheets.

pore: An opening in a membrane or filter matrix.

porosity: The proportion, usually stated as a percentage, of the total volume of material that consists of pore space or voids.

posttreatment: One or more processes that may be used to condition the permeate.

precipitate: A substance separated from a solution by chemical or physical change as an insoluble amorphous or crystalline solid.

pressure filtration: Filtration aided by imposing a pressure differential across an enclosed filter vessel.

pressure vessel (PV): A housing designed to contain membranes and operate with elevated hydraulic pressure. For spiral-wound membranes, the tube-shaped device that houses one or more membrane elements in series.

pretreatment: Processes that may be applied to the feedwater to a membrane system (e.g., filtration, chemical addition, and others) in order to protect the membranes or improve the system performance. For RO and NF systems, chemical addition for scaling protection and/or filtration with cartridge filters are commonly used in pretreatment.

probing: A troubleshooting procedure to find areas of higher salt passage (such as O-ring leaks) within a pressure vessel containing multiple membrane elements.

product channel spacer: The porous spacer material through which permeate water flows after it passes through a flat sheet membrane.

product staging: *See* two-pass system.

product stream: *See* permeate.

profiling: A preventive maintenance procedure in which water quality and/or operating data are collected and archived for each pressure vessel and train to track performance.

PVDF: Polyvinylidene fluoride.

rack: A structural device that supports pressure vessels, membranes, and other devices. *Also see* bank.

recovery: The ratio of the permeate flow to the feedflow, generally expressed as a percentage.

reject: *See* concentrate.

reverse osmosis: The transport of water from a solution having a high salt concentration to one having a low salt concentration through a membrane against the natural osmotic gradient by applying pressure to the more concentrated solution.

RO: reverse osmosis.

salt passage (SP): The ratio of concentration of an ionic constituent(s) in the permeate divided by the concentration of the same constituent(s) in the feed, generally expressed as a percent.

salt rejection (SR): The concentration in the feedwater that is rejected by a membrane, generally expressed as a percent. Equal to 100 percent minus the percent salt passage.

scale inhibitor: *See* antiscalant.

scaling: The precipitation of inorganic salts on the feed–concentrate side of a membrane.

SDI: Silt density index.

semipermeable membrane: A membrane that is permeable only by certain molecules or ions. For RO and NF, a membrane that allows water to pass through but rejects one or more solutes to a high degree.

sequestering agent: A chemical applied to extend the limits of saturation of scaling substances by binding metal ions in a soluble form.

SHMP: Sodium hexametaphosphate.

silt density index (SDI): A dimensionless value resulting from an empirical test used to measure the level of suspended and colloidal material in water. Calculated from the time it takes to filter 500 mL of the test water through a 0.45-µm-pore-diameter filter at 30 psi pressure at the beginning and at the end of a specified test duration. See appendix C.

SMBS: Sodium metabisulfate.

SMCL: Secondary maximum contaminant level.

SOC: Synthetic organic compound.

specific flux: *See* permeability.

spiral-wound element: An RO or NF device, consisting of membrane leaves wound around a central permeate collection tube and including feed and permeate spacers, antitelescoping devices, and a brine seal.

stage: A set of pressure vessels installed in parallel.

supersaturation: A state in which inorganic salts are in solution at a level such that the respective solubility product is exceeded.

SWRO: Abbreviation for seawater desalination using RO.

SWTR: Surface Water Treatment Rule.

TCE: Trichloroethylene.

TDS: Total dissolved solids.

telescoping: A movement of the membrane leaves of a spiral-wound cartridge in the direction of the feed flow, caused by excessive pressure drop across the element.

temperature correction factor (TCF): Correction factor used to normalize relative to a reference temperature.

TTHM: Total trihalomethanes.

thrust collar: A supporting plastic cylinder located between the last spiral-wound element and the end plate in a pressure vessel.

TOC: Total organic carbon.

train: An independent grouping of treatment processes in series. For RO and NF, one of multiple individually controlled and operated membrane elements and pressure vessels. Multiple membrane trains are arranged in parallel and subdivide the overall membrane treatment capacity into more than one segment.

UF: Ultrafiltration.

USEPA: United States Environmental Protection Agency.

VOC: Volatile organic compound.

water transport: The passage of water through a membrane.

Index

AWWA Manuals

M1, *Principles of Water Rates, Fees, and Charges*, Fifth Edition, 2000, #30001PA

M2, *Instrumentation and Control*, Third Edition, 2001, #30002PA

M3, *Safety Practices for Water Utilities*, Sixth Edition, 2002, #30003PA

M4, *Water Fluoridation Principles and Practices*, Fifth Edition, 2004, #30004PA

M5, *Water Utility Management Practices*, Second Edition, 2006, #30005PA

M6, *Water Meters—Selection, Installation, Testing, and Maintenance*, Second Edition, 1999, #30006PA

M7, *Problem Organisms in Water: Identification and Treatment*, Third Edition, 2004, #30007PA

M9, *Concrete Pressure Pipe*, Second Edition, 1995, #30009PA

M11, *Steel Pipe—A Guide for Design and Installation*, Fifth Edition, 2004, #30011PA

M12, *Simplified Procedures for Water Examination*, Fifth Edition, 2002, #30012PA

M14, *Recommended Practice for Backflow Prevention and Cross-Connection Control*, Third Edition, 2003, #30014PA

M17, *Installation, Field Testing, and Maintenance of Fire Hydrants*, Fourth Edition, 2006, #30017PA

M19, *Emergency Planning for Water Utility Management*, Fourth Edition, 2001, #30019PA

M20, *Water Chlorination/Chloramination Practices and Principles*, Second Edition, 2006, #30020PA

M21, *Groundwater*, Third Edition, 2003, #30021PA

M22, *Sizing Water Service Lines and Meters*, Second Edition, 2004, #30022PA

M23, *PVC Pipe—Design and Installation*, Second Edition, 2003, #30023PA

M24, *Dual Water Systems*, Second Edition, 1994, #30024PA

M25, *Flexible-Membrane Covers and Linings for Potable-Water Reservoirs*, Third Edition, 2000, #30025PA

M27, *External Corrosion—Introduction to Chemistry and Control*, Second Edition, 2004, #30027PA

M28, *Rehabilitation of Water Mains*, Second Edition, 2001, #30028PA

M29, *Water Utility Capital Financing*, Third Edition, 2007, #30029PA

M30, *Precoat Filtration*, Second Edition, 1995, #30030PA

M31, *Distribution System Requirements for Fire Protection*, Third Edition, 1998, #30031PA

M32, *Distribution Network Analysis for Water Utilities*, Second Edition, 2005, #30032PA

M33, *Flowmeters in Water Supply*, Second Edition, 2006, #30033PA

M36, *Water Audits and Leak Detection*, Second Edition, 1999, #30036PA

M37, *Operational Control of Coagulation and Filtration Processes*, Second Edition, 2000, #30037PA

M38, *Electrodialysis and Electrodialysis Reversal*, First Edition, 1995, #30038PA

M41, *Ductile-Iron Pipe and Fittings*, Second Edition, 2003, #30041PA

M42, *Steel Water-Storage Tanks*, First Edition, 1998, #30042PA

M44, *Distribution Valves: Selection, Installation, Field Testing, and Maintenance*, Second Edition, 2006, #30044PA

M45, *Fiberglass Pipe Design*, Second Edition, 2005, #30045PA

M46, *Reverse Osmosis and Nanofiltration*, Second Edition, 2007, #30046PA

To order any of these manuals or other AWWA publications, call the Bookstore toll-free at 1-(800)-926-7337.

M47, *Construction Contract Administration*, First Edition, 1996, #30047PA

M48, *Waterborne Pathogens*, Second Edition, 2006, #30048PA

M49, *Butterfly Valves: Torque, Head Loss, and Cavitation Analysis*, First Edition, 2001, #30049PA

M50, *Water Resources Planning*, Second Edition, 2007, #30050PA

M51, *Air-Release, Air/Vacuum, and Combination Air Valves*, First Edition, 2001, #30051PA

M52, *Water Conservation Programs—A Planning Manual*, First Edition, 2006, #30052PA

M53, *Microfiltration and Ultrafiltration Membranes for Drinking Water*, First Edition, 2005, #30053PA

M54, *Developing Rates for Small Systems*, First Edition, 2004, #30054PA

M55, *PE Pipe—Design and Installation*, First Edition, 2006, #30055PA

M56, *Fundamentals and Control of Nitrification in Chloraminated Drinking Water Distribution Systems*, First Edition, 2006, #30056PA

To order any of these manuals or other AWWA publications, call the Bookstore toll-free at 1-(800)-926-7337.

CPSIA information can be obtained
at www.ICGtesting.com
Printed in the USA
BVHW010227030819
554835BV00026B/66/P

9 781583 214916